L7J490

WEYMOUTH COLLEGE

D0274232

Success in Physics

Success Studybooks

Accounting and Costing
Accounting and Costing: Problems and Projects
Biology
Book-keeping and Accounts
British History 1760–1914
British History since 1914
Business Calculations
Chemistry
Commerce
Commerce: West African Edition
Economic Geography
Economics
Economics: West African Edition
Electronics
Elements of Banking
European History 1815–1941
Financial Accounting
Financial Accounting: Questions and Answers
Geography: Human and Regional
Geography: Physical and Mapwork
Insurance
Investment
Law
Management: Personnel
Mathematics
Nutrition
Office Practice
Organic Chemistry
Physics
Principles of Accounting
Principles of Accounting: Answer Book
Statistics
Twentieth Century World Affairs

Success in
PHYSICS

Tom Duncan

John Murray

WEYMOUTH COLLEGE
LIBRARY

ACC.
No. 39509

CLASS
No. 530 D

© Tom Duncan 1985

First published 1985
by John Murray (Publishers) Ltd
50 Albemarle Street, London W1X 4BD

All rights reserved
Unauthorized duplication
contravenes applicable laws

Typeset in Great Britain by
Fakenham Photosetting Ltd, Fakenham, Norfolk
Printed and bound in Great Britain by
Richard Clay (The Chaucer Press) Ltd,
Bungay, Suffolk

British Library Cataloguing in Publication Data

Duncan, Tom
  Success in physics.
  1. Physics
  I. Title
  530   QC21.2

ISBN 0–7195–4191–3

Foreword

Success in Physics is a straightforward introduction to physics which gives comprehensive coverage of O level, 16+ and BTEC I syllabuses and their overseas equivalents. It will also be useful to anyone who wishes to have a knowledge and understanding of basic physics, whether for examination or other purposes.

Part One deals with Physics and Measurement, Part Two with Force, Motion and Energy, Part Three with Molecules and Heat, Part Four with Light and Sound: Waves, Part Five with Electricity and Magnetism and Part Six with Atoms and Electrons. Because of the increasing importance of electronics in basic physics courses, a complete Unit is devoted to this subject. Unit 24 covers topics such as the transistor as a switch and as an amplifier, integrated circuits, logic gates, multivibrators and op amps.

The large number of revision questions and problems (with answers) at the end of Units and the many worked examples make *Success in Physics* particularly suitable for those who are working or revising on their own. The section on mathematics for physics at the end of the book is intended to be used by students as the need arises when they are working through questions and problems.

T.D.

Acknowledgments

I should like to thank Dr Russell Strutt and Dr Malcolm Hawkins for their constructive criticism of the book during its preparation, Dr Jean Macqueen for her expert editing of the text and my wife for producing the typescript.

For permission to use photographs thanks are due to: Addison-Wesley Publishing Company (from *Modern College Physics*, copyright 1962, by Richards, Sears, Wehr and Zemansky) (Fig. 16.13); Airship Industries (UK) Ltd (7.23); Barnaby's Picture Library (5.7(*a*), (*b*)); *British Jeweller and Watchbuyer* (15.10); M. Byrne (8.10(*a*)); Cambridge Consultants Ltd (13.1); D. G. A. Dyson (16.15(*a*)); Philip Harris Limited (2.2(*a*), 2.9, 24.5); D. C. Heath and Co (from *PSSC Physics*, copyright 1965. Educational Development Center) (4.14); Howard Jay (13.15(*a*)); Kodansha Ltd (18.10); Oldham Batteries Ltd (7.24(*b*)); Oxford University Press (from *Ripple Tank Studies of Wave Motion* by W. Llowarch, copyright 1961) (16.6(*a*), (*b*), 16.10(*a*), (*b*), 16.11(*a*)); R. S. Components Ltd (18.12, 19.7(*a*), 19.8(*a*), 24.22, 24.26, 24.27(*a*), 24.28(*a*)); The Royal Society (from *Proceedings, A*, Vol. 104, Plate 16, Fig. 1, 1923) (23.7(*b*)); James R. Sheppard (11.14); A. G. Spalding and Bros Inc (first appeared in article 'Dynamics of the Golf Swing' by Dr D. Williams in *Quarterly Journal of Mathematics and Applied Mathematics*, published by Clarendon Press, Oxford) (4.1); Unilab Ltd (4.6, 18.13(*b*)); C. T. R. Wilson (23.7(*a*)).

Electrical circuit components are shown approximately actual size except where indicated.

T.D.

All the practical work described in this book has been performed many times safely and successfully. But almost any activity may involve risk if sensible precautions and reasonable care are not taken, or if instructions are disregarded. The author and publishers of *Success in Physics* will not accept any liability whatsoever for damage or loss, including consequential loss, suffered or incurred by or inflicted upon any person, creature or property in the course or as a result of the performance of any experiment or other practical work suggested in this book, nor will the author and publishers accept liability for death, personal injury or loss resulting from failure to adhere strictly to the instructions set out in this book, or to seek advice and/or assistance as recommended in it.

Contents

Part Three   Molecules and Heat

Part Five   Electricity and Magnetism

Part Six   Atoms and Electrons

Part One
Physics and Measurement

About Physics

1.1 Matter and Energy

Physics is the study of *matter* and *energy*. It is mankind's attempt to obtain a better understanding of the physical (non-living) world.

(i) **Matter.** Matter is the stuff everything is made of; it may be either *solid*, *liquid* or *gas*. A particular substance is frequently most familiar in one of these conditions but often it is easily changed to the others. For example, water is normally a liquid but it becomes a solid (ice) if it is cooled enough and a gas (steam) if heated sufficiently.

Despite the great variety of matter, it is made up of only about one hundred basic substances, called *elements*. Other substances are combinations of elements, and are called *compounds*. Iron, aluminium, gold, copper, oxygen and hydrogen are elements. Water, salt and sugar are compounds.

The building blocks of matter are *atoms*, which are different for each element. When two or more atoms become bound together, a *molecule* is formed. The molecule of a compound contains two or more different atoms; a water molecule, for example, consists of two hydrogen (H) atoms and one oxygen (O) atom (H_2O). Molecules of elements also exist but these are made from identical atoms; a hydrogen molecule, for example, contains two hydrogen atoms (H_2).

(ii) **Energy.** Energy is that which enables useful jobs to be done. It has various forms: *electrical* energy can turn an electric motor, *thermal* energy can warm your home, *mechanical* energy can drive a pile into the ground and *nuclear* energy can power a submarine. *Light* and *sound* are other forms of energy.

1.2 Making Sense of Physics

(i) **Concepts and laws.** Like all other sciences, physics starts with observations and experiments (usually involving measurements) designed to obtain *facts*. The investigation of electricity, for example, began when it was noticed that amber (a glass-like fossil) attracts small objects when it is rubbed with a cloth.

To help to make sense of the facts of physics and to explain the behaviour of matter and energy, physicists use *concepts*. These concern quantities that can be measured and experiments show that in many cases, relationships called *laws* or *principles* exist between these quantities, and summarize a large number of facts. For instance, Hooke's law tells us how a spring behaves when it is stretched and relates the concepts of force and length. Boyle's law describes how gases respond when squeezed, using the concepts of pressure and volume. Newton's laws of motion deal with the action of forces on objects and the accelerations they produce. Ohm's law in electricity connects the rather abstract concepts of voltage and current.

The so-called 'laws of nature' are man-made, being extracted from the facts, and have limitations; for example, Hooke's law is only true if the spring is not stretched too far. Moreover, the discovery of new facts may show further limitations in existing 'laws'; for instance, Einstein showed that Newton's laws of motion do not apply to objects moving at very high speeds. Nevertheless, it is by inventing concepts and discovering laws that we are able to make the physical world seem reasonable and to obtain some control over it.

(ii) **Theories.** Frequently in physics what we are dealing with is not directly accessible to our senses and in such cases *theories* or 'thought-models' are used to help us to 'explain' things. For example, the *wave theory* is used to make sense of some of the properties of light and sound and draws on our knowledge of the behaviour of real waves—water waves, for example. The *kinetic theory* gives us insight into the properties of matter, especially gases, and considers that in some respects the molecules of matter are not unlike visible particles.

Remember, however, that scientific theories are aids to understanding which, like geographical maps, are representations or analogies of reality and are not complete descriptions of it.

1.3 Physics and Technology

It has been said that a scientific discovery is incomplete and immature until it has a practical application, which is the concern of technology. Technology has three aspects.

(i) **Technology the friend.** Engineering and technology use man's inventiveness and knowledge of physics (and other sciences) to improve his material well-being. There are many examples.

Electrical generators, the source of electricity in power stations, are the outcome of discoveries made by Faraday over 150 years ago. So too are electric motors, the heart of so many of today's appliances (including robots, which are becoming increasingly important in manufacturing industry), while radio and television arose from the theoretical ideas of the physicist Clerk Maxwell, concerning the connection between light, electricity and magnetism. Predictions about the paths taken by artificial satellites and space vehicles are based on Newton's laws of motion, formulated around 300 years ago; nuclear power stations are possible because of the basic work done by Rutherford on the structure of the atom at the beginning of this century; modern medicine uses a host of devices, from X-ray machines to lasers, developed by physicists for the diagnosis and treatment of disease.

Electronics, which arose from J. J. Thomson's discovery of the electron at the end of the nineteenth century, is today being used to an ever-increasing extent in communication, control and computer systems as well as in domestic products and for medical care. Modern telephone exchanges have electronic switching and are controlled by computers. They are linked to exchanges in other countries via large dish aerials at earth-stations, which send signals to earth-orbiting communication satellites for amplification and onward transmission.

(ii) **Technology the foe.** If not used wisely, technology can create social and environmental problems such as unemployment and pollution, not to mention the ultimate folly of global nuclear war. It is for mankind to use technology responsibly.

(iii) **Interplay.** The interaction between physics and technology is a two-way process. Not only does technology depend on physics; the advances in technology are often in turn used to further the work of the physicists by providing them with new tools and techniques.

1.4 Physics and Mathematics

Mathematics is an essential tool of physics. Many laws are written as mathematical equations which may have to be manipulated. Simple arithmetic is also required at times and graphs are often used to represent results pictorially.

A reference section explaining how to deal with some of the basic mathematics needed for physics is given at the end of this book. Use it whenever you find it necessary.

1.5 Revision Questions

1. With what is the study of physics concerned?

2. (a) How does a compound differ from an element? (b) How does a molecule differ from an atom?

3. What is a scientific concept? Name six concepts.

4. What does a 'law of nature' tell us? Name three laws.

5. What is the purpose of a theory? Name two theories.

6. List three kitchen appliances that contain an electric motor.

7. State three uses for an electric motor in a car.

8. Computers are products of physics and technology. Mention two ways in which they can be used (a) for the benefit, (b) to the detriment, of mankind.

Unit Two

Measurement

2.1 Quantities and Units

In physics only five quantities are considered to be *basic*. They are length, mass and time (considered in this Unit), temperature and electric current (which we shall consider in Units 9 and 18). All other quantities, such as volume, density, force, acceleration and voltage, are *derived* from these.

Before a measurement can be made, a standard or *unit* must be chosen. A unit must be easily reproduced and must not vary; for example, the metre is taken as the unit of length and defined exactly. The size of the quantity to be measured is then found with an *instrument* having a scale calibrated in the unit; for example, a ruler is used to measure length. The value of the quantity is stated as a number followed by a unit.

In science, SI (*Système Internationale d'Unités*) units are used. This is a decimal system in which units are multiplied or divided by 10 to give larger or smaller units. Tables of the basic quantities and the commoner derived quantities with their symbols and units are given in Appendix 1 (page 431), along with the prefixes for SI multiple and submultiple units.

2.2 Standard Form: Significant Figures

(i) **Standard form or scientific notation.** This is a neat way of writing numbers, especially those that are very large or very small. It is most easily explained by using examples. Look at the following:

$4000 = 4 \times 10 \times 10 \times 10 = 4 \times 10^3$ (this is stated as

'four times ten to the power three')

$400 = 4 \times 10 \times 10 \qquad = 4 \times 10^2$
$40 = 4 \times 10 \qquad\qquad = 4 \times 10^1$
$4 = 4 \times 1 \qquad\qquad = 4 \times 10^0$
$0.4 = 4/10 \qquad = 4/10^1 \quad = 4 \times 10^{-1}$ (this is stated as

'four times ten to the power minus one')

$0.04 = 4/100 \quad = 4/10^2 \quad = 4 \times 10^{-2}$
$0.004 = 4/1000 = 4/10^3 \quad = 4 \times 10^{-3}$

The small figures 1, 2, 3 in these examples are called *powers of ten* or *exponents* and specify how many times the number before the multiplication sign has to be multiplied by 10 if the number concerned is greater than 1, and divided by

10 if it is less than 1. The number 1 itself is also written as 10^0; for numbers less than 1, the power has a negative sign. Numbers in standard form are less likely to be copied incorrectly than are numbers consisting of long strings of digits—40 000 000 and 400 000 000, for instance, are all too easily confused.

In calculations involving the multiplication or division of numbers in standard form, certain rules have to be followed. They are given in the section on *Mathematics for Physics* (page 423).

(ii) **Significant figures.** Every measurement of a quantity is an attempt to find its true value and is subject to errors arising from limitations of the apparatus and the experimenter. The number of figures, called *significant* figures, in the stated value of a quantity indicates how accurate we think it is, and more should not be given than the experiment justifies. For example, a value of 4.5 given for a measurement has two significant figures; 0.0385 has three significant figures, 3 being the most significant figure and 5 the least, that is, it is the one we are least sure about—it might be 4 or it might be 6 and perhaps had to be estimated by the experimenter because the reading was between two marks on a scale.

When doing a calculation your answer should contain the same number of significant figures as the measurements used in the calculation. For example, if your calculator gave an answer of 3.4185062, you should write this as 3.4 if the measurements had two significant figures and as 3.42 if they had three. In deciding what the least significant figure should be, you look at the number on its right. If this is less than 5 you leave the least significant figure as it is (hence 3.41 to two significant figures becomes 3.4) but if it is equal to or greater than 5 you increase the least significant figure by 1 (hence 3.418 to three significant figures becomes 3.42).

Where a number is expressed in standard form, the number of significant figures is the number of digits before the power of ten, for example, 2.73×10^3 has three significant figures.

2.3 Length

The SI unit of length is the *metre* (symbol m) and is the distance, believed never to alter, occupied by a certain number of wavelengths (1 650 763.76) of orange light. (Previously it was defined as the distance between two marks on a particular metal bar.) Submultiples of the metre are:

$$
\begin{aligned}
1 \text{ decimetre (dm)} &= 1/10 \text{ m} = 10^{-1} \text{ m} \\
1 \text{ centimetre (cm)} &= 1/100 \text{ m} = 10^{-2} \text{ m} \\
1 \text{ millimetre (mm)} &= 1/1000 \text{ m} = 10^{-3} \text{ m} \\
1 \text{ micrometre } (\mu\text{m}) &= 10^{-6} \text{ m} \\
1 \text{ nanometre (nm)} &= 10^{-9} \text{ m}
\end{aligned}
$$

A multiple for large distances is

$$1 \text{ kilometre (km)} = 10^3 \text{ m (about } \tfrac{5}{8} \text{ mile)}$$

Many length measurements are made using a ruler marked in centimetres and millimetres. The correct reading is obtained only when your eyes are right over the mark on the ruler: other viewing positions cause errors due to *parallax*. (There is parallax between two objects—such as a pointer and a mark on a scale—if they appear to separate and move in opposite directions when you move your head sideways. Objects that coincide move together without separating; parallax arises when objects do not coincide.) This is true of any scale-reading instrument where the point being measured and the line on the scale do not coincide. In Fig. 2.1, where they are separated by the thickness of the ruler, the correct reading is 7.6 cm and the 'wrong' position reading is 7.7 cm.

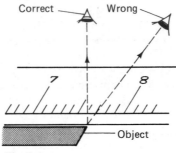

Fig. 2.1

The circumference (the outline) of a circle is a length, and equals $2\pi r$, where r is the radius of the circle and $\pi = 22/7$ or 3.14. You can check this by drawing a circle of radius 5 cm, fitting a piece of string around its circumference and then measuring the length of the string.

2.4 Vernier Scales

When a reading is between two marks on a scale it can be found more accurately with the help of a *vernier* scale. Such scales are used on calipers (Fig. 2.2(a)), which are used for finding the outside or inside diameter of a tube, and on barometers.

A vernier scale for use with a millimetre scale is 9 mm long and has ten equal divisions (Fig. 2.2(b)):

$$1 \text{ vernier division} = \tfrac{9}{10} \text{ mm} = 0.9 \text{ mm}$$

The object in Fig. 2.2(c) is between 13 mm and 14 mm long. The next figure is obtained by finding the mark on the vernier scale which is exactly opposite (or

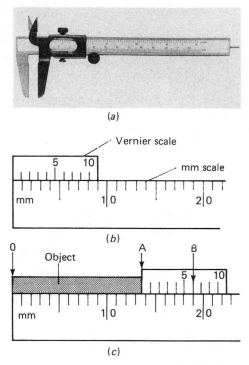

(a)

(b)

(c)

At B the 6th mark on the vernier is *exactly* opposite a mark on the mm scale

Fig. 2.2

nearest to) a mark on the mm scale. Here it is the sixth mark and the reading is 13.6 mm, since

$$OA = OB - AB = 19.0 - 6 \times 0.9$$
$$= 19.0 - 5.4$$
$$= 13.6 \, mm$$

2.5 Micrometer Screw Gauge

A micrometer screw gauge (Fig. 2.3) measures very small lengths, such as the diameter of a wire.

The drum is joined to the screw, and one complete turn of the drum opens the jaws by one division on the scale on the shaft, which is usually 0.5 mm. (The *pitch* of the screw is said to be 0.5 mm.) If the drum has a scale of 50 divisions round it, turning it by one division opens the jaws by

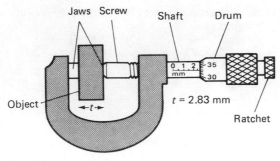

Fig. 2.3

0.5/50 =0.01 mm. The reading is taken when the ratchet turns without closing the jaws any more. The thickness t of the object shown is given by

t =2.5 mm on shaft scale +33 divisions on drum scale
   =2.5 +33 ×0.01
   =2.83 mm

A micrometer screw gauge is accurate to 0.01 mm, vernier calipers to 0.1 mm and a metre rule to 1 mm.

2.6 Area

The square in Fig. 2.4(*a*) has sides 1 cm long, and its area is 1 square centimetre (1 cm^2). The rectangle in Fig. 2.4(*b*) measures 4 cm by 3 cm and has an area of $4 \times 3 = 12$ cm^2, since it has the same area as twelve squares each of area 1 cm^2. The area of a square or rectangle is given by

$$area =length \times breadth$$

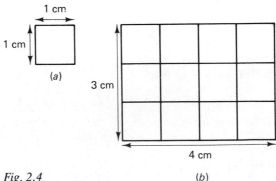

Fig. 2.4   (*b*)

The SI unit of area is the *square metre* (m^2), which is the area of a square with sides 1 m long. Note that

$$1\,cm^2 = \frac{1}{100}\,m \times \frac{1}{100}\,m = \frac{1}{10\,000}\,m^2 = 10^{-4}\,m^2$$

You can make an estimate of the area of an irregular shape by dividing it up into squares, each of area, say, $1\,cm^2$. Count the incomplete squares having an area of $\frac{1}{2}\,cm^2$ or more as complete squares, and ignore those of area less than $\frac{1}{2}\,cm^2$.

A reasonable estimate for the shaded area in Fig. 2.5 is $13\,cm^2$. Use the same method to estimate the area of a circle of radius 5 cm. Check your answer using the expression

$$\text{area of circle} = \pi r^2$$

where $\pi = 22/7$ or 3.14.

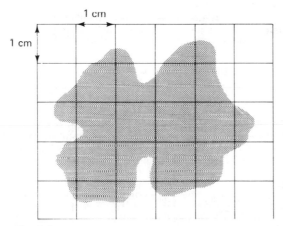

Fig. 2.5

2.7 Volume

Volume is the amount of space occupied. The SI unit is the *cubic metre* (m^3) but as this is rather large for most purposes, the cubic centimetre (cm^3) is generally used. It is the volume of a cube with sides 1 cm long. Note that

$$1\,cm^3 = \frac{1}{100}\,m \times \frac{1}{100}\,m \times \frac{1}{100}\,m = \frac{1}{1\,000\,000}\,m^3 = 10^{-6}\,m^3$$

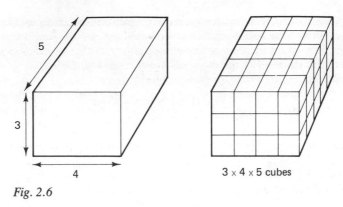

Fig. 2.6

(i) **Regular solids.** The volume of regularly shaped solids can be calculated. For example, as Fig. 2.6 shows,

$$\text{volume of a rectangular block} = \text{length} \times \text{breadth} \times \text{height}$$

The volumes of two other simple shapes are given by:

$$\text{volume of a cylinder} = \pi \times \text{radius}^2 \times \text{height}$$

and
$$\text{volume of a sphere} = \frac{4}{3} \times \pi \times \text{radius}^3$$

(ii) **Liquids.** The volume of a liquid may be found by pouring it into a measuring cylinder (Fig. 2.7(*a*)) and reading the level. A given volume can be obtained more accurately by running it off from a burette (Fig. 2.7(*b*)) or a

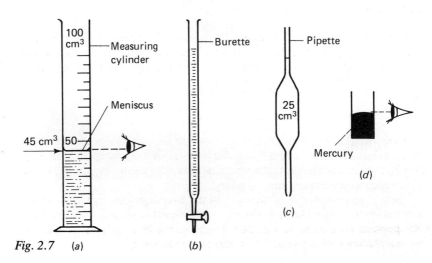

Fig. 2.7   (*a*)   (*b*)

pipette (Fig. 2.7(c)). When making a reading, the vessel must be upright and the eye level with the bottom of the curved liquid surface (the *meniscus*). The meniscus formed by mercury is curved oppositely to that of other liquids, however, and the level of the meniscus *top* is read (Fig. 2.7(d)).

Liquid volumes are also expressed in *litres*, where

$$1 \text{ litre (l)} = 1000 \text{ cm}^3 = 1 \text{ dm}^3$$
$$1 \text{ millilitre (ml)} = 1 \text{ cm}^3$$

(iii) **Irregular solids.** The volume can be measured by displacing water in a measuring cylinder as in Fig. 2.8, where the volume of the pebble is $(V_2 - V_1)$. For a solid that floats in water, such as a cork, another object of known volume—a brass weight, for example—has to be attached to it.

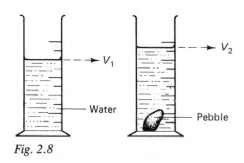

Fig. 2.8

2.8 Mass

The mass of an object is a measure of the amount of matter in it. The SI unit of mass is the *kilogram* (kg) and is the mass of a piece of platinum alloy at the Office of Weights and Measures in Paris. Submultiples and multiples are

$$1 \text{ gram (g)} = 1/1000 \text{ kg} = 10^{-3} \text{ kg}$$
$$1 \text{ milligram (mg)} = 1/1000 \text{ g} = 10^{-3} \text{ g}$$
$$1000 \text{ kg} = 1 \text{ tonne}$$

The term *weight* is often used when mass is really meant. In science the two terms are distinct and have different units, as we will see later (in Unit 3.2). The confusion is not helped by the fact that *mass* is measured on a balance by a process we unfortunately call 'weighing'.

There are several kinds of balance. In the *lever* balance a system of levers acts against the mass placed in the pan, and a direct reading is obtained from the position on a scale of a pointer joined to the lever system. A modern *top-pan* balance with a digital read-out is shown in Fig. 2.9.

Fig. 2.9

2.9 Time

The SI unit of time is the *second* (symbol s) which was previously based on the length of a day, this being the time for the earth to revolve once on its axis. Days are not all of exactly the same duration, however, and the second is now defined as the time interval for a certain number of cycles of radiation (9 192 631 770) to be emitted from the caesium atom. (Caesium is an alkali metal, like sodium.)

(i) **Clocks and watches.** Time-measuring devices rely on some kind of constantly repeating vibrations that occur at a steady rate. In spring-operated clocks and watches a small wheel (the balance wheel) rotates to and fro. In many modern clocks and watches the vibrations are produced by a tiny quartz crystal. In a 'grandfather' clock the swings of a pendulum are used.

(ii) **Simple pendulum.** A simple pendulum consists of a piece of thread which is fixed at one end and has a small ball, called the bob, on the other end. The *periodic time T* of the pendulum is the time for a complete swing or oscillation from O to A to O to B to O again. The *length l* of the pendulum is the distance from the point of support to the centre of the bob. The *amplitude* of a swing is the angle between the extreme and rest positions of the thread (Fig. 2.10).

Experiments show that if the amplitude does not exceed 10° or so, T depends only on l and is unaffected by either the mass of the bob or the amplitude. The connection between T and l is

$$T \propto \sqrt{l} \text{ or } T^2 \propto l$$

That is, $T = $ a constant $\times \sqrt{l}$

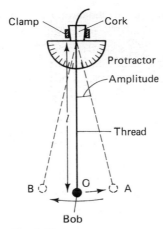

Fig. 2.10

In words, *the periodic time is directly proportional to the square root of the length of the pendulum*, that is, when *l* is quadrupled (say from 25 to 100 cm), *T* doubles. A graph of *T* against $\sqrt{l}$ (or T^2 against *l*) is a straight line through the origins of both axes.

2.10 Density

(i) **Definition.** In everyday language lead is said to be 'heavier' than wood. By this is meant that a certain volume of lead is heavier than the same volume of wood. In physics such comparisons are made by using the concept of *density*. This is the *mass per unit volume* of a substance and is calculated from

$$\text{density} = \frac{\text{mass}}{\text{volume}}$$

The density of lead is 11 grams per cubic centimetre (11 g/cm^3 or 11 g cm^{-3}); this means that a piece of lead of volume 1.0 cm^3 has mass 11 g. A volume of 5.0 cm^3 of lead would have mass $11 \times 5.0 = 55$ g. Knowing the density of a substance, the mass of *any* volume can be calculated.

The SI unit of density is the *kilogram per cubic metre* (kg/m^3 or kg m^{-3}). To convert a density from g/cm^3, normally the most suitable unit for the size of sample we use, to kg/m^3, we multiply by 10^3; for example, the density of water is 1.0 g/cm^3 or 1.0×10^3 kg/m^3. (This simple value is due to the fact that originally 1 kg was taken as the mass of 1000 cm^3 of pure water at 4°C.)

The shorthand way of writing the unit of density, that is, kg/m^3, is a reminder that density is calculated by dividing mass by volume.

The approximate densities of some common substances are given in Table 2.1.

Table 2.1 Densities of some common substances

Solids	Density g/cm³	kg/m³	Liquids and gases	Density g/cm³	kg/m³
aluminium	2.7	2700	methylated spirit	0.80	800
copper	8.9	8900	paraffin	0.80	800
iron	7.9	7900	petrol	0.80	800
gold	19.3	19 300	pure water	1.0	1000
glass (window)	2.5	2500	mercury	13.6	13 600
wood (teak)	0.80	800	air	0.0013	1.3
ice	0.90	900	oxygen	0.0014	1.4
polythene	0.90	900	hydrogen	0.00009	0.09

(ii) **Calculations.** Using the symbols d for density, m for mass and V for volume, the expression for density is

$$d = \frac{m}{V}$$

Rearranging the equation gives

$$m = V \times d \quad \text{and} \quad V = \frac{m}{d}$$

These are useful if d is known and m or V has to be calculated. (The Greek letter ρ (rho) is also used as the symbol for density.) If you do not see how they are obtained, refer to the *Mathematics for Physics* section at the end of this book. The triangle in Fig. 2.11 is an aid to remembering them. If you cover the quantity you want—say m—with a finger, its value equals what you can still see, that is, $V \times d$. To find V, cover V and you get $V = m/d$.

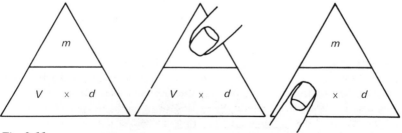

Fig. 2.11

(iii) **Worked example.** Taking the density of copper as 9.0 g/cm^3, find (a) the mass of 5.0 cm^3 of copper and (b) the volume of 63 g of copper.

(a) $d = 9.0 \, \text{g/cm}^3$, $V = 5.0 \, \text{cm}^3$ and m is to be calculated.

$$\therefore m = V \times d = 5.0 \, \text{cm}^3 \times 9.0 \, \text{g/cm}^3 = 45 \, \text{g}$$

(b) $d = 9.0 \, \text{g/cm}^3$, $m = 63 \, \text{g}$ and V is to be calculated.

$$\therefore V = \frac{m}{d} = \frac{63 \, \text{g}}{9.0 \, \text{g/cm}^3} = 7.0 \, \text{cm}^3$$

2.11 Measuring Density

If the mass m and volume V of a material are known, its density d can be calculated from $d = m/V$.

(i) **Regularly shaped solid.** The mass is found on a balance and the volume calculated as in Unit 2.7(i), measuring the dimensions with a ruler, vernier calipers or a micrometer screw gauge, depending on the size.

(ii) **Irregularly shaped solid.** The solid—a pebble or glass stopper, for example—is weighed and its volume found by the displacement method described in Unit 2.7(iii).

(iii) **Liquids.** A known volume is transferred from a burette, pipette or measuring cylinder into a weighed beaker which is then reweighed; the difference between the weighings gives the mass of liquid.

(iv) **Air.** A 500 cm³ round-bottomed flask made of hard glass such as Pyrex is fitted with a rubber stopper, tube and clip and weighed on a sensitive top-pan balance, first when it is full of air (Fig. 2.12), and then after the air is removed using a vacuum pump. The difference gives the mass of air that was in the flask. The volume of the flask (and so that of the air) is found by filling the flask with water and then emptying it into a measuring cylinder.

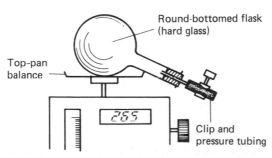

Fig. 2.12

The density of air is about 1.3 kg/m^3, which is small compared with those of solids and liquids but even so it means that the mass of air in a normal-sized laboratory is about one-quarter of a tonne (1 tonne $= 1000 \text{ kg}$).

2.12 Relative Density

The relative density tells you how many times a substance is denser than water, that is,

$$\text{relative density} = \frac{\text{density of substance}}{\text{density of water}} \qquad 1$$

The density of aluminium is 2.7 g/cm^3 and that of water is 1.0 g/cm^3; the relative density of aluminium is therefore 2.7. Relative density has no units and equals numerically the density of the substance in g/cm^3.

Another expression for relative density, which can be obtained from equation 1, is

$$\text{relative density} = \frac{\text{mass of substance}}{\text{mass of same volume of water}} \qquad 2$$

Using equation 2, the relative density and so also the density of a substance can be found just by weighing the sample. In the simple methods outlined in Unit 2.11, the volume measurement is usually less accurate than is the mass measurement using a top-pan balance. Other methods of measuring relative density are described in Units 7.10 and 7.12.

2.13 Revision Questions

1. Name the basic SI units of length, mass and time.

2. Write the following in standard form:
   4000; 200 000; 1 000 000; 2500; 186 000; 0.1; 0.05; 0.29; 0.0076; 0.000 0013.

3. What does it mean if a length is given as (a) 2.5 cm, (b) 2.53 cm?

4. To what accuracy can you read with confidence (a) a metre rule, (b) vernier calipers, (c) a micrometer screw gauge? State one use for each.

5. Write expressions for (a) the circumference of a circle radius r, (b) the area of a circle radius r, (c) the volume of a sphere radius r, and (d) the volume of a cylinder radius r and height h.

6. Name two kinds of balance.

7. Define the term *density* and state two units in which it is measured.

8. How would you measure the density of air?

9. Define the term *relative density*.

2.14 Problems

Length and Volume

1. How many millimetres are there in (*a*) 1 cm, (*b*) 4 cm, (*c*) 0.5 cm, (*d*) 6.7 cm, (*e*) 1 m?

2. Write down these lengths in metres: (*a*) 300 cm, (*b*) 550 cm, (*c*) 870 cm, (*d*) 43 cm, (*e*) 100 mm.

3. How would you use a metre rule to measure (*a*) the circumference of a football, and (*b*) the thickness of a sheet of paper?

4. The pages of a book are numbered 1 to 200 and each leaf is 0.10 mm thick. If each cover is 0.20 mm thick, what is the thickness of the book?

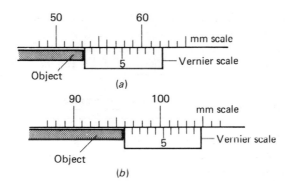

Fig. 2.13

Fig. 2.14   (a)   (b)

5. What are the lengths of the objects in Figs. 2.13(*a*) and (*b*)?

6. What are the screw gauge readings in Figs. 2.14(*a*) and (*b*)?

7. A metal block measures 10 cm ×2.0 cm ×2.0 cm. What is its volume? How many blocks each 2.0 cm ×2.0 cm ×2.0 cm would make up the same value?

8. How many blocks of ice cream each 10 cm ×10 cm ×4.0 cm can be stored in the compartment of a deep-freeze measuring 40 cm ×40 cm ×20 cm?

9. A rectangular block has measurements l=4.1 cm, b=2.8 cm, d=2.1 cm. Calculate its volume, if each measurement is correct to two significant figures.

Density

10. (*a*) If the density of wood is 0.5 g/cm³, what is the mass of (i) 1 cm³, (ii) 2 cm³, (iii) 10 cm³?

(*b*) Find the densities of two objects of (i) mass 100 g and volume 10 cm³, (ii) volume 3 m³ and mass 9 kg?

(*c*) The density of gold is 19 g/cm³. Find the volume of (i) 38 g, (ii) 95 g, of gold.

11. A piece of steel has a volume of 12 cm³ and a mass of 96 g. What is its density in (*a*) g/cm³, (*b*) kg/m³?

12. What is the mass of 5.0 m³ of cement of density 3000 kg/m³?

13. What is the mass of air in a room measuring 10 m × 5.0 m × 2.0 m if the density of air is 1.3 kg/m³?

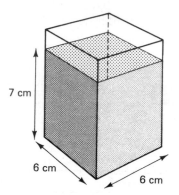

7 cm

6 cm

6 cm

Fig. 2.15

14. A plastic box has a 6 cm square base and contains water to a height of 7 cm (Fig. 2.15).

(*a*) A pebble is lowered into the water so as to be completely covered and the water rises to a height of 9 cm. What is the volume of the stone?

(*b*) If the pebble has mass 180 g, what is its density?

15. If 200 cm³ of water (density 1.0 g/cm³) is mixed with 300 cm³ of methylated spirit (density 0.80 g/cm³), what is the density of the mixture?

16. What is the mass of a metal sphere of density 8400 kg/m³, if its radius is 1.0 × 10⁻² m? (π = 22/7.)

17. A thread of mercury in a narrow glass tube is 0.28 m long and weighs 3.0 × 10⁻³ kg. If the density of mercury is 13 600 kg/m³, find the average diameter of the inside of the tube (that is, its *bore*). (π = 22/7.)

Part Two
Force, Motion and Energy

Unit Three

Forces at Rest

3.1 About Forces

A force is a *push* or a *pull* exerted by one object or *body* on another. It may cause a body at rest to move or one in motion to change its speed or direction; it may also change the shape or size of the body.

Contact forces are those which, like the muscular force you apply when you push an object, involve actual contact between the bodies concerned.

Action-at-a-distance forces act through space and do not need one body to touch the other. Magnetic, electrical and gravitational forces are of this type, and vary with the distance between the bodies.

The SI unit of force is the *newton* (N). The definition, given in Unit 5.4, is based on the change of speed a force can produce on a body. As an illustration, the force to pull the tab off a can of drink is about 20 N.

Forces can be measured by a spring balance calibrated in newtons. A force pulling on the hook stretches the spring until the spring provides an equal opposing force; the greater the force, the more the spring stretches.

3.2 Weight

We all constantly experience the force of gravity, that is, the pull of the earth. It is this force that causes an unsupported body to fall from rest to the ground.

The *weight* of a body is *the force of gravity on it*. The nearer a body is to the centre of the earth, the more the earth attracts it. Since the earth is not a perfect sphere but is slightly flattened at the poles, the weight of a body varies over the earth's surface. It is greater at the poles than at the equator (the mass of a body is the same wherever it is, because it does not depend on the presence of the earth).

Weight, being a force, is expressed in newtons. The weight of an average-sized apple is 1 N or so. It is useful to remember that over most of the earth's surface

the weight of a body of mass 1 kg is 9.8 N.

Often, for convenience, this is taken as 10 N. A mass of 2 kg has a weight of about 20 N, and so on.

While mass is measured by a beam, lever or top-pan balance, weight—being a force—is conveniently measured by a spring balance. Many old spring balances are marked in kilograms or grams; a reading of 1 kg would correspond to 10 N, and a reading of 100 g to 1 N (on earth).

3.3 Stretching Springs and Hooke's Law

The difference between the length of an unstretched spring and its length when it is stretched is called the *extension* of the spring. The arrangement in Fig. 3.1 may be used to show that the extension depends on the stretching force. The bottom of the hanger can act as a 'pointer' for reading the mm scale; it gives the zero extension reading with no load on the hanger. If 100 g masses are added one at a time, the stretching force increases by steps of 1 N and the extension can be read on the mm scale; the extension may then be checked as the masses are removed one by one.

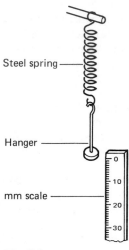

Steel spring

Hanger

mm scale

Fig. 3.1

If you carry out this experiment, you will probably find that at the start—up to a load of about 5 N, perhaps—each extra 1 N of force stretches the spring by the same amount, say 10 mm. Putting it another way, if the force doubles from 1 N to 2 N, the extension doubles as well, from 10 mm to 20 mm; if the force trebles from 1 N to 3 N, the extension trebles from 10 mm to 30 mm, and so on. In other words, the extension is directly proportional to the stretching force, or:

$$\text{extension} \propto \text{stretching force}$$

This is called *Hooke's law*.

You can confirm this by plotting the results of the experiment on a graph of stretching force against extension; Fig. 3.2 illustrates a typical graph, which shows that for extensions up to E, the *elastic limit*, the graph is a straight line through the origin. If the force for a point on the graph beyond E, such as A, is

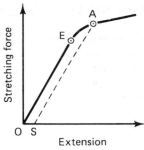

Fig. 3.2

applied to the spring the elastic limit is passed, and on removing the force the spring remains permanently stretched by the length OS.

Hooke's law makes it easy to use a spring as a force-measurer, as in a spring balance.

3.4 Forces and Materials

(i) **Mechanical properties.** When selecting a material for a particular job we need to know how it behaves when forces act on it, that is, what its mechanical properties are.

1. *Strength*. A strong material requires a large force to break it. The strength of some materials depends on how the force is applied. Concrete, for example, is strong when compressed but weak when stretched (that is, in *tension*).

2. *Stiffness*. A stiff material resists forces which tend to change its shape or its size, or both. It is not flexible. All materials 'give' to some extent, although the change may be very small. Steel is strong and stiff, putty is neither. Rope is not stiff but can be strong in tension.

3. *Elasticity*. An elastic material recovers its original shape and size after the force deforming it has been removed. Rubber is elastic; so are steel and most other metals, although the deformations produced in metal objects are usually very small. A material which does not recover but is deformed permanently, like Plasticine, is *plastic*. (Man-made 'plastics' are not always plastic in this sense; they are so called because during manufacture they behave in that way.)

4. *Ductility*. Ductile materials can be rolled into sheets, drawn into wires or worked into other useful shapes without breaking. Metals owe much of their usefulness to this property.

5. *Brittleness*. A brittle material is fragile and breaks suddenly. Bricks and cast iron are brittle; so too is glass, if the force is applied suddenly (for instance, when a tumbler is dropped).

(ii) **Stretching a wire.** Useful information about mechanical properties is

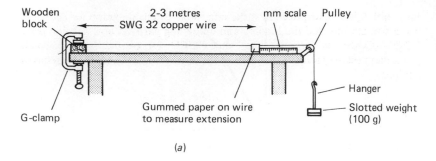

(a)

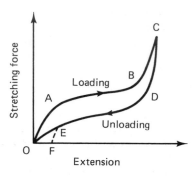

Fig. 3.3　　　　　　　　　(b)

obtained from stretching a long wire of material by gradually loading it using the apparatus in Fig. 3.3(a).

The graph obtained by plotting stretching force against the extension of a wire is similar to that for a spring (Fig. 3.2). Between O and the elastic limit E it is a straight line, showing that Hooke's law holds. At A, the *yield point*, the wire 'runs' and a given increase of stretching force produces a greater extension than before.

Up to E, stretching the wire merely pulls the atoms in the material slightly farther apart; the deformation is elastic and the wire recovers its original length when the load is removed. Beyond A, layers of atoms slip over each other; the deformation is plastic and if unloaded the wire does not return to its original length. A brittle material like glass gives a graph that ends at E, because it breaks almost immediately after the elastic stage, with little or no plastic deformation—that is, glass is non-ductile.

Metals used in engineering structures should carry only loads which deform them elastically.

(iii) **Rubber.** Many materials, including most metals and glass, obey Hooke's law; rubber is an exception. A stretching force–extension graph for rubber is not a straight line and the loading and unloading parts do not coincide (Fig. 3.3(*b*)—OABC is for stretching and CDEO for contracting). A small permanent set may remain as shown by the dotted line EF. Polythene behaves similarly.

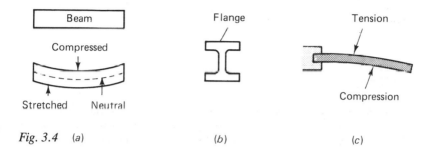

Fig. 3.4   (*a*)   (*b*)   (*c*)

3.5 Beams and Structures

(i) **Beams.** Beams are the simplest and the commonest parts of larger structures. When a beam bends one side is compressed and the other is stretched; the centre (a neutral plane) is unstressed (Fig. 3.4(*a*)). I-shaped steel girders (Fig. 3.4(*b*)) are in effect beams that have had material removed from the neutral plane and so have the advantage of lightness. The top and bottom flanges withstand the compression and tension forces due to loading. In a cylindrical beam the removal of unstressed material so as to form a hollow tube gives similar advantages.

A cantilever (Fig. 3.4(*c*)) is a beam which is supported at only one end. An aircraft wing is a cantilever.

(ii) **Bridges.** An arched stone bridge (Fig. 3.5(*a*)) is designed so that the stone is in compression, since stone is weak in tension. In arch-supported beam bridges (Fig. 3.5(*b*) and (*c*)) the arch may be of steel or concrete.

A girder bridge (Fig. 3.6(*a*)) has no material in the neutral plane and is strengthened by diagonal bars. The top of the bridge is under compression and the bottom under tension.

Fig. 3.5 (*a*)   (*b*)   (*c*)

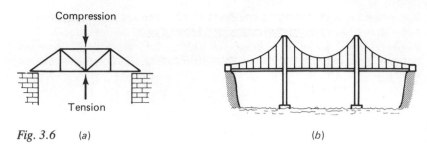

Fig. 3.6   (a)   (b)

Suspension bridges are in effect supported beams (Fig. 3.6(*b*)). Some of the largest bridges in the world are of this type.

(iii) **Cracks and fracture.** A notch, crack or scratch on the surface of a brittle material like concrete or glass spreads more readily under tension than under compression (Fig. 3.7). Hence one kind of pre-stressed concrete contains steel rods that are in tension because they were stretched while the concrete was poured on them and set. As well as resisting tension forces, they keep the concrete in compression even if the whole structure is not.

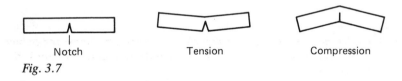

Notch   Tension   Compression

Fig. 3.7

When a structure is designed, the effect of notches must be guarded against, for example, by designing the structure so that the parts are under compression (as in the arch of a bridge). Another method is to use a laminated material consisting of alternate strong and weak layers, in which any cracks that pass through a strong layer spread out and are stopped when they reach a layer of more yielding material. The same principle applies in the use of fibres of glass or carbon to reinforce plastics. In the manufacture of safety glass, the formation of notches is avoided by making the glass surface very smooth.

3.6 Moment of a Force

(i) **Definition.** Sometimes a force acting on a body makes it turn, as a door turns on its hinge when it is opened or closed. Opening a door is easy, because the handle is fixed at the outside edge; a much larger force would be needed if the handle were near the hinge. Similarly it is easier to turn a nut with a long spanner than with a short one.

The *turning effect* or *moment of a force* about a point depends on both the size of the force and how far it is applied from the turning point, called the

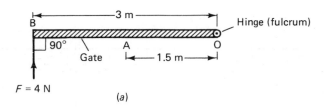

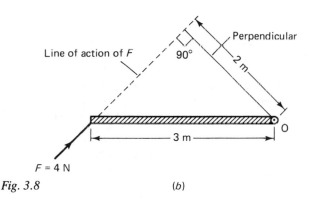

Fig. 3.8 (b)

pivot or *fulcrum*. It is calculated by multiplying the force by the perpendicular distance of the line of action of the force from the fulcrum. The unit is the *newton metre* (N m).

moment of a force about a point
=force ×perpendicular distance from the point

In Fig. 3.8(*a*) a force *F* acts on a gate at right angles:

moment of *F* about O =4 N ×3 m =12 N m

In Fig. 3.8(*b*), the force acts on the gate at an angle, so that

moment of *F* about O =4 N ×2 m =8 N m

The calculated turning effect of *F* is thus greater in (*a*) than in (*b*); this agrees with our experience that a gate opens most easily when it is pulled at right angles.

In (*a*) the moment of *F* about A, the mid-point of the gate, is only 6 N m and that about B is zero (since it is at zero distance from it, and 4 N ×0 m =0).

A *clockwise moment* tries to produce turning in a clockwise direction about the point being considered: thus *F* has a clockwise moment about O in Figs. 3.8(*a*) and (*b*). An *anticlockwise moment* has a turning effect in an anticlockwise direction about the point.

Where several forces act in the same direction, the moments about a given point can be added together.

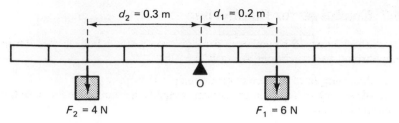

Fig. 3.9

(ii) **Principle of moments.** In Fig. 3.9 a metre rule (or similar rod) is supported at its centre and different known masses hung from it at various points along its length, so that a series of different forces is applied to it. The rule is balanced or, as we say, *in equilibrium* if the clockwise turning effect equals the anticlockwise turning effect.

This illustrates the *principle of moments*, which is stated as follows:

When a body is in equilibrium the sum of the clockwise moments about any point equals the sum of the anticlockwise moments about the same point.

In Fig. 3.9, taking moments about O:

$$\text{clockwise moment} = F_1 \times d_1 = 6\,\text{N} \times 0.2\,\text{m} = 1.2\,\text{N m}$$
$$\text{anticlockwise moment} = F_2 \times d_2 = 4\,\text{N} \times 0.3\,\text{m} = 1.2\,\text{N m}$$

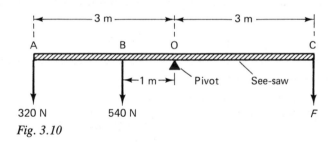

Fig. 3.10

(iii) **Worked example.** If the see-saw in Fig. 3.10 is balanced, find F. Taking moments about O:

$$\text{clockwise moment} = (F \times 3)\,\text{N m}$$
$$\text{anticlockwise moments} = 540 \times 1 + 320 \times 3$$
$$= 540 + 960 = 1500\,\text{N m}$$

By the principle of moments,

$$\text{clockwise moment} = \text{anticlockwise moments}$$
$$\therefore F \times 3 = 1500$$
$$\therefore F = 500\,\text{N}$$

3.7 Conditions for Equilibrium

(i) **Parallel forces.** If a number of parallel forces act on a body so that it is in equilibrium, two conditions are satisfied:

1. the principle of moments must apply;
2. the sum of the forces in one direction equals the sum of the forces in the opposite direction.

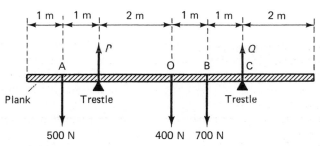

Fig. 3.11

As an example consider Fig. 3.11, which shows diagrammatically two people of weights 500 N and 700 N standing at A and B on a plank resting on two trestles. The whole weight of the plank (400 N) may be taken to act vertically downwards at its centre, O (we shall discuss the reason for this in Unit 3.8). If P and Q are the upwards forces exerted by the trestles on the plank (called *reactions*) then we have from (2) above:

$$P + Q = 500 + 400 + 700 = 1600 \text{ N}$$

Moments can be taken about any point, but taking them about C eliminates the moment due to the force Q.

clockwise moment $= (P \times 4) \text{ N m}$
anticlockwise moments $= (700 \times 1 + 400 \times 2 + 500 \times 5) \text{ N m}$
$= 700 + 800 + 2500 \text{ N m}$
$= 4000 \text{ N m}$

Since the plank is in equilibrium we have, from (1):

$$4P = 4000$$
$$\therefore P = 1000 \text{ N}$$

But $P + Q = 1600 \text{ N}$
$$\therefore Q = 600 \text{ N}$$

(ii) **Couples.** Two equal but opposite parallel forces form a *couple*; a couple causes rotation. When you steer a bicycle round a bend with both hands on the handle-bars (Fig. 3.12) you apply a couple.

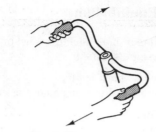

Fig. 3.12

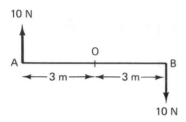

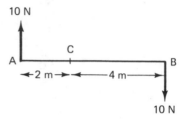

(a) Clockwise moment
    about O = 10 × 3 + 10 × 3
            = 60 N m

(b) Clockwise moment
    about C = 10 × 2 + 10 × 4
            = 60 N m

Fig. 3.13

The *moment of a couple* can be found by taking the moments of the forces about any point and then adding them. In Fig. 3.13 the moment of a couple is calculated about two different points, O and C; clearly, the result obtained is the same whichever point is taken, and is given by

moment of a couple = force × perpendicular distance between forces
$$= 10\,N \times 6\,m = 60\,N\,m$$

A couple can only be balanced by an equal and opposite couple.

3.8 Centres of Gravity

A body behaves as if its whole weight were concentrated at one point, called its *centre of gravity* (c. of g.) or *centre of mass*, even though the earth attracts every part of it. The c. of g. of a metre rule is at its centre and when supported there it balances (Fig. 3.14(a)). If it is supported at any other point it topples (Fig.3.14(b)), because the moment of its weight W about the point of support is not zero.

The c. of g. of a regularly shaped body of the same density all over is at its

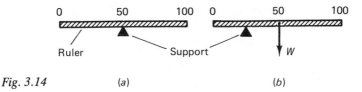

Fig. 3.14   (a)   (b)

centre (which means that for some objects, such as hoops or hollow balls, it is not even in the body). For other bodies it can be found by experiment.

(i) **Finding the c. of g. of a flat object.** For an irregularly shaped lamina (a thin sheet) of cardboard, a hole A is made in it so that it can swing freely on a nail

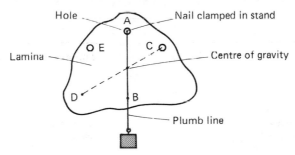

Fig. 3.15

clamped in a stand (Fig. 3.15). It comes to rest with its c. of g. vertically below A. A vertical line AB is drawn on the lamina through A by tying a plumb line (a thread and weight) to the nail and marking its position on the lamina. The c. of g. lies on AB.

If the lamina is now hung from another position C and the plumb line position CD marked, then the c. of g. also lies on CD. It must therefore be at the point where AB and CD intersect.

The experiment can be repeated for a third position such as E, to check that the third line passes through the same point.

(ii) **Stability.** The position of the c. of g. of a body affects whether or not it topples over easily.

In Fig. 3.16(*a*), for instance, the can has been tilted but is in *stable equilibrium*; this means that, when released, it returns to its rest position because of the restoring action of the moment of its weight *W*. If a body is in stable equilibrium its c. of g. rises when it is slightly displaced and the vertical line from its c. of g. falls inside the base.

In Fig. 3.16 (*b*) the displaced can is in *unstable equilibrium*, that is, it topples when released: the c. of g. falls and the vertical line from the c. of g. falls outside the base of the can.

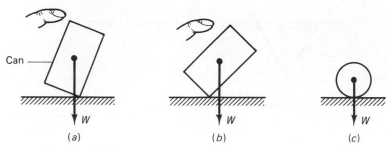

Fig. 3.16 (a) Stable, (b) unstable, (c) neutral

In Fig. 3.16(c) the can is on its side and is in *neutral equilibrium*—when displaced it stays in its new position and the c. of g. neither rises nor falls.
   A stable body will have

1. a low c. of g., and
2. a base with a proportionately large area.

When such a body is displaced, the chance of the vertical line from the c. of g. falling outside the base is slight. Racing cars have a low c. of g. and a wide wheelbase.

3.9 Adding Forces

(i) **Resultant of two forces.** When two forces act at the same point it is sometimes useful to know the size and direction of the single force, called the *resultant*, which would have exactly the same effect as the two forces.

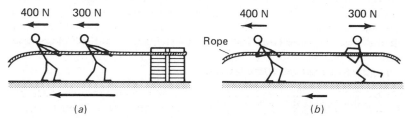

Fig. 3.17 (a) Resultant 700 N to left, (b) resultant 100 N to left

If the forces act in the same direction, as the 300 N and 400 N forces do in Fig. 3.17(a), the resultant is found by simple addition—700 N. If they act in opposite directions (Fig. 3.17(b)) simple subtraction gives the resultant, 100 N. If the forces act at an angle to each other, their resultant is found using the *parallelogram law*.

(ii) **Parallelogram law.** Suppose we have to find the resultant of the two forces of 300 N and 400 N acting at a point O, at the angle shown in Fig. 3.18(a). The procedure is as follows:

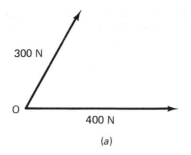

(a)

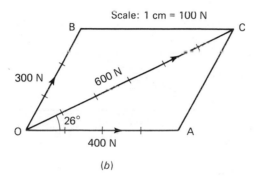

Fig. 3.18   (b)

1. From O, draw two lines in the directions in which the forces act, with lengths OA and OB representing the sizes of the forces to some scale (here 1 cm = 100 N is convenient).

2. Draw two more lines AC and BC to complete the parallelogram.

3. Draw the diagonal OC and measure its length (Fig. 3.18(b)).

The parallelogram law states that OC represents the resultant in both magnitude (size) and direction. In this example it is a force of 600 N at an angle of 26° to the 400 N force.

The general statement of the law is as follows:

If two forces acting at a point are represented in size and direction by the sides of a parallelogram drawn from the point, their resultant is represented in size and direction by the diagonal of the parallelogram drawn from the same point.

(iii) **Vectors and scalars.** A *vector* quantity is one which is described completely only if both its magnitude and its direction are stated. Force is an example of a vector quantity. A vector can be represented by a straight line whose length represents the magnitude of the quantity and whose direction gives its line of action. An arrow on the line shows which way along the line the vector acts. Vectors are added by the parallelogram law.

A *scalar* quantity has magnitude only. Mass is an example of a scalar quantity and is completely described when its value is known. Scalars are added by ordinary arithmetic: a mass of 300 kg added to one of 400 kg always gives a mass of 700 kg. By contrast, a force of 300 N added to one of 400 N gives a resultant of anything between 100 N and 700 N depending, as we have seen, on the direction of the forces.

3.10 Resolving a Force

The parallelogram law enables two forces to be replaced by one. Sometimes the reverse is needed, and one force has to be split or *resolved* into two forces called its *components*, which together have the same effect as the single force. Usually it is most useful to take the components at right angles to each other.

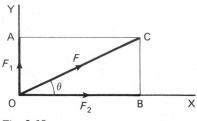

Fig. 3.19

Suppose that in Fig. 3.19 OC represents a force F and that we want to find the components of F along OX and OY where angle XOY is 90°. If the rectangle OACB is drawn, its sides OA and OB represent the required components F_1 and F_2 on the same scale on which OC represents F. For example, if $F = 200$ N and angle COB is 30°, then a scale drawing will show that $F_1 = 100$ N and $F_2 = 173$ N.

By applying simple trigonometry to triangle COB you can show that

$$F_2 = F \cos \theta \text{ and } F_1 = F \sin \theta$$

Resolving a force helps to explain how a boat can be towed along a canal by a rope pulled from the bank. In Fig. 3.20, F is the actual force pulling the boat at

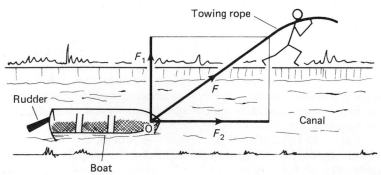

Fig. 3.20

O. F_2 is the useful part of F which moves the boat along. F_1 just tries to pull it into the bank and is counteracted by using the rudder to point the boat slightly away from the towing bank. A yacht is able to sail into the wind for similar reasons.

3.11 Friction

Friction is the force that opposes a surface while it is moving, or trying to move, over another. Friction arises, firstly, because all surfaces have minute 'humps' and 'hollows' which catch in each other and, secondly, because the molecules of the two surfaces tend to 'stick' together when they are pressed into contact.

Friction can be a help or a hindrance. We could not walk if there was no friction between the soles of our shoes and the ground. Our feet would slip backwards, as they tend to when we walk on ice. It is also used in most vehicle braking systems. On the other hand, engineers try to reduce friction in the moving parts of machinery to a minimum, by using lubricating oils and ball bearings.

(i) **Static and dynamic friction.** When a gradually increasing force P is applied through a spring balance to a block on a table (Fig. 3.21), the block does not move at first. This is because an equally increasing but opposing frictional force F acts where the block and table touch.

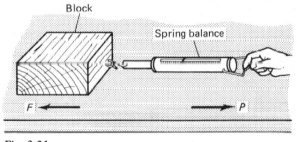

Fig. 3.21

If P is increased further the block eventually moves; at the instant that it does so F has its maximum value, called *starting* or *static* friction. When the block is moving at a steady speed the balance reading is slightly less than this maximum: *sliding* or *dynamic* friction is therefore less than static friction.

Putting a mass on the block increases the force pressing the surfaces together and increases friction.

(ii) **Fluid friction.** Friction also opposes the motion of bodies moving through fluids (that is, through liquids and gases), and *increases with speed*. Fluid friction, in the form of air resistance, is the largest of all the frictional forces opposing a car travelling at high speed. Car body design attempts to reduce it to a minimum.

3.12 Revision Questions

1. Name (*a*) five effects a force can have on a body, and (*b*) the unit of force.

2. What is meant by the weight of a body? How is it measured and in what unit? Is it always the same for a given body? Explain your answer.

3. (*a*) How does a spring behave if it obeys Hooke's law?
   (*b*) What is meant by the elastic limit?

4. Explain the following terms used to describe the mechanical properties of materials: (*a*) strength, (*b*) stiffness, (*c*) elasticity, (*d*) ductility, (*e*) brittleness.

5. (*a*) Draw a diagram to show which parts of a loaded beam are under (i) compression, (ii) tension.
   (*b*) Why are steel girders (beams) often I-shaped?
   (*c*) Name three types of bridge.
   (*d*) Why is it important not to have a brittle material under tension in a structure?

6. (*a*) What is meant by the moment of a force? How is it measured?
   (*b*) State the principle of moments.

7. If a body is in equilibrium under the action of a number of parallel forces, what two conditions must be satisfied?

8. What is a couple? What effect does it have on a body, and how is this effect measured?

9. What is meant by the centre of gravity (mass) of a body? How would you find it for an irregularly shaped lamina?

1   2   3

Fig. 3.22

10. (*a*) State two ways in which the stability of a body can be increased.
    (*b*) Fig. 3.22 shows a ball in three different situations. State for each whether it is in stable equilibrium, unstable equilibrium or neutral equilibrium.

11. (*a*) What is meant by the resultant of two forces?
    (*b*) What is the parallelogram law used for?

12. Distinguish between a scalar quantity and a vector quantity, and give an example of each.

13. What is meant by resolving a force?

14. (*a*) When does friction occur?
   (*b*) Give one example where friction is a help and one where it is a nuisance.
   (*c*) Distinguish between static and dynamic friction.

3.13 Problems

Weight and Springs
1. If a body of mass 1.0 kg has weight 10 N at a certain place, what will be the weight of bodies of mass (*a*) 100 g, (*b*) 5.0 kg, (*c*) 50 g?

2. The force of gravity on the moon is one-sixth of that on earth. What would a mass of 12 kg weigh (*a*) on the earth and (*b*) on the moon?

3. Fig. 3.23 shows four diagrams of the same spring, which obeys Hooke's law. What is (*a*) the length *x*, (*b*) the mass *M*?

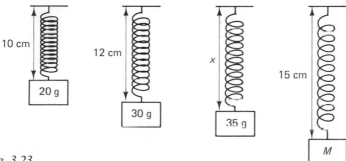

Fig. 3.23

4. In a stretched spring experiment the following measurements were obtained:

Mass hung from spring (g)	0	100	200	300	400	500	600	700	800
Stretching force (N)									
Length of spring (mm)	60	72	84	96	108	120	132	150	180
Extension (mm)									

(*a*) Copy and complete the table.
(*b*) Plot a graph of stretching force against extension.
(*c*) Mark the elastic limit of the spring and say over which region Hooke's law is obeyed.

5. Write down the reading of each of the spring balances marked X and Y in Fig. 3.24.

Moments and Centres of Gravity
6. The half-metre rules in Fig. 3.25 are marked off at intervals of 5 cm. Identical metal discs are placed on the rules as shown. State whether each rule turns clockwise, turns anticlockwise or is balanced. Explain your answers.

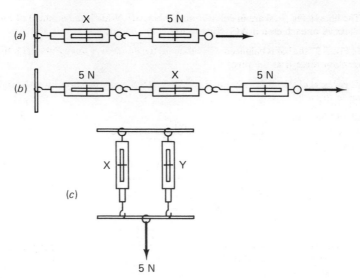

Fig. 3.24

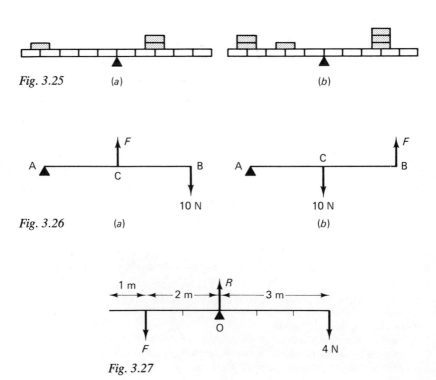

Fig. 3.25   (a)   (b)

Fig. 3.26   (a)   (b)

Fig. 3.27

7. The bars in Fig. 3.26 are in equilibrium (balanced). What is the moment of force F about A in each case if AC=CB=1 m?

8. In Fig. 3.27 the bar is balanced. Calculate (*a*) the moment of force F about O, (*b*) the reaction force R at the pivot.

9. The weight of the uniform bar in Fig. 3.28 is 10 N. Does it balance, tip to the right or tip to the left?

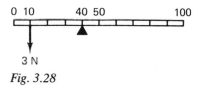

Fig. 3.28

10. The uniform plank in Fig. 3.29 weighs 200 N, rests on two trestles and supports a boy of weight 500 N. P and Q are the reaction forces at A and B.
    (*a*) Write down the moment of each force about A.
    (*b*) Use the principle of moments to calculate Q.
    (*c*) What is the total upward force $P+Q$?
    (*d*) What is the value of P?

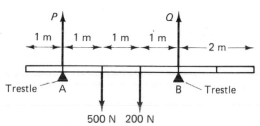

Fig. 3.29

11. What is the moment of the couple in Fig. 3.30?

Fig. 3.30

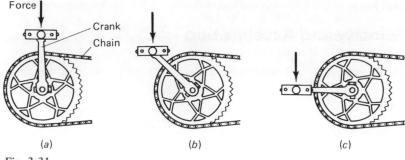

Force

Crank

Chain

(a)   (b)   (c)

Fig. 3.31

12. Three positions of the pedal on a bicycle which has a crank 0.10 m long are shown in Fig. 3.31. If a cyclist exerts the same vertically downwards push of 25 N with his foot, in which case is the turning effect (i) $25 \times 0.2 = 5\,N\,m$, (ii) 0, (iii) between 0 and $5\,N\,m$? Explain your answers.

Adding and Resolving Forces

13. Forces of 3 N and 4 N act at the same point.
    (*a*) What is the largest resultant they can produce?
    (*b*) What is the smallest resultant they can produce?
    (*c*) If they act at right angles to each other, find by a scale drawing (or otherwise) the size and direction of their resultant.

14. Using a scale of 1 cm to represent 10 N, find the size and direction of the resultant of forces of 30 N and 40 N acting (*a*) at right angles to each other, (*b*) at 60° to each other.

15. Tom, Dick and Harry are pulling a metal ring. Tom pulls with a force of 100 N and Dick with a force of 140 N at an angle of 70° to Tom. If the ring does not move, what force is Harry exerting?

16. The roller in Fig. 3.32 is being pushed with a force of 200 N at an angle of 30° to the ground.
    (*a*) What are the vertical and horizontal components of the force?
    (*b*) The roller weighs 500 N. What is the total downward force on the ground when it is pushed?
    (*c*) If the roller is pulled with the same force (instead of being pushed), what is the total downward force on the ground?

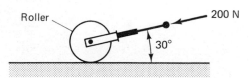

Roller   200 N

30°

Fig. 3.32

Velocity and Acceleration

4.1 Speed

The *average speed* of a moving object can be calculated from the formula

$$\text{average speed} = \frac{\text{distance moved}}{\text{time taken}}$$

If distance is measured in metres (m) and time in seconds (s), the speed is given in metres per second (m/s or m s^{-1}). A car which travels 1000 m in 100 s has an average speed of 1000 m/100 s = 10 m/s.

Unless the car is on a straight, traffic-free road, however, its speed is likely to change during the time it takes to travel 1000 m. To find its *actual speed* at any instant we would need to know the distance covered in a very short time interval. This can be found using multiflash photography. For example, the golfer in Fig. 4.1 was photographed while a flashing lamp illuminated him 100 times a second. The actual speed of the club-head as it hit the ball was about 50 m/s.

Fig. 4.1

4.2 Velocity

Speed is the distance travelled in unit time; *velocity* is the distance travelled in unit time *in a stated direction*. It is calculated from the relationship

$$\text{velocity} = \frac{\text{distance moved in a stated direction}}{\text{time taken}}$$

Clearly, if two cars travel due north at 20 m/s, they have the same speed of 20 m/s and the same velocity of 20 m/s due north. If one travels north and the other south, their speeds are the same but their velocities are different, since their directions of motion are different. Speed is a scalar; velocity, on the other hand, is a vector quantity (see Unit 3.9(iii)) and velocities can, like forces, be added by the parallelogram law.

Distance moved in a stated direction is called *displacement*. It is a vector, unlike distance which is a scalar. It follows from the formula above that velocity is also given by

$$\text{velocity} = \frac{\text{displacement}}{\text{time taken}}$$

The velocity of a body is *uniform* or *constant* if it moves with a steady speed in a straight line (that is, if the direction of motion stays the same). If either the speed or the direction changes, the velocity changes. In this Unit we will consider only straight-line motion, so that the only velocity changes we shall deal with are due to changes in speed alone.

The units of speed and velocity are the same—metres per second, kilometres per hour. It is useful to remember that

$$72 \text{ km/h} = 72\,000 \text{ m}/3600 \text{ s} = 20 \text{ m/s}$$

4.3 Acceleration

A body *accelerates* when its velocity increases. If a car starting from rest (0 m/s) on a straight road has a velocity of 2 m/s after 1 second, its velocity has increased by 2 m/s in 1 second. We say that its acceleration is 2 m/s per second, which is written 2 m/s^2 (or 2 m s^{-2}).

Acceleration is the *change of velocity in unit time*. In this example the change is an increase and the acceleration is calculated from

$$\text{acceleration} = \frac{\text{increase of velocity}}{\text{time taken}}$$

In real life, it is usually average accelerations that concern us. Acceleration is also a vector quantity and strictly speaking both its magnitude (size) and direction should be stated. Since we are at present dealing only with straight-line motion, however, we can for simplicity's sake take acceleration as the change of speed in unit time.

Velocity: 0 m/s   5 m/s   10 m/s   15 m/s   20 m/s

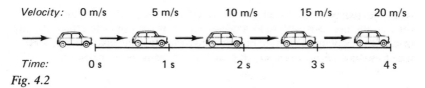

Time: 0 s   1 s   2 s   3 s   4 s

Fig. 4.2

The speeds of the accelerating car shown in Fig. 4.2 after successive seconds are given below:

Time (s)	0	1	2	3	4
Speed (m/s)	0	5	10	15	20

The speed increases by 5 m/s every second. The acceleration is *uniform* and equals 5 m/s². If the speed of the car then decreased by 5 m/s every second, it would have a *deceleration* or *retardation* of 5 m/s², that is, an acceleration of -5 m/s².

4.4 Distance–Time Graphs

It is often useful to represent the motion of a body by plotting a graph of distance moved against time taken.

(i) **Uniform velocity.** A body travelling with uniform velocity covers equal distances in equal times. Its distance–time graph is a straight line, as in Fig. 4.3(*a*), which is drawn for a body travelling with uniform velocity of 10 m/s. The slope or gradient of the line (given by y/x) $=40/4=10$, which is the value of the velocity. It is true in general that

the gradient of a distance–time graph equals the value of the velocity.

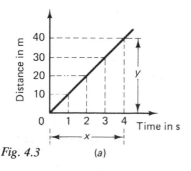

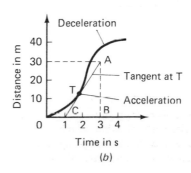

Fig. 4.3   (a)   (b)

(ii) **Changing velocity.** When a body accelerates the gradient of the distance–time graph increases with time; deceleration has the opposite effect. At any instant the slope of the tangent gives the velocity at that time. In Fig. 4.3(b), which is drawn for a body which first accelerates and then decelerates, the slope of the tangent at T is AB/BC = 30/2 = 15, that is, the velocity at the time corresponding to T is 15 m/s.

4.5 Velocity–Time Graphs

If the velocity of a body is plotted against time, a velocity–time graph is obtained which gives information about the distance moved by the body and its acceleration at different times. It enables us to solve problems on motion, using two rules.

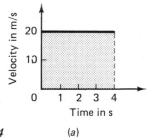 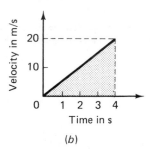

Fig. 4.4   (a)   (b)

(i) **Rule 1:** *area under graph equals distance moved.* Fig. 4.4(a) shows the velocity–time graph for a body moving with a uniform velocity of 20 m/s. After 4 seconds it will have moved 20 m/s ×4 s =80 m. This is the shaded area under the graph using the values on the graph scales (*not* distances on the graph paper); the unit of time *must* be the same on both axes.

A velocity–time graph for uniform acceleration from rest is given in Fig. 4.4(b). Using the rule, we can write:

$$\text{distance moved in 4 s} = \text{area of shaded triangle}$$
$$= \tfrac{1}{2} \times \text{base} \times \text{height}$$
$$= \tfrac{1}{2} \times 4\,\text{s} \times 20\,\text{m/s}$$
$$= 40\,\text{m}$$

This rule works even if the acceleration is not uniform.

(ii) **Rule 2:** *gradient of graph equals acceleration.* For instance, in Fig. 4.4(a) the gradient of the graph is zero, as is the acceleration. In Fig. 4.4(b), the gradient is 20/4 = 5 giving an acceleration of 5 m/s^2, that is, the velocity has increased by 5 m/s at the end of successive time intervals of 1 second.

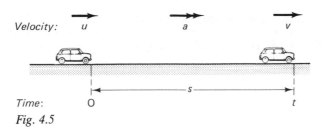

Fig. 4.5

4.6 Equations of Motion

Problems on bodies moving with *uniform acceleration* can often be solved quickly using one or more of the equations of motion. Look, for example, at Fig. 4.5, where

u = initial velocity of the car, that is, its velocity at the point where timing starts;

a = uniform acceleration of the car,

v = final velocity of the car, that is, its velocity at the point where timing ends,

t = time for the car's velocity to increase from u to v, and

s = distance car travels in time t (the displacement).

These quantities can be shown to be connected by the following equations (if you are interested in seeing how they are obtained you will find their derivation in Appendix 2):

$$v = u + at \qquad \qquad \qquad 1$$
$$s/t = (u + v)/2 \qquad \qquad 2$$
$$s = ut + \tfrac{1}{2}at^2 \qquad \qquad 3$$
$$v^2 - u^2 + 2as \qquad \qquad 4$$

If we know any *three* of u, a, v, t and s, the others can be found from the equations.

4.7 Worked Example

A cyclist starts from rest and accelerates at $1.0\,\text{m/s}^2$ for 20 seconds. He then travels with constant velocity for 1 minute and finally decelerates at $2.0\,\text{m/s}^2$ until he stops. Find his maximum velocity and the total distance travelled.

First stage (acceleration):

$\qquad\qquad u = 0$ (since he starts from rest),

$\qquad\qquad a = 1.0\,\text{m/s}^2$,

$\qquad\qquad t = 20\,\text{s}$, and

$\qquad\qquad v$ is the maximum velocity to be found.

The equation containing all these quantities is

$$v = u + at$$
$$\therefore \quad v = 0 + 1.0 \times 20 = 20 \text{ m/s}$$

To find the distance s moved in the first stage we use
$$s = ut + \tfrac{1}{2}at^2$$
$$= 0 \times 20 + \tfrac{1}{2} \times 1.0 \times 20^2$$
$$= 200 \text{ m}$$

Second stage (constant velocity):
$$\text{velocity} = 20 \text{ m/s}$$
$$\text{time} = 60 \text{ s}$$
$$\therefore \quad \text{distance} = \text{velocity} \times \text{time (since velocity is constant)}$$
$$= 20 \times 60 \text{ m}$$
$$= 1200 \text{ m}$$

Third stage (deceleration):
$$u = \text{velocity at start of deceleration} = 20 \text{ m/s}$$
$$v = \text{final velocity} = 0$$
$$a = \text{deceleration} = -2.0 \text{ m/s}^2$$
s is the distance travelled in coming to rest.

The equation containing all these quantities is

$$v^2 = u^2 + 2as$$

$$\therefore s = \frac{v^2 - u^2}{2a} = \frac{0 - (20)^2}{2(-2)} = \frac{-400}{-4}$$

$$= 100 \text{ m}$$

$$\therefore \text{ Total distance travelled} = 200 + 1200 + 100$$
$$= 1500 \text{ m}$$

4.8 Tickertape Timer

The motion of a trolley in the laboratory can be studied using a tickertape timer (Fig. 4.6). Equal time intervals are marked by dots on tickertape attached to the trolley. The dots occur at 1/50 s (0.02 s) intervals, so that the distance between successive dots equals the distance moved by the trolley in 0.02 s, that is, its average velocity in cm per 'tick' where 1 tick = 0.02 s. The greater the velocity, the further apart are the dots.

Tape charts can be made by sticking consecutive strips of tape (usually ten-tick or ten-dot lengths, that is, each representing 0.2 s) side by side, and these enable velocities and accelerations to be measured. The chart in Fig. 4.7 represents a body moving with *uniform velocity*, since equal distances are

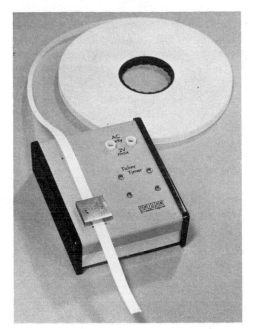

Fig. 4.6

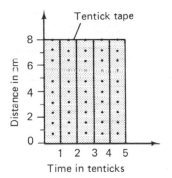

Fig. 4.7

covered in each tentick interval. The velocity is 8 cm/tentick = 8 cm/0.2 s = 40 cm/s.

The chart in Fig. 4.8(*a*) is for *uniform acceleration*; the 'steps' are of equal size showing that the velocity increased by the same amount in every tentick. The average velocity during the *first* tentick is 2 cm/0.2 s or 10 cm/s. During the *sixth* tentick it is 12 cm/0.2 s or 60 cm/s. And so during this interval of 5

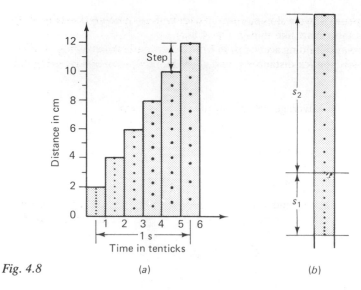

Fig. 4.8   (a)   (b)

tenticks (that is, $5 \times 0.2\,\text{s} = 1\,\text{s}$), the change of velocity is $(60 - 10)\,\text{cm/s} = 50\,\text{cm/s}$. We can therefore find the average acceleration, since

$$\text{acceleration} = \frac{\text{increase of velocity}}{\text{time taken}}$$

$$= \frac{50\,\text{cm/s}}{1\,\text{s}}$$

$$= 50\,\text{cm/s}^2$$

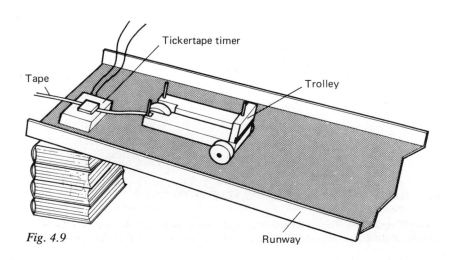

Fig. 4.9

A trolley runs down a sloping runway with uniform acceleration (Fig. 4.9) and gives a tape chart like that in Fig. 4.8(*a*).

Another way of finding acceleration from tickertape is shown in Fig. 4.8(*b*). Two *successive* tentick distances s_1 and s_2 are marked, each one covering 0.2 seconds.

$$\text{average velocity } v_1 \text{ over } s_1 = \frac{s_1}{0.2} = 5s_1$$

$$\text{average velocity } v_2 \text{ over } s_2 = \frac{s_2}{0.2} = 5s_2$$

$$\therefore \text{ change in velocity} = v_2 - v_1 = 5(s_2 - s_1)$$

We can consider v_1 and v_2 as the velocities at the middle of successive 0.2-second intervals, so the change in velocity $(v_2 - v_1)$ occurs in 0.2 seconds.

$$\therefore \text{ acceleration} = \frac{5(s_2 - s_1)}{0.2}$$

$$\text{or} \quad \underline{\underline{a = 25(s_2 - s_1)}}$$

It is useful to remember this expression.

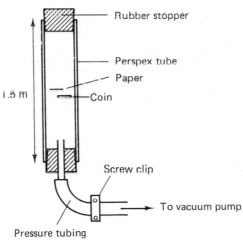

Fig. 4.10

4.9 Acceleration and Falling Bodies

(i) **Falling bodies.** If you drop a coin and a bit of paper at the same moment, the coin falls faster than the paper does. In a vacuum they fall at the same rate, however, as may be shown with the apparatus of Fig. 4.10. In air the paper is slowed down much more than the coin is, because of the action of *air resistance*. As we will see in Unit 5.9, this affects light objects—especially if they have a large surface area—more than it affects heavy ones.

Experiment shows that all bodies falling freely under the force of gravity do so with *uniform acceleration* if air resistance is negligible, as it is for small dense objects falling short distances. A tape chart consisting of successive one-tick lengths, obtained using the arrangement in Fig. 4.11 for a falling mass, will confirm that this is so by having equal 'steps'.

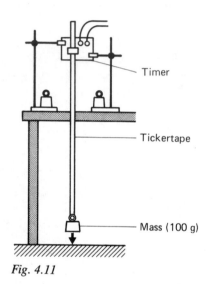

Fig. 4.11

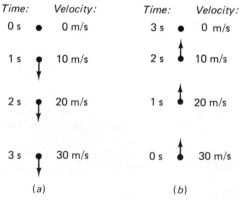

Fig. 4.12 (a) Falling body, (b) rising body

(ii) **Acceleration due to gravity.** The acceleration of a freely falling body, called the *acceleration due to gravity*, is denoted by the italic letter g. Its value is about 9.8 m/s^2 (for approximate purposes it can be taken as 10 m/s^2 but it does vary slightly from one place on earth to another). Thus where air resistance is negligible, the velocity of a falling body increases by 10 m/s every second (Fig. 4.12(a)). On the other hand an object shot straight upwards with a velocity of 30 m/s *decelerates* by 10 m/s every second and reaches its highest point after 3 seconds (Fig. 4.12(b)).

In calculations using the equation of motion, g replaces a. It is given a positive sign for falling bodies (that is, $a = +10 \text{ m/s}^2$) and a negative sign for rising bodies since they are decelerating ($a = -10 \text{ m/s}^2$).

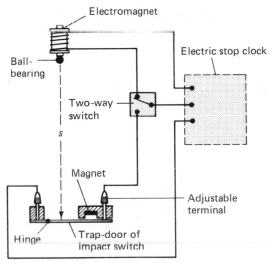

Fig. 4.13

4.10 Measuring g

A method of finding the value of g directly is shown in Fig. 4.13, where the time for a steel ball bearing to fall a known distance is measured accurately by an electric stop clock.

When the two-way switch is turned to the 'down' position, the electromagnet releases the ball and simultaneously the clock starts. At the end of its fall the ball opens the 'trap-door' on the impact switch and the clock stops.

The result is calculated from $s = ut + \frac{1}{2}at^2$ where s is the distance fallen (in metres), t is the time taken in seconds, $u = 0$ (the ball starts from rest) and $a = g$ (in m/s^2). Hence

$$s = \tfrac{1}{2}gt^2 \text{ or } g = 2\,s/t^2$$

4.11 Worked Example

An object is shot vertically upwards with an initial velocity of 30 m/s. Find (*a*) its maximum height, (*b*) the time it takes to return to its starting point. Neglect air resistance, and take $g = 10 \, \text{m/s}^2$.

(*a*) We have $u = 30$ m/s, $a = -10$ m/s^2 (a deceleration) and $v = 0$ since the object is momentarily at rest at its highest point. Substituting in

$$v^2 = u^2 + 2\,as,$$
$$0 = 30^2 + 2(-10)s \text{ or } -900 = -20\,s$$

$$\therefore s = \frac{-900}{-20} = 45 \, \text{m}$$

(*b*) If t is the time to reach the highest point, we have from

$$v = u + at$$
$$0 = 30 + (-10)\,t \text{ or } -30 = -10\,t$$

$$\therefore t = \frac{-30}{-10} = 3.0 \, s$$

The downward trip takes exactly the same time as the upward one and so the time taken to return to the starting-point is 6 s.

4.12 Projectiles

The photograph in Fig. 4.14 was taken while a lamp emitted regular flashes of light. One ball was dropped from rest and the other, a *projectile*, was thrown sideways at the same time. Their vertical accelerations due to gravity are equal, showing that a projectile falls like a body which is dropped from rest. Its horizontal velocity remains constant (ignoring the small effect of air resistance) and does not affect its vertical motion. *The horizontal and vertical motions of a projectile are independent and can be treated separately.*

For example, if a ball is thrown horizontally from the top of a cliff and takes 2 seconds to reach the sea below we can calculate the height of the cliff by considering the vertical motion only. We have $u = 0$ (since the ball has no vertical motion initially), $a = g = +10$ m/s^2 and $t = 2$ s. The height s of the cliff is given by $s = ut + \frac{1}{2}at^2 = 0 \times 2 + \frac{1}{2}(+10)2^2 = 20 \, \text{m}$.

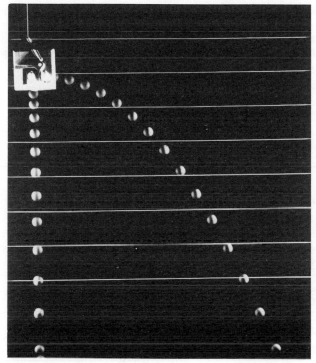

Fig. 4.14

4.13 Revision Questions

1. How does velocity differ from speed?

2. How does acceleration differ from velocity? State a unit in which each is measured.

3. Explain the terms (*a*) uniform velocity, (*b*) uniform acceleration.

4. What does the gradient of a distance–time graph tell you?

5. Say how you could obtain from a velocity–time graph (*a*) the distance moved in a certain time, (*b*) the acceleration at a certain time.

6. Write down the four equations for uniform acceleration, stating what each symbol means.

7. Describe the motion of a body falling freely under gravity if air resistance is negligible.

8. Does the horizontal motion of a projectile affect its vertical motion?

4.14 Problems

Speed, Velocity, Acceleration
1. Calculate the average speed of (*a*) a car which travels 400 m in 20 s, (*b*) an athlete who runs 1500 m in 4 minutes.

2. A train increases its speed steadily from 10 m/s to 20 m/s in 1 minute.
   (*a*) What is its average speed during this time in m/s?
   (*b*) How far does it travel while increasing its speed?

3. A motor cyclist starts from rest and reaches a speed of 6 m/s after travelling with uniform acceleration for 3 s. What is his acceleration?

4. A vehicle moving with a uniform acceleration of 2 m/s^2 has a velocity of 4 m/s at a certain time. What will its velocity be (*a*) 1 s later, (*b*) 5 s later?

5. If a body travelling at 20 m/s is subject to a steady deceleration of 5.0 m/s^2, how long will it take to come to rest?

6. An aircraft flying at 600 km/h accelerates steadily at 10 km/h per second. Taking the speed of sound as 1100 km/h at the aircraft's altitude, how long will it take to reach the 'sound barrier'?

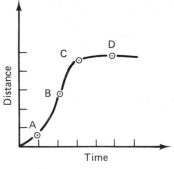

Fig. 4.15

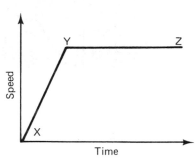

Fig. 4.16

Distance–Time and Velocity–Time Graphs
7. The distance–time graph for a vehicle on a straight road is shown in Fig. 4.15. Describe the motion at A, B, C and D.

8. The speed–time graph for a moving object is shown in Fig. 4.16. Describe the motion along (*a*) XY, (*b*) YZ.

9. The graph in Fig. 4.17 represents the distance travelled by a car plotted against time.
   (*a*) How far has the car moved at the end of 5 s?
   (*b*) What is the average speed of the car during the first 5 s?
   (*c*) What has happened to the car's motion after A?

10. Fig. 4.18 shows an uncompleted velocity–time graph for someone running a distance of 100 m.
    (*a*) What is the acceleration during the first 4 s?
    (*b*) What distance is covered during (i) the first 4 s, (ii) in the next 10 s?

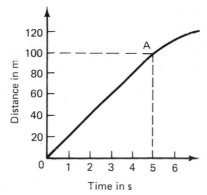

Fig. 4.17

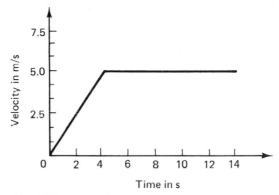

Fig. 4.18

(c) Copy and complete the graph to find how long this person takes to run 100 m (assuming the velocity stays constant at 5 m/s).

Equations of Motion

11. A body starts from rest and reaches a speed of 5 m/s after travelling with uniform acceleration for 2 s. Calculate its acceleration.

12. An object starts from rest and moves with a steady acceleration of 2 m/s^2.
    (a) What is its velocity after 5 s?
    (b) How far has it travelled in this time?
    (c) When will it be 100 m from its starting-point?

13. A car accelerates from 4.0 m/s to 20 m/s in 8.0 s. How far does it travel in this time?

14. A motor cyclist travelling at 12 m/s decelerates at 3.0 m/s^2.
    (a) How long does he take to come to rest?
    (b) How far does he travel in coming to rest?

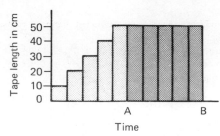

Fig. 4.19

Tape Charts

15. Each strip in the tape chart of Fig. 4.19 is for a time interval of 1 tentick.

(*a*) If the timer makes 50 dots per second, what time intervals are represented by OA and OB?

(*b*) Find the acceleration between O and A in (i) cm/tentick^2, (ii) cm/s per tentick, (iii) cm/s^2.

(*c*) What is the acceleration between A and B?

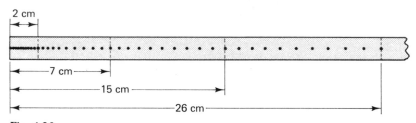

Fig. 4.20

16. The tape in Fig. 4.20 was pulled through a timer by a trolley travelling down a runway. It was marked off in tentick lengths.

(*a*) What can you say about the trolley's motion?

(*b*) Find its acceleration in cm/s^2.

Acceleration due to Gravity

Ignore air resistance, and take $g = 10$ m/s^2.

17. A stone falls from the top of a high tower.

(*a*) Find its velocity after (i) 1 s, (ii) 2 s, (iii) 3 s, (iv) 5 s.

(*b*) Calculate how far it will have fallen after (i) 1 s, (ii) 2 s, (iii) 3 s, (iv) 5 s.

18. An object is dropped from a height of 80 m.

(*a*) How long does it take to reach the ground?

(*b*) What is its velocity as it hits the ground?

19. An object is shot upwards from the ground with a velocity of 30 m/s.

(*a*) Find its velocity after (i) 1 s, (ii) 2 s, (iii) 3 s, (iv) 5 s, (v) 6 s.

(*b*) How high does it rise?

Projectiles

20. An object is released from an aircraft travelling horizontally with a constant velocity of 200 m/s at a height of 500 m.

    (a) How long does the object take to reach the ground?

    (b) What is the horizontal distance travelled by the object between leaving the aircraft and reaching the ground?

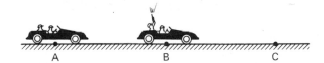

Fig. 4.21   A   B   C

21. A gun pointing vertically upwards is fired from an open car B moving with uniform velocity. When the bullet returns to the level of the gun, car B has travelled to C and another car A has reached the position occupied by B when the gun was fired (Fig. 4.21). Are the occupants of A or B in danger?

Unit Five

Newton's Laws of Motion

5.1 First Law

If the engine of a moving car is switched off, friction and air resistance bring it to rest. If these and other opposing forces were absent we believe that a body, once set in motion, would go on moving for ever with a constant speed in a straight line. That is, force is not needed to keep a body moving with uniform velocity so long as no opposing forces act on it.

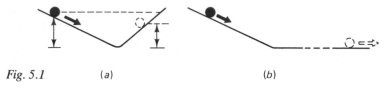

Fig. 5.1   (a)   (b)

This idea was proposed by Galileo (1564–1642) and arose from his 'two inclined planes experiment', shown diagrammatically in Fig. 5.1(a), in which he found that a ball allowed to roll down one smooth slope, rose to very nearly the same height on the other. He felt that only friction stopped the ball from reaching the height on the second slope that it had started from on the first. He predicted that if the second plane was horizontal (Fig. 5.1(b)) and if friction was absent, the ball would go on moving for ever (or until a force stopped it).

Newton (1642–1727) developed Galileo's work into the three laws of motion, the first being a summary of Galileo's ideas:

A body stays at rest, or if moving it continues to move with uniform velocity, unless an external force makes it behave differently.

It seems that the question we should ask about a moving body is not 'what keeps it moving?' but 'what changes or stops its motion?'. The smaller the external forces opposing a moving body, the smaller is the force needed to keep it moving with uniform velocity.

5.2 Mass and Inertia

Newton's first law is another way of saying that all matter has a built-in opposition to being moved if it is at rest or, if it is moving, to having its motion changed. This property of matter is called *inertia*.

Its effect is evident on the occupants of a car which stops suddenly; they

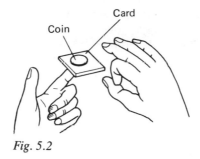

Fig. 5.2

lurch forward in an attempt to continue moving. The reluctance of a stationary object to move can be shown by placing a large coin on a piece of card on your finger (Fig. 5.2); if the card is flicked *sharply* the coin stays where it was while the card flies off.

The larger the mass of a body the greater is its inertia, that is, the more difficult it is to move when at rest and to stop when in motion. Because of this we consider that the *mass of a body measures its inertia*. This is a better definition of mass than the one given in Unit 2.8, where it was stated to be the 'amount of matter' in a body.

5.3 Effect of Force and Mass on Acceleration

To accelerate, a body must be acted on by a resultant force. The acceleration a produced depends on both the size of the force F and the mass m of the body. The relationship between a, F and m can be investigated using trolleys on a runway and a timer. Stretched lengths of elastic provide the forces acting on the trolleys. The runway should first be compensated for friction by raising one end until the trolley runs down with uniform velocity when pushed. There is then no resultant force on the trolley and any acceleration produced during the experiment will be due only to the force caused by the stretched elastic.

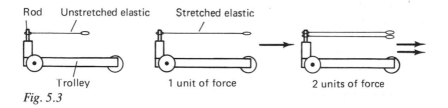

Fig. 5.3

(i) **F and a (m constant).** Three different forces are applied in turn to one trolley by fixing first one, then two and finally three identical elastics to the rod at the back of the trolley and stretching them until the other end is level with the front of the trolley (Fig. 5.3). A tape chart is produced for each force and the corresponding acceleration worked out from it (as in Unit 4.8) in cm/tentick^2. The unit of force is taken as one elastic stretched to a certain length, and the unit of mass as the mass of one trolley.

The results should show, firstly, that a steady force produces a steady acceleration. They should also show that if F is doubled, a roughly doubles; if F is trebled, a is trebled. That is, a is *directly proportional* to F when m is constant.

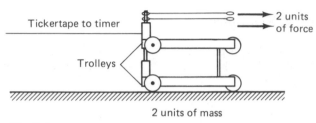

Fig. 5.4

(ii) **m and a (F constant).** The experiment is carried out as in (i), using two elastics (that is, F is constant) to accelerate first one trolley, then two stacked one on top of the other (Fig. 5.4), and finally a stack of three. Accelerations are again worked out from the tape charts.

This experiment should show that a is halved if m is doubled, and reduced to a third if m is trebled. That is, a is *inversely proportional* to m when F is constant.

5.4 Second Law

From the experiment in Unit 5.3, we can say that

1. if the mass is constant, the acceleration a is directly proportional to the force F producing it, that is, $a \propto F$, and

2. for a fixed force, the acceleration a is inversely proportional to the mass m, that is, $a \propto 1/m$.

Combining these two relationships into one equation gives

$$a \propto F/m \text{ or } F \propto ma$$

In words, the force is directly proportional to the quantity 'mass $\times$ acceleration'. This can be written as a mathematical equation in the form

$$F = kma$$

where k is a constant of proportionality.

If we now define the unit of force—the *newton* (N)—as *the force which gives a mass of 1 kg an acceleration of 1 m/s^2*, this equation simplifies. From the definition of the newton, if $m=1$ kg and $a=1$ m/s² then $F=1$ N. Substituting in $F=kma$ gives $1=k\times1\times1$, so that $k=1$, and we can write

$$F=ma$$

This is the mathematical statement of Newton's second law of motion. Notice two points about it: first, F is the *resultant* or *unbalanced* force causing the acceleration a; second, F must be in N, m in kg and a in m/s² (otherwise k is not 1).

5.5 Worked Examples

1. A block of mass 2 kg is pushed along a table with a constant velocity by a force of 5 N. When the push is increased to 9 N, what is (*a*) the resultant force, (*b*) the acceleration?

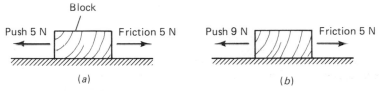

Fig. 5.5 (a) Resultant =0, (b) resultant =4 N

When the block moves with constant velocity its acceleration a is zero and the resultant force F on it must also be zero (from $F=ma$). The forces acting on it are balanced and so the force of friction opposing its motion must be 5 N (Fig. 5.5(*a*)).

(*a*) When the push is increased to 9 N, the resultant (unbalanced) force F on the block is now $(9-5)$ N (since the frictional force is still 5 N) $=4$ N (Fig. 5.5(*b*)).

(*b*) The acceleration a is obtained from $F=ma$ where $F=4$ N and $m=2$ kg,

$$\therefore 4=2\times a$$
$$a=2\text{ m/s}^2$$

2. A car of mass 1200 kg travelling at 20 m/s is brought to rest in 4.0 s. Find (*a*) the average deceleration, (*b*) the average braking force, (*c*) the distance moved during the deceleration.

(*a*) The deceleration is found from $v=u+at$ where $v=0$, $u=20$ m/s and $t=4.0$ s. Hence

$$0=20+a\times4.0 \text{ or } -20=4a$$
$$\therefore a=-20/4=-5.0\text{ m/s}^2$$

(b) The average braking force F is given by $F=ma$ where $m=1200$ kg and $a=-5.0$ m/s². Therefore

$$F=1200 \times (-5.0) = -6000 \text{ N}$$

(c) To find the distance moved s we use $s=ut+\frac{1}{2}at^2$:

$$\therefore s=20 \times 4.0 + \frac{1}{2} \times (-5.0) \times (4.0^2)$$
$$= 80-40 = 40 \text{ m}$$

5.6 Weight and Gravity

The weight W of a body is the force of gravity acting on it, which gives it an acceleration g when it is falling freely near the earth's surface. If the body has mass m, we can use the relationship $F=ma$ to calculate W, by putting $F=W$ and $a=g$. This gives

$$W=mg$$

If we take $g=10$ m/s² and $m=1$ kg, this equation gives $W=10$ N, that is, a body of mass 1 kg has weight 10 N. Similarly, a body of mass 2 kg has weight 20 N and so on. While the mass of a body is always the same, its weight varies depending on the value of g. On the moon the acceleration due to gravity is only about 1.6 m/s² which means a 1 kg mass has a weight of just 1.6 N there.

The weight of a body is directly proportional to its mass, which explains why g is the same for all bodies. Thus the greater the mass of a body, the greater is the force of gravity acting on it; it does not accelerate faster when falling, however, because of its greater inertia (that is, its greater resistance to acceleration).

5.7 Gravitational Field Strength

The force of gravity acts through space; it is an action-at-a-distance force. We 'explain' it by saying that the earth is surrounded by a *gravitational field* which exerts a force on any body in the field. (Later in this book we shall introduce magnetic and electric fields to explain other action-at-a-distance forces.)

The strength of a gravitational field is defined as the gravitational force acting on unit mass in the field.

Near the earth's surface the gravitational field strength is therefore 10 N/kg since a mass of 1 kg experiences a force of 10 N (that is, its weight is 10 N). It is denoted by g, the symbol used for the acceleration due to gravity.

We now have two ways of regarding g. First, when considering bodies falling freely near the earth's surface we can think of it as an *acceleration* of approximately 10 m/s². Second, we can think of it as the *gravitational force* of 10 N acting on each kg of mass of a body near the earth's surface.

5.8 Third Law

Forces never occur singly but always in pairs as a result of the action between two bodies. For example, when you step forward from rest your foot pushes backwards on the earth and the earth exerts an equal but opposite force forward on you: two bodies and two forces are involved. The small force you exert on the large mass of the earth gives no noticeable acceleration to the earth but the equal force it exerts on your very much smaller mass causes you to accelerate. The equal and opposite forces do not act on the *same* body, of course; if they did, there could never be any resultant forces and acceleration would be impossible.

This behaviour of forces is summed up by Newton's third law of motion:

*If a body A exerts a force on body B, then body B
exerts an equal but opposite force on body A.*

The law is sometimes stated in the form:

To every action there is an equal and opposite reaction.

Fig. 5.6

You really need to appreciate the third law and the effect of friction when stepping from a rowing boat (Fig. 5.6). You push backwards on the boat and, although the boat pushes you forwards with an equal force, it is itself now moving backwards (because friction with the water is slight); this reduces your forwards motion by the same amount—and you might fall in!

5.9 Air Resistance

When an object falls in air, the air resistance opposing its motion increases as its speed rises, so reducing its acceleration. Eventually, air resistance acting upwards equals the weight of the object acting downwards. The resultant force on the object is then zero (since the two opposing forces balance) and the object falls with a constant velocity called its *terminal velocity* whose value depends on its size, shape and weight.

A small dense object such as a steel ball-bearing has a high terminal velocity and falls a considerable distance with a constant acceleration of about 10 m/s^2 before air resistance equals its weight. A light object such as a raindrop, or one with a large surface area such as a parachute, has a low terminal velocity and accelerates over only a comparatively short distance before air resistance equals its weight. A 'sky diver' has a terminal velocity of more than 50 m/s (100 miles per hour).

5.10 Momentum and Impulse

Momentum is a useful quantity to consider when bodies are involved in collisions and explosions. It is defined as the mass of the body multiplied by its velocity:

$$\text{momentum} = \text{mass} \times \text{velocity}$$

If mass is measured in kg and velocity in m/s, momentum is measured in kg m/s. A 2.0 kg mass moving at 10 m/s has momentum 20 kg m/s, the same as the momentum of a 5.0 kg mass moving at 4.0 m/s.

(i) **Force and momentum.** If a steady force F acting on a body of mass m increases its velocity from u to v in time t, the acceleration a is given by

$$a = (v - u)/t \qquad (\text{from } v = u + at)$$

Substituting for a in $F = ma$ gives

$$F = \frac{m(v - u)}{t} = \frac{mv - mu}{t} \qquad\qquad 1$$

where mv is the final momentum and mu the initial momentum. Therefore

$$\text{force} = \frac{\text{change of momentum}}{\text{time}} = \text{change of momentum per second}$$

This is another version of the second law of motion. For some problems it is more useful than $F = ma$.

(ii) **Impulse and momentum.** Rearranging equation 1 gives

$$Ft = mv - mu$$

In words,

$$\text{force} \times \text{time} = \text{change of momentum}$$

The quantity 'force $\times$ time' (Ft) is called the *impulse* of the force on the body. It is measured in N s (if F is in N and t in s) or kg m/s. We can therefore write

$$\text{impulse} = \text{change of momentum}$$

(a)

(b)

Fig. 5.7

(iii) **Sport and momentum.** The good cricketer or tennis-player 'follows through' with the bat or racquet when striking the ball (Fig. 5.7(a) and (b)). The force applied then acts for a longer time, the impulse is greater and so also is the gain of momentum (and velocity) of the ball.

When we want to stop a moving body such as a cricket ball, however, its momentum has to be reduced to zero. An impulse is then required in the form of an opposing force acting for a certain time. While any number of combinations of force and time will give a particular impulse, the 'sting' can be removed from the catch by drawing back the hands as the ball is caught. A smaller average force is then applied for a longer time.

5.11 Conservation of Momentum

(i) **Principle of conservation of momentum.** This is an important principle which can be deduced from the second and third laws of motion and confirmed by experiment.

> *When two or more bodies act on one another, as in a collision,*
> *the total momentum of the bodies remains constant,*
> *provided no external forces (such as friction) act.*

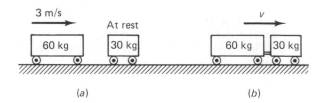

(a)   (b)

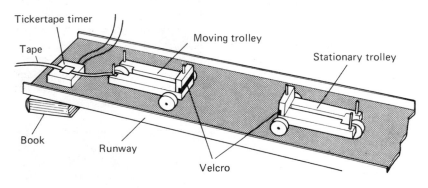

Fig. 5.8   (c)

The principle can be useful in solving problems. Suppose, for example, a truck of mass 60 kg moving with velocity 3.0 m/s collides and couples with a stationary truck of mass 30 kg (Fig. 5.8(a)). The two move off together with the same velocity v (Fig. 5.8(b)). We can use the principle of conservation of momentum to find v.

Total momentum before collision $=(60 \times 3.0 + 30 \times 0)$ kg m/s
$\qquad\qquad\qquad\qquad\qquad\qquad = 180$ kg m/s

Total momentum after collision $\quad=(60 + 30)\, v$ kg m/s
$\qquad\qquad\qquad\qquad\qquad\qquad = 90\, v$ kg m/s

Since momentum is not lost, $90\, v = 180$ or $v = 2.0$ m/s

The principle follows from the fact that when two bodies collide, each exerts the same force on the other for the same time and so they receive *equal but opposite impulses*. As a result, from the impulse–momentum equation in Unit 5.10(ii), we can conclude that the momentum lost by one equals that gained by the other, that is, none is lost.

An experimental test of the principle may be made using the simple arrangement in Fig. 5.8(c) for inelastic ('no bounce') collisions. The trolley at the top of the friction-compensated runway (see Unit 5.3) is given a push; when it hits the stationary trolley halfway down the runway, the Velcro strips stick to each other and the trolleys move on together with the same velocity. The velocities are found from the tickertape attached to the top trolley and passing through a timer. The total momentum before the collision can then be calculated taking 'one trolley' as the unit of mass.

The procedure may be repeated with another trolley stacked on top of the one to be pushed, so that two are moving before the collision and three afterwards.

(ii) **Explosions.** Momentum, like velocity, is a vector quantity since it has both magnitude (size) and direction. Vectors cannot be added by ordinary addition unless they act in the same direction. If they act in exactly opposite directions, the smaller subtracts from the greater; if they are equal they cancel.

Momentum is conserved in an explosion such as that which occurs when a rifle is fired. Before firing, the total momentum is zero since both rifle and bullet are at rest. During the firing the rifle and the bullet receive *equal* but *opposite* amounts of momentum so that the total momentum after firing is zero.

For example, if a rifle fires a bullet of mass 0.010 kg with a velocity of 300 m/s (Fig. 5.9(a) overleaf), then

forward momentum of bullet $\quad =0.010 \text{ kg} \times 300 \text{ m/s}$
$\qquad\qquad\qquad\qquad\qquad\qquad =3.0 \text{ kg m/s}$
$\therefore$ backward momentum of rifle $\quad =3.0 \text{ kg m/s}$

If the rifle has mass m, it recoils (kicks back) with a velocity v such that

$$mv = 3.0 \text{ kg m/s}$$

Taking $m = 6$ kg gives

$$v = 3.0/6.0 = 0.5 \text{ m/s}$$

The principle of conservation of momentum can be tested experimentally for 'explosions' with the arrangement in Fig. 5.9(b). One tape from each trolley goes to a tickertape timer. When one of the buffer rods is tapped, the spring inside is released and the trolleys fly apart. The velocities v_1 and v_2 of each can be worked out from the tapes. Since the trolleys are initially at rest, the total momentum before the explosion is zero. Therefore the total momentum afterwards should also be zero, that is, $m_1v_1 - m_2v_2 = 0$ where m_1 and m_2 are the masses of the trolleys; if $m_1 = m_2$ then v_1 should equal v_2 in size (although, of course, v_1 and v_2 are in opposite directions).

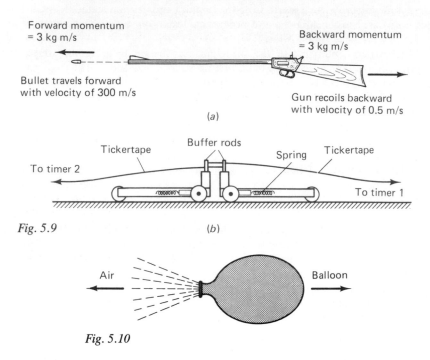

Forward momentum = 3 kg m/s

Backward momentum = 3 kg m/s

Bullet travels forward with velocity of 300 m/s

Gun recoils backward with velocity of 0.5 m/s

(a)

Tickertape   Buffer rods   Spring   Tickertape

To timer 2

To timer 1

Fig. 5.9   (b)

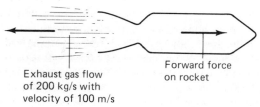

Air   Balloon

Fig. 5.10

5.12 Rockets and Jets

(i) **Principle.** If an inflated balloon is released with its neck open, it flies off in the direction opposite to that of the escaping air. In Fig. 5.10 the air has momentum to the left and the balloon moves to the right with equal momentum.

This is the principle of rockets and jet engines (see Units 12.3 and 12.4). In both, a high-velocity stream of hot gas is produced by burning fuel and leaves the exhaust with large momentum. The rocket or jet engine itself acquires an equal forward momentum.

Exhaust gas flow of 200 kg/s with velocity of 100 m/s

Forward force on rocket

Fig. 5.11

(ii) **Worked example.** Exhaust gas leaves the rocket in Fig. 5.11 at the rate of 200 kg/s with a velocity of 100 m/s. What is the forward force on the rocket?

The momentum form of the second law of motion states:

$$\text{force} = \text{change of momentum per second}$$

Here, 200 kg of gas increases its velocity from 0 to 100 m/s in 1 second, therefore

$$\text{change of momentum of gas per second} = 200 \text{ kg} \times 100 \text{ m/s per s}$$
$$= 20\,000 \text{ kg m/s per s}$$
$$\text{Hence, forward force on rocket} = 20\,000 \text{ N}$$

5.13 Circular Motion

You will be very familiar with examples of bodies moving in paths that are circular or nearly so—chair-o-planes at a fun fair, clothes in a spin dryer, the planets going round the sun and the moon circling the earth. When a car turns a corner it may follow an arc of a circle. Throwing the hammer is a sport practised at highland games in Scotland, in which the hammer is whirled round and round before it is released.

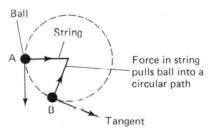

Fig. 5.12

(i) **Centripetal force.** In Fig. 5.12 a ball attached to a string is being whirled round in a horizontal circle. Its direction of motion is constantly changing. At A it is along the tangent at A; shortly afterwards, at B, it is along the tangent at B and so on.

Velocity is speed in a stated direction and if the direction of a moving body changes, even if its speed does not, then its velocity changes too. A change of velocity is an acceleration and so during its whirling motion the ball is accelerating.

It follows from the first law of motion that if we consider a body moving in a circle to be accelerating, then there must be a force acting on it to cause the acceleration. The force accelerating the whirling ball is provided by the string pulling inwards on the ball. Like the acceleration, the force acts towards the centre of the circle and keeps the ball at a fixed distance from the centre. A larger force F is needed if

1. the speed v of the ball is increased, since this increases the rate of change of the ball's direction, that is, the acceleration;
2. the radius r of the circle (the length of the string) is decreased, since this also increases the acceleration;
3. the mass m of the ball is increased—this follows from $F=ma$, since if m increases while a is kept constant, F must also increase.

It can be shown that $a = v^2/r$, and therefore these quantities are related by

$$F = ma = mv^2/r$$

Should the force become greater than the string can bear, the string breaks and the ball flies off with steady speed in a straight line along the tangent, that is, in the direction it had when the string broke (as the first law predicts). It is not thrown outwards.

The force which acts *towards the centre*, so keeping a body in a circular path, is called the *centripetal force* (centre-seeking force). Whenever a body moves in a circle (or circular arc) there must be a centripetal force acting on it. In throwing the hammer, the centripetal force is the pull of the athlete's arms acting on the hammer towards the centre of the whirling path. When a car rounds a bend a frictional force is exerted inwards by the road on the tyres.

(ii) **Universal gravitation.** Newton proposed the theory that all objects in the universe attract each other with a force he called *gravitation*. The gravitational attraction between two ordinary objects, such as two 1 kg bags of sugar 1 m apart, is extremely small and difficult to detect. The greater the masses of the objects and the smaller their separation, the more they attract each other.

Newton suggested that the gravitational attraction of the sun for the planets was the centripetal force which kept the planets in near-circular orbits round the sun. He regarded gravity as the gravitational attraction of the earth for nearby objects and saw it as being responsible for holding the moon in its orbit round the earth. Newton united the physics of earthly and celestial bodies by showing that the same laws applied to both.

5.14 Space Travel

(i) **Satellite orbits.** To put an artificial satellite or a space capsule into a circular orbit at a certain height above the earth it must enter the orbit at the correct speed. If it does not, the force of gravity, which decreases with increasing height, will not be equal to the centripetal force needed for the orbit. The nearer the orbit is to the earth, the greater must be the speed (Fig. 5.13). Doubling the mass of a satellite doubles the centripetal force required, and the extra force is provided by the gravitational pull of the earth being twice as great. A satellite may move in an ellipse-shaped orbit if it does not have the correct speed for a circular orbit.

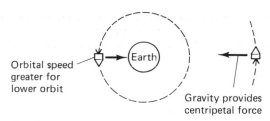

Orbital speed greater for lower orbit

Gravity provides centripetal force

Fig. 5.13

At a height of 200 km or so (that is, just above the earth's atmosphere) an orbit speed of about 8 km/s is required. The earth's natural satellite, the moon, has an orbit speed of 1 km/s. To escape completely from the earth an object must be launched at 11 km/s, called the *escape speed*.

(ii) **Weightlessness.** An astronaut orbiting the earth in a space vehicle with its rocket motors off is sometimes described as being 'weightless'. If weight means the pull of the earth on a body, then the statement, although commonly used, is misleading. A body is not truly weightless unless it is outside the earth's (or any other) gravitational field, whereas in fact it is gravity that keeps an astronaut and his vehicle in orbit.

On earth, we are made aware of our weight because the ground (or whatever supports us) exerts an *upward* push on us as a result of the *downward* push our feet exert on the ground. It is this upward push which makes us 'feel' the force of gravity. When a lift suddenly starts upwards the push of the floor on our feet increases and we feel heavier; on the other hand, if the support is reduced when the lift starts moving downwards we seem to be lighter. In fact we judge our weight from the upward push exerted on us by the floor. If our feet are completely unsupported we experience weightlessness. Passengers in a lift which had a continuous downward acceleration equal to *g* would get no support from the floor, since they too would be falling with the same acceleration as the lift. There would be no upward push on them and they would feel no sensation of weight.

An astronaut in an orbiting space vehicle is not unlike a passenger in a freely falling lift. The astronaut is moving with constant speed along the orbit, but since he is travelling in a circle he has a centripetal acceleration, which is of the same value as that of his space vehicle and is equal to *g* at that height. The walls of the vehicle exert no force on him; he is unsupported and floats about with no apparent weight—he appears to be 'weightless'. To be strictly accurate we should not apply the term to him, however, unless by weight we were to mean the force exerted on (or by) a body by (or on) its support and usually we do not.

5.15 Revision Questions

1. State Newton's first law of motion.

Fig. 5.14

2. What is meant by the term *inertia*? How is it measured for a body?

3. Explain (*a*) why it is dangerous to step off a moving train on to a platform (Fig. 5.14), (*b*) why an umbrella can be 'dried' by turning it upside down and rapidly closing and opening it, and (*c*) why drops of water on the roof of a car fall off at the back when the car starts and at the front when it stops.

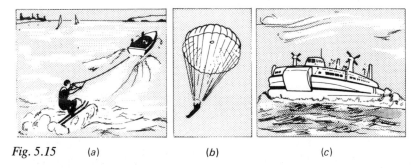

Fig. 5.15   (a)   (b)   (c)

4. In Fig. 5.15 the water skier in (*a*), the parachutist in (*b*) and the hovercraft in (*c*) are moving in a straight line with constant speed. State what forces are acting on each, and say how they compare in size.

5. (*a*) What is the mathematical statement of Newton's second law of motion?
   (*b*) Define the SI unit of force.

6. (*a*) Define the term *gravitational field strength*.
   (*b*) What is its value near the earth's surface?

7. (*a*) State Newton's third law of motion.
   (*b*) Two pairs of action–reaction forces exist when a book lies at rest on a table. What are they?

8. The forces acting on a falling raindrop are shown in Fig. 5.16. *A* is the force causing it to fall and *B* is the force opposing its motion.
   (*a*) What is *A* called?

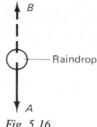

Fig. 5.16

(b) What is B called?
(c) What happens to the raindrop when A = B?

9. (a) How is the momentum of a body calculated?
   (b) What is the unit of momentum?
   (c) What is the momentum form of Newton's second law of motion?
   (d) How is the impulse of a force calculated?

10. State the principle of conservation of momentum.

11. Explain the principle on which rockets and jet engines work.

12. (a) Why is a body moving in a circle with constant speed accelerating?
    (b) What is the name of the force needed to keep a body moving in a circle?

5.16 Problems

Laws of Motion

1. Which of the diagrams in Fig. 5.17 shows the arrangement of forces which gives the
   block M the greatest acceleration?

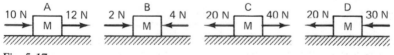

Fig. 5.17

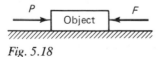

Fig. 5.18

2. In Fig. 5.18, if P is a force of 20 N and the object moves with constant velocity, what
   is the value of the opposing force F?

3. What force produces an acceleration of 5.0 m/s² in a car of mass 1000 kg? What force
   would be required to give the same acceleration to a truck of mass 2000 kg?

4. What acceleration is produced in a mass of 2.0 kg by a force of 30 N? If twice this force acted on half the mass, what would be the acceleration?

5. A car of mass 500 kg accelerates steadily from rest to 40 m/s in 20 s.
   (a) What is its acceleration?
   (b) What force produces this acceleration?
   (c) The actual force will be greater than your answer to (b). Why?

6. A block of mass 500 g is pulled from rest on a horizontal frictionless bench by a steady force F and travels 8.0 m in 2.0 s. Find (a) the acceleration, (b) the value of F.

7. A rocket has a mass of 500 kg.
   (a) What is its weight on earth where the gravitational field strength is 10 N/kg?
   (b) At lift-off the rocket engine exerts an upward force of 25 000 N. What is the resultant force on the rocket? What is its initial acceleration?

Momentum and Impulse

8. The velocity of a body of mass 10 kg increases from 4.0 m/s to 8.0 m/s when a force acts on it for 2.0 s.
   (a) What is the momentum of the body before the force has acted?
   (b) What is the momentum of the body after the force acts?
   (c) What is the momentum gain per second?
   (d) What is the value of the force?

9. (a) What is the impulse of a force of 5 N acting for 2 s?
   (b) How great is the impulse which gives a 10 kg mass a change of velocity of 2 m/s?
   (c) What happens to the velocity of a 3 kg mass when an impulse of 6 N s is applied to it?

10. A football of mass 0.50 kg has a velocity of 20 m/s after a kick lasting 0.025 s. Find (a) the gain of momentum of the ball, (b) the impulse, and (c) the average force exerted on the ball.

11. A boy catches a 0.15 kg cricket ball travelling towards him at 20 m/s. Calculate (a) the loss of momentum of the ball, (b) the impulse, and (c) the average force exerted by the boy if the catch takes 0.1 s.

12. A girl of mass 60 kg jumps from a wall and lands with a speed of 5.0 m/s. Find the force exerted on her by the ground during landing if (a) she bends her knees and takes 1.0 s to land, (b) she forgets to bend her knees and stops quickly in 0.01 s.

Conservation of Momentum

13. A ball X of mass 1 kg travelling at 2 m/s has a head-on collision with an identical ball Y at rest. X stops and Y moves off. Calculate (a) the momentum of each ball before the collision, (b) the momentum of each ball after the collision, and (c) the velocity of Y after the collision.

14. A boy of mass 50 kg running at 5.0 m/s jumps on to a 20 kg trolley travelling in the same direction at 1.5 m/s. Find (a) the total momentum of boy and trolley before he jumps on, and (b) their common velocity after he jumps on.

15. A trolley of mass 2 kg collides with a stationary trolley of mass 1 kg and sticks to it. If they move on together with a velocity of 4 m/s, what was the original velocity of the 2 kg trolley?

16. A girl of mass 50 kg jumps out of a rowing boat of mass 300 kg on to the river bank

with a horizontal velocity of 3.0 m/s. With what velocity does the boat begin to move backwards?

17. A rocket launched vertically sends out 50 kg of exhaust gas every second with a velocity of 200 m/s.

(a) What is the upward force on the rocket?

(b) If the mass of the rocket is 500 kg, what is its initial upward acceleration? ($g = 10$ N/kg.)

Circular Motion

18. An apple is whirled round in a horizontal circle on the end of a string which is tied to the stalk. It is whirled faster and faster and at a certain speed the apple is torn from the stalk. Why?

19. A car rounds a bend travelling in an arc of a circle.

(a) What provides the centripetal force?

(b) Is a larger or a smaller centripetal force required if (i) the car travels faster, (ii) the bend is more gradual, (iii) the car has more passengers?

20. A space shuttle is in orbit round the earth at a certain height.

(a) What provides the centripetal force to keep it in orbit?

(b) If the shuttle reduces its mass by launching a communications satellite, how does this affect the centripetal force?

(c) If the shuttle moves to a higher orbit, does there have to be an increase or a decrease in (i) the centripetal force, (ii) the orbit speed?

Unit Six

Work, Energy and Machines

6.1 Work and its Measurement

In science the word *work* has a more exact meaning than in everyday life. Scientifically speaking, *work is only done when a force causes movement.* The force produced by a boat when it pulls a water skier does work. The force applied by a crane to lift a load also does work. No work, in the scientific sense, is done by someone holding a pile of books, however; an upward force is exerted but no motion results.

The greater the force and the further it moves, the greater is the amount of work done. We therefore measure work using the equation

work = force × distance moved in direction of force

or, in symbols,

$$W = F \times s$$

The SI unit of work is the *joule* (J). It is *the work done when a force of 1 newton moves through a distance of 1 metre in the direction in which it is acting.*

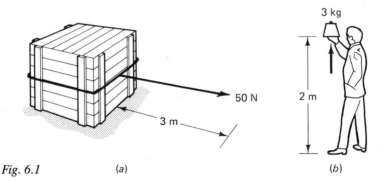

Fig. 6.1   (a)   (b)

For example, if you have to pull with a force of 50 N to move a box 3.0 m in the direction of the force (Fig. 6.1(a)) the work done is 50 N × 3.0 m = 150 N m = 150 J. Or again, if you lift a mass of 3.0 kg vertically through 2.0 m (Fig. 6.1(b)) you have to exert a vertically upward force equal to the weight of the mass, that is, 30 N (approximately), and the work done is 30 N × 2.0 m = 60 N m = 60 J.

In calculations, always remember to take the distance *in the direction in which the force acts.*

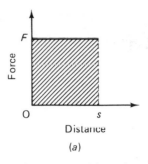
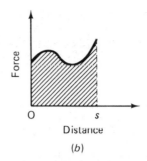

Fig. 6.2   (a)   (b)

Work can be measured by using a graph of force against distance moved. The graph in Fig. 6.2(a) is for a constant force F acting on a body through a distance s. The work done $=F\times s$, and clearly this is represented by the shaded area under the graph. It can also be shown that if the force varies with distance —as in Fig. 6.2(b), for instance—the work done over distance s is again represented by the shaded area.

6.2 Energy and its Forms

Energy is what people and machines must have before they can do work. It is measured in *joules* and occurs in many different forms.

(i) **Chemical energy.** Foods of all kinds and fuels like coal, oil and gas are stores of chemical energy which, when they combine with oxygen (in our bodies or in engines), release other forms of energy. Chemical energy is an important basic form of energy because of the major role it plays in every living thing, as well as in the growth of our civilization.

(ii) **Potential energy (p.e.).** This is energy which a body has because its *position* or *condition* allows it to do work when released. The weight at the top of a pile-driver has p.e. which is used to do work when it falls and forces a pile into the ground for the foundations of a building. Water in a mountain reservoir has p.e. which enables it to do work by driving an electrical generator when it falls to a hydroelectric power station.

Wound-up watch springs and stretched elastic bands have p.e. because of their 'strained' condition.

(iii) **Kinetic energy (k.e.).** A *moving* body has k.e., and the faster it moves the more k.e. it has. For example, as a hammer strikes a nail it exerts a force and does work because of the k.e. it has due to its motion. Rotating bodies also have k.e.

Kinetic and potential energy are classed as *mechanical energy*.

(iv) **Other forms of energy.** These include thermal energy (also referred to as internal energy and heat energy), electrical energy, sound energy, radiation energy (such as light and X-rays) and nuclear energy. All will be considered later in this book.

6.3 Energy Changes

One of the useful things about energy is that it can be changed from one form to another by suitable devices.

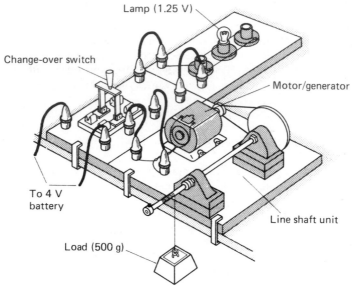

Lamp (1.25 V)

Change-over switch

Motor/generator

To 4 V battery

Line shaft unit

Load (500 g)

Fig. 6.3

(i) **Demonstration.** The apparatus in Fig. 6.3 may be used to show some energy changes. Chemical energy of the battery becomes electrical energy when it is connected by the change-over switch to the motor. In the motor, electrical energy is changed to k.e. by making it rotate. The motor raises the load so giving it p.e.

If the change-over switch is then connected to the lamp and the load allowed to fall, the load loses p.e. and makes the line shaft unit rotate the motor. The motor is now being driven and has k.e. It acts as a generator and produces electrical energy which is changed to light and thermal energy in the lamp.

(ii) **Conservation of energy.** In all energy changes the *principle of conservation of energy* is found to hold. It is stated as follows:

> *Energy cannot be created or destroyed but it can be changed from one form into another.*

To measure energy changes we use the fact that in such a change work is done. For example, if you have to exert an upwards force of 10 N to raise a stone through a vertical distance of 1.5 m, the work done is 15 J. This is also the amount of chemical energy transferred *from* your muscles *to* the p.e. of the stone.

Sometimes in an energy change it seems that some energy has disappeared. Very often, the 'lost' energy has been converted into thermal energy. For example, when a brick falls its p.e. becomes k.e. As it hits the ground, its temperature and that of the ground rises and thermal energy (and a little sound energy) is produced.

6.4 Calculating k.e. and p.e.

It is often useful to be able to calculate how much bodies have of these two forms of mechanical energy.

(i) **Kinetic energy.** Suppose a body of mass m is at rest and is acted on by a steady force F which gives it a uniform acceleration a, so that the velocity of the body is v after it has moved a distance s. We can use the equation $v^2 = u^2 + 2as$ and, since $u = 0$,

$$v^2 = 2as \quad \text{or} \quad a = v^2/2s$$

Substituting in $F = ma$,

$$F = m \left(\frac{v^2}{2s} \right) \quad \text{or} \quad F \times s = \tfrac{1}{2} mv^2$$

$F \times s$ is the work done on the body to give it velocity v and therefore equals its k.e. Hence

$$\text{kinetic energy} = E_k = \tfrac{1}{2} mv^2$$

If m is in kg and v in m/s, the k.e. is in J. For example, a cricket ball of mass 0.20 kg moving with velocity 20 m/s has k.e. $= \tfrac{1}{2} mv^2 = \tfrac{1}{2} \times 0.20 \times (20)^2 = 0.10 \times 400 = 40$ J.

Since k.e. depends on v^2, a train travelling at 200 km/h (125 m.p.h.) has four times the k.e. it has at 100 km/h.

(ii) **Potential energy.** A body above the earth's surface is considered to have an amount of gravitational p.e. equal to the work that has been done against gravity by the force used to raise it. To lift a body of mass m through a *vertical* height h needs a force equal and opposite to the weight mg of the body, where g is the earth's gravitational field strength at that place. Hence

$$\text{work done by force} = \text{force} \times \text{vertical height}$$
$$= mg \times h$$
$$\therefore \text{potential energy} = E_p = mgh$$

When m is in kg, g in N/kg (or m/s^2) and h is in m, the p.e. is in J. For example, if $g = 10$ N/kg, the p.e. gained by a 0.10 kg (100 g) mass raised vertically by 1.0 cm is 0.10 kg $\times$ 10 N/kg $\times$ 1 m = 1.0 N m = 1.0 J.

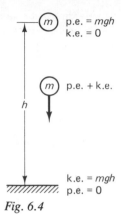

p.e. = mgh
k.e. = 0

p.e. + k.e.

k.e. = mgh
p.e. = 0

Fig. 6.4

(iii) **Changes of p.e. to k.e.** The p.e. of a mass m at height h above the ground (Fig. 6.4) is given by

$$E_p = mgh \qquad\qquad 1$$

When it falls, its velocity increases and it gains k.e. at the expense of its p.e. If it starts from rest and air resistance is negligible, its velocity v on reaching the ground can be calculated from

$$v^2 = u^2 + 2\,as = 0 + 2\,gh = 2\,gh \qquad\qquad 2$$

Also, as it reaches the ground, its k.e. is given by

$$E_k = \tfrac{1}{2} mv^2$$

But from equation 2, $v^2 = 2gh$,

$$\therefore E_k = \tfrac{1}{2} m \times 2\,gh = mgh \qquad\qquad 3$$

Hence, from equations 1 and 3,

$$\text{loss of p.e.} = \text{gain of k.e.}$$

That is, energy is conserved.

When a pendulum swings, k.e. and p.e. are interchanged continuously. The energy of the bob is all p.e. at the end of the swing and all k.e. as it passes through its central position. In other positions it has both p.e. and k.e. (Fig. 6.5). Eventually, when the swings stop, all its mechanical energy (that is, p.e. + k.e.) becomes thermal energy as a result of overcoming air resistance and warming the air.

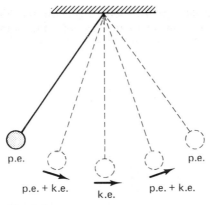

Fig. 6.5

6.5 Power

(i) **Definition.** The more powerful a car is, the faster it can ascend a hill, that is, the faster it does work. The *power* of a device is the work it does per second—*the rate at which it does work*. This is the same as *the rate at which it changes energy* from one form to another. Therefore

$$\text{power} = \frac{\text{work done}}{\text{time taken}} = \frac{\text{energy change}}{\text{time taken}}$$

The unit of power is the *watt* (W), which is a rate of working of 1 joule per second, that is, $1\,\text{W} = 1\,\text{J/s}$. Larger units are the *kilowatt* ($1\,\text{kW} = 1000\,\text{W} = 10^3\,\text{W}$) and the *megawatt* ($1\,\text{MW} = 1\,000\,000\,\text{W} = 10^6\,\text{W}$).

If 500 J of work are done in 10 s, the power is $500\,\text{J}/10\,\text{s} = 50\,\text{J/s} = 50\,\text{W}$. A small car develops a maximum power of about 25 kW.

(ii) **Human power.** You can measure your own power if you know your mass m in kilograms and the time t in seconds that you take to run up a flight of steps through a known *vertical* height h in metres (h = number of steps × height of one step). Then

$$\text{gravitational p.e. you gain} = mgh$$
$$\therefore \text{ work you have done in lifting}$$
$$\text{your weight up the stairs} = mgh$$

$$\text{Hence your power} = \frac{\text{work done}}{\text{time taken}} = \frac{mgh}{t}$$

where $g = 10\,\text{N/kg}$. For example, if $m = 50\,\text{kg}$, $h = 3.0\,\text{m}$ and $t = 3.0\,\text{s}$ then

$$\text{your power} = 50 \times 10 \times 3/3 = 500\,\text{W}$$

A non-SI unit of power is 1 horsepower (h.p.), which was introduced when steam engines replaced horses for doing work: 1 h.p. ≈ 750 W.

6.6 Sources of Energy

Energy is a necessary 'raw material' in the modern world.

(i) **Fossil fuels.** Oil, natural gas and coal are fossil fuels formed from the decayed remains of animals and plants which lived millions of years ago on earth, and which originally received their energy from the sun. At present, most other useful forms of energy (such as electricity) come from fossil fuels.

Unfortunately the world's reserves of oil and gas are unlikely to last much beyond the end of the twentieth century, though coal may not run out for another 200 or so years. As a result there is worldwide concern to make the best use of what fossil fuels remain and to develop *alternative* sources, despite their bulkier and less convenient nature.

(ii) **Solar energy.** The sun's energy can be harnessed directly using large curved mirrors to focus the sun's rays on to a small area. The energy can then be used to turn water to steam for driving the turbine of an electrical generator in a power station. The large reflector at Mont Louis in the French Pyrenees consists of 3500 small mirrors. It produces temperatures of over 3000 °C and follows the sun by rotating on a track.

Roof-top solar collectors for solar water-heating systems in buildings like houses and schools are common in hot climates. We shall consider them in Unit 11.9.

(iii) **Geothermal energy.** Scientists have discovered that huge amounts of heat are stored throughout the earth deep in certain rocks, such as granite, in volcanic and earthquake regions. At a depth of 2 km the temperature is typically 80 °C, and at 6 km about 200 °C. To tap these 'heat reservoirs', two holes are drilled and cold water pumped down one comes up the other as hot water or steam. The latter can be used to generate electricity or to heat buildings.

(iv) **Wind and wave energy.** Electrical generators driven by giant windmills are being developed for use in windy situations.

Wave energy is also being investigated, using the rocking motion of a floating object to operate a generator.

(v) **Nuclear energy.** The principles applied when operating a nuclear power station will be considered in Unit 23.10. Although these stations can present *safety* problems if a fault develops and radiation leakage occurs and *environmental* problems arising from the disposal of dangerous waste materials, it seems likely that nuclear energy in some form will be essential in the future. There are risks in not using it as well as in using it and people have different views as to what is the best course to follow.

(vi) **The future.** If developing countries are to enjoy the standards of living of industrialized nations additional energy will be required, as well as that needed to meet the extra demands also made by the world's ever-increasing population.

At present, half the energy used in the world comes from oil, which like coal and gas is not renewable. Renewable sources such as sun, winds and waves are more or less inexhaustible but require considerable development before they can replace fossil fuels on a substantial scale and at reasonable cost.

For the immediate future, one solution to the energy crisis is to use nuclear energy to generate electricity—one tonne (1000 kg) of uranium produces more energy than 20 000 tonnes of coal—and to preserve the remaining fossil fuel stocks for making plastics, fertilizers, medicines and other useful chemicals. This makes economic sense since uranium has few commercial uses apart from electricity generation. Today nuclear power stations produce up to 60 per cent of the electricity in some industrialized countries as cheaply or cheaper than other types of power station.

6.7 Energy of Food

When food is eaten it reacts with the oxygen we breathe into our lungs and is slowly 'burnt'. As a result chemical energy stored in food becomes *thermal energy* to warm the body and *mechanical energy* for muscular movement.

The calorific value of a substance is the amount of energy released when 1 kg is completely oxidized.

Calorific value is measured in J/kg. Dieticians sometimes use kilocalories instead of joules. The calorie was the previously used unit of thermal energy and equals 4.2 J. The calorific values of some foods are given below in megajoules per kilogram (MJ/kg):

Fat	38	Sugar	16	Ice cream	9	Milk	2.9
Butter	31	Flour	15	Eggs	7	Apples	2.6
Cheese	21	Beef	10	Potatoes	4	Carrots	1.7

Foods with high values are 'fattening' and if more food is eaten than the body really needs, the extra is stored as fat. The average person requires about 12 MJ per day.

Our muscles change chemical energy into mechanical energy when we exert a force—to lift a weight, for example. Unfortunately, they are not too good at doing this; of every 100 J of chemical energy they use, they can convert only 25 J into mechanical energy (that is, they are only 25 per cent efficient at changing chemical energy into mechanical energy). The other 75 J become thermal energy, much of which the body gets rid of by sweating (see Unit 10.10(ii)).

6.8 Machines

Machines let us do work more easily but they do not reduce the amount that has to be done for a particular job. Simple machines such as levers, pulleys, screws and gear wheels are used to build more complicated ones.

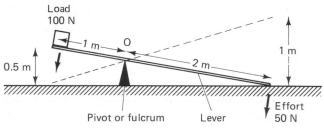

Fig. 6.6

(i) **Levers.** A lever is any device which can turn about a pivot or fulcrum. The one in Fig. 6.6 is being used (like a crowbar) to lift a load of 100 N through 0.5 m by applying a force, called the *effort*, at the opposite end. Using the measurements given, the effort can be calculated from the principle of moments (see Unit 3.6(ii)). Taking moments about the pivot O, we can say that as the effort just begins to raise the load,

$$\text{clockwise moment} = \text{anticlockwise moment}$$
$$\text{effort} \times 2\,\text{m} = \text{load} \times 1\,\text{m} = 100\,\text{N} \times 1\,\text{m}$$
$$\therefore \text{effort} = 100/2 = 50\,\text{N}$$

The lever has therefore enabled the effort to raise a load twice as large as itself, but only by moving twice as far as the load does (for example, through 1 m when the load rises 0.5 m).

(ii) **Mechanical advantage and velocity ratio.** The mechanical advantage of a machine is defined as follows:

$$\text{mechanical advantage (M.A.)} = \frac{\text{load}}{\text{effort}}$$

The lever in Fig. 6.8 has an M.A. of 100/50 = 2—this would be larger if the load was nearer the pivot or the effort farther away. Machines with M.A. greater than 1 allow heavy loads to be moved by smaller efforts, that is, they are *force-multipliers*.

Another useful concept is that of the velocity ratio, where

$$\text{velocity ratio (V.R.)} = \frac{\text{distance moved by effort}}{\text{distance moved by load}}$$

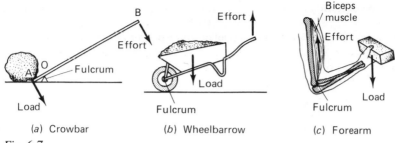

| (a) Crowbar | (b) Wheelbarrow | (c) Forearm |

Fig. 6.7

The lever in Fig. 6.8 has a V.R. of 2, which equals its M.A. In machines with V.R. greater than 1, the effort moves farther than the load does, but this is the price that has to be paid to obtain a force gain.

(iii) **Everyday levers.** Some examples of levers are shown in Fig. 6.7. The M.A. (and also the V.R.) is greater than 1 for a crowbar and a wheelbarrow. It is less than 1 for the human forearm because the effort (applied by the biceps muscle) is much greater than the load. Just a small effort movement is needed to move the load a large distance, however; that is, the V.R. is small. The forearm is a *distance-multiplier*.

(iv) **Efficiency.** The efficiency of a machine is defined by

$$\text{efficiency} = \frac{\text{work output}}{\text{work input}} = \frac{\text{power output}}{\text{power input}}$$

It is usually expressed as a percentage. In practice efficiency is always less than 100 per cent because some of the work (power) input is wasted in overcoming friction and in moving parts of the machine.

There is a useful relation between M.A., V.R. and efficiency. From the above equation, and using the relationship

$$\text{work} = \text{force} \times \text{distance}$$

it follows that

$$\text{efficiency} = \frac{\text{work done in lifting load}}{\text{work done by effort}}$$

$$= \frac{\text{load} \times \text{distance load moves}}{\text{effort} \times \text{distance effort moves}}$$

$$= \text{M.A.} \times \frac{1}{\text{V.R.}}$$

$$\therefore \text{ percentage efficiency} = \frac{\text{M.A.}}{\text{V.R.}} \times 100\%$$

In a perfect machine, no work is wasted and the efficiency is 100 per cent. Then M.A. =V.R., as in the lever in Fig. 6.6 where it was assumed that there was no friction at the pivot and that the lever was weightless.

6.9 Pulleys

A pulley is a wheel with a groove in its rim which, with the help of a rope wound round it, allows heavy loads to be lifted. Various systems are used.

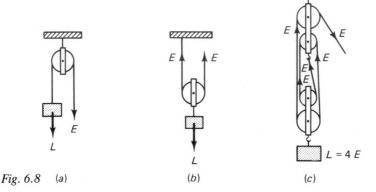

Fig. 6.8   (a)   (b)   (c)

(i) **Single fixed pulley** (Fig. 6.8(*a*)). This enables a load *L* to be *raised* more conveniently by applying a *downward* effort *E*. *E* need be only slightly greater than *L* and if friction in the pulley bearings is negligible then *E*=*L* and M.A. =1. *E* moves down as far as *L* moves up making V.R. =1. The arrangement is sometimes used on building sites.

(ii) **Single movable pulley** (Fig. 6.8(*b*)). If the effort applied to the free end of the rope is *E*, the total upward force on the pulley is 2*E* since two parts of the rope support it. A load *L* =2*E* can therefore be raised if the pulley and rope are frictionless and weightless. That is, M.A. =2 (but less in practice).

To raise the load by 1 m requires each side of the rope to shorten by 1 m. The free end has to take up 2 m of slack and so V.R. =2.

(iii) **Block and tackle** (Fig. 6.8(*c*)). This type of pulley system is used in cranes, in lifts and in garages. It consists of two blocks, each with one or more pulleys. In the diagram the pulleys in the blocks are shown one above the other for clarity; in practice they are the same size, mounted side by side on the same axle. The rope passes round each pulley in turn.

The total upward force on the lower block is 4*E* since it is supported by four parts of the rope and a load *L* =4*E* can be raised. Hence the M.A. =4 if the pulleys are frictionless and weightless. The V.R. =4 as well; this can be shown simply by counting the number of times the rope passes from one block to the other.

In fact, some of the effort is required to raise the lower pulley block and to overcome friction at the pulleys, so in practice a load of perhaps only $3E$ might be lifted. In that case, M.A. $=3/4=0.75$ or 75 per cent. This value increases as the load increases, because the energy loss (due to friction and the lower pulley block) becomes a smaller proportion of the total energy input.

6.10 Other Simple Machines

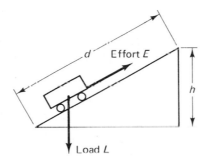

Fig. 6.9

(i) **Inclined plane (ramp).** It is easier to push a barrel up a plank on to a lorry than to lift it vertically. In Fig. 6.9, to raise the load L through a *vertical* height h, the smaller effort E moves a greater distance d equal to the length of the incline.

$$V.R. \text{ of incline} = \frac{\text{distance moved by effort}}{\text{vertical distance moved by load}}$$

$$= \frac{\text{length of incline}}{\text{height of incline}} = \frac{d}{h}$$

The M.A. of a perfect incline may be calculated from the principle of conservation of energy by assuming

$$\text{work done raising load} = \text{work done by effort}$$
$$\text{or} \qquad L \times h = E \times d$$

$$\therefore \text{M.A.} = \frac{L}{E} = \frac{d}{h}$$

In fact, because of friction, it will be less than the calculated value.

(ii) **Screw jack.** In a car jack a screw passes through a nut carrying an arm that fits into the car chassis (Fig. 6.10(a)). When the effort applied to the lever at the top of the screw makes one complete turn, the screw (and the load) rises a

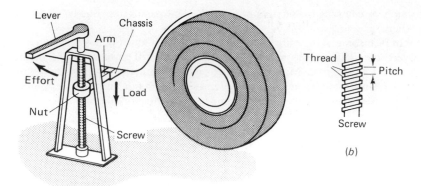

Fig. 6.10   (a)

distance equal to its pitch (the distance between successive threads) (Fig. 6.10(b)).

$$\text{V.R. of screw jack} = \frac{\text{circumference of circle made by effort}}{\text{pitch of screw}}$$

The M.A. of a perfect jack can also be calculated. A typical jack has a V.R. of about 500 and a M.A. of 200 or so.

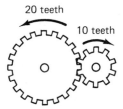

Fig. 6.11

(iii) **Gears.** The V.R. and M.A. of a machine can be changed by gears. In Fig. 6.11 the gear wheel with 10 teeth makes two revolutions for each complete revolution of the one with 20 teeth. The V.R. is therefore 2 if the effort is applied to the shaft of the small gear wheel which drives the large one. Hence

$$\text{V.R. of gears} = \frac{\text{number of teeth on driven gear wheel}}{\text{number of teeth on driving gear wheel}}$$

A car gearbox has several different gear wheels which can be connected in various ways to give different V.R.s. In bottom gear, the driving wheel has one-quarter of the teeth on the driven wheel and turns four times faster (V.R. = 4). In top gear, both wheels have the same number of teeth and turn at the same speed (V.R. = 1).

(iv) **Wheel and axle.** A screwdriver and the steering wheel of a car both (Fig. 6.12) use the wheel and axle principle. This is shown in Fig. 6.13(a); the effort

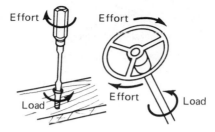

Fig. 6.12

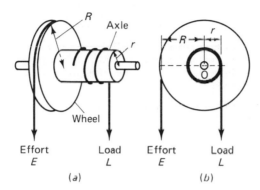

Fig. 6.13   (a)   (b)

E is applied to a rope wound round the wheel and the load L is raised by another rope wound oppositely on the axle. For one complete turn of the wheel, the effort moves a distance $2\pi R$ (that is, the circumference of the wheel), and the load a distance $2\pi r$. Hence

$$\text{V.R.} = \frac{2\pi R}{2\pi r} = \frac{R}{r}$$

The M.A. of a frictionless wheel and axle is also R/r, as can be proved from Fig. 6.13(b) by taking moments about O. We have

$$L \times r = E \times R$$

$$\therefore \text{M.A.} = \frac{L}{E} = \frac{R}{r}$$

6.11 Revision Questions

1. (a) What is meant by *work* in science?
   (b) How is work measured?
   (c) State and define the SI unit of work.

2. (a) Explain the term *energy*.
   (b) Name seven forms of energy.
   (c) State the principle of conservation of energy.

3. Name for each case one device which changes (a) electrical energy to light, (b) sound to electrical energy, (c) chemical energy to electrical energy, (d) potential energy to kinetic energy, and (e) electrical energy to kinetic energy.

4. Write down an equation for the calculation of (a) kinetic energy, (b) potential energy.

5. (a) What is meant by *power*?
   (b) State and define the SI unit of power.

6. Name six sources of energy. State one disadvantage of each.

7. Name two forms of energy that are produced when food is eaten.

8. (a) How can a machine make work easier?
   (b) Name two kinds of simple machine.
   (c) What is meant by (i) the mechanical advantage, (ii) the velocity ratio and (iii) the efficiency, of a machine?

9. Scissors, a hammer and a spade are levers. Show by diagrams the positions of the effort, load and fulcrum in each.

6.12 Problems

Take $g = 10\,\text{N/kg} = 10\,\text{m/s}^2$.

Work, Kinetic and Potential Energy
1. How much work is done when (a) a force of 10 N moves an object a distance of 5.0 m, (b) a mass of 3.0 kg is lifted vertically through 6.0 m?

2. A walker climbs a hill 400 m high. If his mass is 50 kg, what work does he do in lifting himself to the top of the hill?

3. Calculate the k.e. of (a) a 1 kg trolley travelling at 2 m/s, (b) a 10 kg mass with a velocity of 10 m/s, (c) a 10 kg mass with a velocity of 20 m/s, (d) a 500 kg car travelling at 72 km/h. (Remember to change km/h to m/s.)

4. What is the velocity of an object of mass 1.0 kg which has 200 J of kinetic energy?

5. A force F acting on a body increases its k.e. by 400 J over a distance of 2.0 m.
   (a) Neglecting friction, how much work was done on the body?
   (b) What is the value of F?

6. Calculate the p.e. of a 5 kg mass when it is (a) 3 m, (b) 6 m, above the ground.

7. At what height above the ground does an 8.0 kg mass have p.e. 160 J?

8. A boulder of mass 4.0 kg rolls over a cliff and reaches the beach below with a velocity of 20 m/s.
   (a) What is the k.e. of the boulder just before it lands?
   (b) What is its p.e. on the cliff?
   (c) How high is the cliff?

9. A ball of mass 0.10 kg falls from a height of 1.8 m on to a plate and rebounds to a height of 1.25 m. Find (a) the p.e. of the ball before the fall, (b) its k.e. as it hits the plate, (c) its velocity on hitting the plate, (d) its k.e. as it leaves the plate on the rebound, and (e) its velocity of rebound.

10. A hammer head of mass 0.5 kg has a speed of 2 m/s just before it drives a nail 0.01 m into a piece of wood. Find (a) the k.e. of the hammer head, and (b) the average resisting force of the wood.

Power

11. A boy of mass 40 kg runs up a flight of stairs of vertical height 5.0 m in 8.0 s. What is his average power output?

12. A 500 kg mass is lifted through a vertical height of 10 m in 25 s by a crane. Calculate the power output of the motor driving the crane.

13. How long will it take an electric motor of power output 25 kW to raise a lift of mass 1000 kg through 20 m?

14. It is estimated that 7×10^6 kg of water pours over the Niagara Falls every second. If the Falls are 50 m high, and if all the energy of the falling water could be harnessed, what power would be available?

Machines and Efficiency

15. The frictionless, weightless lever in Fig. 6.14 is used to raise a load L of 1000 N.
   (a) What effort E must be applied?
   (b) What is the M.A. of the lever?
   (c) How far will E have to move down for L to move up 0.1 m?
   (d) What is the V.R. of the lever?

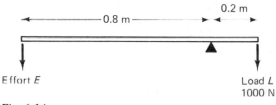

Fig. 6.14

16. An effort of 250 N raises a load of 1000 N through 5.0 m in a pulley system. If the effort moves 30 m, find (a) the work done in raising the load, (b) the work done by the effort, (c) the efficiency of the pulley system.

17. For each pulley system in Fig. 6.15(a), (b) and (c) on page 94, what are (i) the M.A., (ii) the V.R. and (iii) the efficiency?

18. A pulley system has an efficiency of 60 per cent and a V.R. of 5.
   (a) What is its M.A.?
   (b) If the load is 150 N, what is the value of the effort?
   (c) The load is raised by 2 m. (i) How far does the effort move? (ii) How much work does the effort do? (iii) How much energy is wasted?

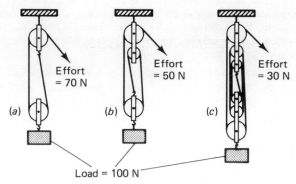

Fig. 6.15

19. An electric motor has a power output of 400 W.
    (a) How much work does it do in 10 s?
    (b) If its efficiency is 80 per cent, what power is supplied to it?

20. A trolley of weight 10 N is pulled from the bottom to the top of the inclined plane in Fig. 6.16 by a force of 2 N. What are (a) the M.A., (b) the V.R. and (c) the efficiency?

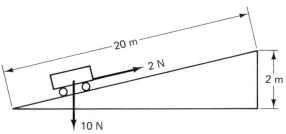

Fig. 6.16

21. If gear wheel A has 30 teeth and drives gear wheel B with 75 teeth, how many times does A rotate for each rotation of B?

Unit Seven

Pressure in Liquids and Gases

7.1 Pressure

(i) **Meaning.** Sometimes when a force acts on a body we can only make sense of its effect if we consider not only the *force* but also the *area* on which it acts. For example, a tractor with wide wheels can move over soft ground because its weight is spread over a large area. As a result, the pressure on the ground is less and it does not sink so deeply. On the other hand, a nail can be driven into wood because the very high pressure exerted over the small area of the point is more than the wood can stand.

The greater the area over which a force acts the less is the pressure; conversely, the smaller the area, the greater the pressure. Pressure is calculated from

$$\text{pressure} = \frac{\text{force}}{\text{area}}$$

or, in symbols,

$$p = \frac{F}{A}$$

Pressure is thus the force (or thrust) acting at right angles on a surface of unit area. If force is measured in N and area in m^2, the pressure is in N/m^2 or *pascal* (Pa). 1 Pa, the SI unit of pressure, is quite a small pressure. An apple in your hand exerts about 1000 Pa.

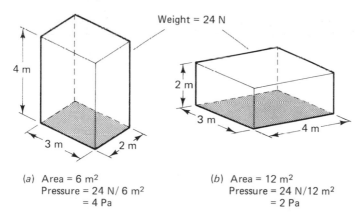

Weight = 24 N

4 m   3 m   2 m

2 m   3 m   4 m

(a) Area = 6 m²
     Pressure = 24 N/ 6 m²
             = 4 Pa

(b) Area = 12 m²
     Pressure = 24 N/12 m²
             = 2 Pa

Fig. 7.1

Consider the pressure exerted on the floor by the same box (*a*) standing on end, (*b*) lying flat, as in Fig. 7.1. The same force of 24 N—the weight of the box—acts in each case but the area over which it acts in (*b*) is twice that in (*a*) and so the pressure in (*b*) is half that in (*a*).

(ii) **Worked example.** A man stands on the ice of a frozen pond.

(*a*) If he weighs 1000 N and his feet are in contact with an area of 0.050 m² of ice, what pressure does he exert on the ice?

(*b*) If the ice breaks when the pressure exceeds 16 000 Pa, by how much is he 'overweight'?

(*a*) The pressure *p* on the ice is given by

$$p = \frac{F}{A}$$

$$= \frac{1000\,\text{N}}{0.050\,\text{m}^2} = \underline{\underline{20\,000\,\text{Pa}}}$$

(*b*) To calculate the maximum weight the man can have without breaking the ice, that is, the greatest force he can exert on the ice, we rearrange the pressure equation to get

$$F = p \times A$$
$$= 16\,000\,\text{Pa} \times 0.050\,\text{m}^2$$
$$= 800\,\text{N}$$

He is 'overweight' by $(1000 - 800) = \underline{\underline{200\,\text{N}}}$

7.2 Liquid Pressure

The weight of a liquid pulls it down into its container, causing a pressure on the container and on any object in the liquid.

(i) **Laws of liquid pressure.** These summarize the behaviour of a liquid in an open vessel.

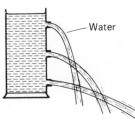

Fig. 7.2

1. *Pressure in a liquid increases with depth*, because the farther down you go the greater the weight of liquid above. In Fig. 7.2 water spurts out fastest and farthest from the lowest hole. The dam of a reservoir must be thicker at the bottom than at the top, because the water pressure is greater at the bottom.

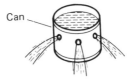

Can

Fig. 7.3

2. *Pressure at one depth acts equally in all directions.* The can of water in Fig. 7.3 has similar holes all round it at the same level. Water comes out as fast and as far from each hole.

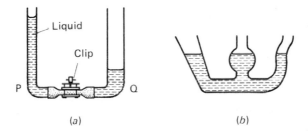

Liquid

Clip

P   Q

Fig. 7.4   (a)   (b)

3. *A liquid finds its own level.* In the U-tube of Fig. 7.4(*a*), the liquid pressure at the foot of P is greater than that at the foot of Q, because the left-hand column is higher than the right-hand one. When the clip is opened the liquid flows from P to Q until the pressures and levels are the same, that is, the liquid finds its own level. Although the weight of liquid in Q is now greater than that in P, it acts over a greater area since tube Q is wider. In Fig. 7.4(*b*) the liquid is at the same level in each tube; the experiment shows that the pressure at the foot of a liquid column depends only on the *vertical* depth of the liquid and not on the width or shape of the tube.

4. *Pressure depends on the density of the liquid.* The denser the liquid, the greater the pressure at any given depth.

(ii) **Calculating liquid pressure.** The pressure p at a depth h in a liquid of density d can be found by considering a horizontal area A (Fig. 7.5). The force acting vertically downwards on A equals the weight of the liquid column of height h and cross-sectional area A above it. Then

$$\text{volume of liquid column} = hA$$

Since mass = volume × density, we can say

$$\text{mass of liquid column} = hAd$$
$$\text{weight of liquid column} = \text{mass} \times g$$
$$= hAdg$$
$$\therefore \quad \text{force on area } A = hAdg$$

$$\therefore \quad \text{pressure} = \frac{\text{force}}{\text{area}} = \frac{hAdg}{A}$$

$$\therefore \quad p = hdg$$

This pressure acts equally in all directions at depth h vertically below the surface and depends only on h and d. For example, if $h = 2.0$ m, $d = 1000$ kg/m^3 and $g = 10$ N/kg, then

$$p = 2.0\,\text{m} \times 1000\,\text{kg/m}^3 \times 10\,\text{N/kg}$$
$$= 20\,000\,\text{Pa}$$

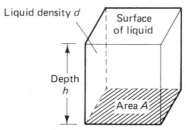

Fig. 7.5

7.3 Hydraulic Machines

Hydraulic machines enable work to be done more conveniently, like those containing pulleys, levers or gears, but they use liquid pressure.

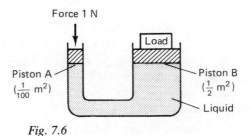

Fig. 7.6

(i) **Principle.** Their action depends on two facts about liquids. First, they are almost incompressible (that is, their volume cannot be reduced by squeezing) and, second, they pass on to all parts any pressure applied to them.

The principle of hydraulic machines is illustrated in Fig. 7.6. Suppose a downward force of 1 N acts on a piston A of area $1/100\,m^2$. The pressure transmitted through the liquid is

$$\text{pressure} = \frac{\text{force}}{\text{area}} = \frac{1}{1/100} = 100\,\text{Pa}$$

This pressure acts on piston B of area $\frac{1}{2}\,m^2$. The total upward force on B is given by

$$\text{force} = \text{pressure} \times \text{area} = 100 \times \tfrac{1}{2} = 50\,\text{N}$$

Hence, if there are no frictional losses, a load of 50 N can be lifted by an effort of 1 N, so that the M.A. = load/effort = 50/1 = 50. The force-multiplication is achieved by the effort moving fifty times farther than the load does, that is, V.R. = 50.

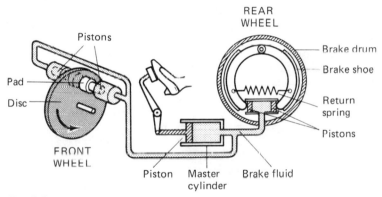

Fig. 7.7

(ii) **Hydraulic car brakes** (Fig. 7.7). When the brake pedal is pushed the piston in the master cylinder exerts a force on the brake fluid and the resulting pressure is transmitted equally to eight other pistons (four are shown). These force the brake shoes or pads against the wheels and stop the car.

(iii) **Other hydraulic machines.** A *hydraulic jack* (Fig. 7.8) has a platform on top of piston B and is used in garages to lift cars. Both valves open only to the right and they allow B to be raised when A is moved up and down repeatedly. A *hydraulic fork lift truck* works in a similar way.

A *hydraulic press* is constructed similarly, but with a fixed plate above B; sheets of steel are placed between B and the plate and pressed into the shapes required for making products such as car bodies.

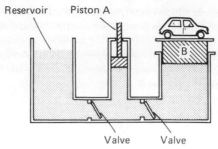

Fig. 7.8

7.4 Atmospheric Pressure

Although the air forming the earth's atmosphere stretches upwards for hundreds of kilometres, it thins out very rapidly after ten kilometres or so. Like a liquid, it exerts a pressure in all directions which decreases with height. At sea level, atmospheric pressure is very large and equals about 100 000 Pa = 100 kPa.

We do not normally feel atmospheric pressure because the pressure inside our bodies is almost the same as that outside. Our ears are sensitive to pressure changes, however; you may have experienced ear 'popping' in an aircraft at take-off. This is due to the outside air pressure falling as the aircraft climbs, so that a pressure difference is created between the air in the middle part of the ear and that in the outer ear, and the eardrum becomes distorted. Swallowing helps to equalize the pressures. Modern high-flying aircraft have pressurized cabins in which the air pressure is increased sufficiently above that outside to safeguard the crew and passengers from difficulty with breathing.

The existence of air pressure may be shown if the air from an empty oil can is removed by a vacuum pump (Fig. 7.9(*a*)). The can collapses (Fig. 7.9(*b*))

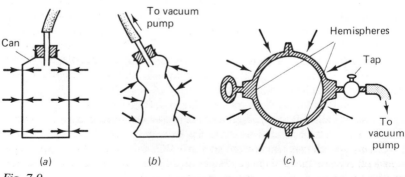

Fig. 7.9

because the air pressure inside becomes less than that outside, and the balance between them is upset. A space from which all the air has been withdrawn is a *vacuum*.

The large value of atmospheric pressure was first demonstrated by von Guericke, the Mayor of Magdeburg, who invented the vacuum pump. About 1650 he fitted together two large hollow metal hemispheres to give an airtight sphere, which he then evacuated. So good was his pump that it took two teams, each of eight horses, to separate the hemispheres. A similar experiment can be done by two people with small brass hemispheres (Fig. 7.9(*c*)).

7.5 Using Air Pressure

(i) **Drinking straw** (Fig. 7.10(*a*)). When you suck, your lungs expand and air passes into them from the straw. Atmospheric pressure pushing down on the surface of the liquid in the bottle is now greater than the pressure of the air in the straw and so forces the liquid up to your mouth.

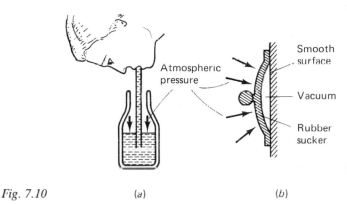

Fig. 7.10   (*a*)   (*b*)

(ii) **Rubber sucker** (Fig. 7.10(*b*)). When the sucker is moistened and pressed on a smooth flat surface, the air inside is pushed out. Atmospheric pressure then holds it firmly against the surface. Suckers are used as towel holders in the home and in industry for lifting metal sheets.

(iii) **Vacuum cleaner** (Fig. 7.11). The fan creates a partial vacuum in the bag which causes air, carrying dust, to rush through the cleaning attachment into the bag.

(iv) **Power brakes** (Fig 7.12). In some vehicles atmospheric pressure supplies an extra force to the brakes. The engine removes air from both sides of a piston in a cylinder which links the braking system to the brake pedal. When the latter is pushed, a valve opens to let air into the right-hand side of the piston and the resulting pressure difference forces the piston to the left.

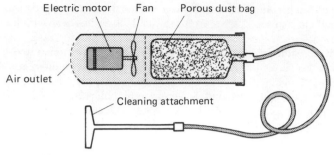

Fig. 7.11

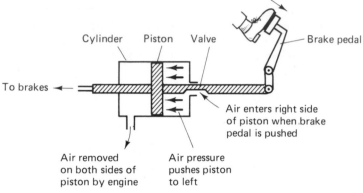

Fig. 7.12

(v) **Breathing.** When you breathe in, your lungs expand and atmospheric pressure forces air into them through your nose. When you breathe out, your lungs contract and the air is expelled.

7.6 Pressure Gauges

These measure the pressure exerted by a fluid, that is, by either a liquid or a gas.

(i) **Bourdon gauge.** This works like the rolled-up paper whistle in Fig. 7.13(a): the harder you blow into the tube, the more it uncurls. When a fluid pressure is applied in a Bourdon gauge (Fig. 7.13(b)), the curved metal tube unwinds slightly and rotates a pointer over a scale. These devices are used as car oil-pressure gauges and on gas cylinders.

(ii) **U-tube manometer.** In Fig. 7.14(a) each surface of the liquid is acted on equally by atmospheric pressure and the levels are the same. If one side is

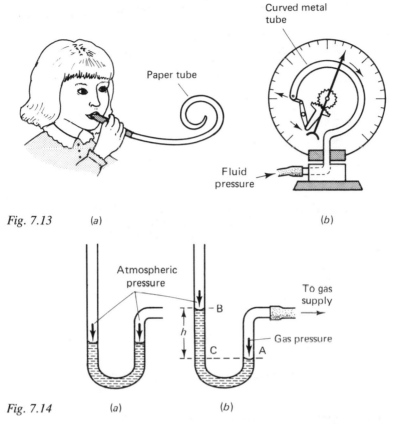

Fig. 7.13   (a)   (b)

Fig. 7.14   (a)   (b)

connected to a gas supply (Fig. 7.14(b)), the gas exerts a pressure on surface A and level B rises until

pressure of gas = atmospheric pressure + pressure due to liquid column BC

The pressure of the liquid column BC equals hdg (in Pa) where h is the vertical height of BC (in m) and d is the density of the liquid (in kg/m^3). The height h is called the *head of liquid* and sometimes, instead of stating a pressure in Pa, we say that it is so many mm of water (or mercury for higher pressures).

7.7 Barometers

A barometer is an instrument for measuring atmospheric pressure.

(i) **Mercury barometer.** A simple barometer can be made from a thick-walled glass tube about 1 m long, filled with mercury. When it is inverted into a bowl of mercury, the mercury in the tube falls until it is about 760 mm above the

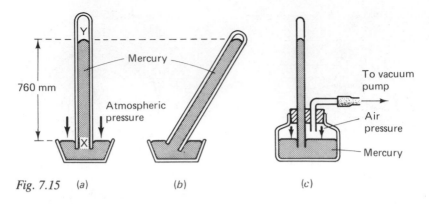

Fig. 7.15   (a)   (b)   (c)

level in the bowl (Fig. 7.15(*a*)). The pressure at X due to the weight of the column of mercury XY equals the atmospheric pressure on the surface of the mercury in the bowl. XY measures the atmospheric pressure in mm of mercury (mmHg).

The *vertical* height of the column is unchanged if the tube is tilted (Fig. 7.15(*b*)), or its width altered. The space above the mercury in the tube is a vacuum (as can be checked by tilting the tube sufficiently for the mercury to fill it completely).

The apparatus in Fig. 7.15(*c*) may be used to show that it is atmospheric pressure that holds up the column. When the air above the mercury in the bottle is pumped out, the column falls.

Note. For safety reasons liquid mercury should *not* be touched nor its very poisonous vapour inhaled.

Standard atmospheric pressure is the pressure of a column of mercury 760 mm high and is also called 1 atmosphere (atm). Its value p in Pa can be found by substituting $h = 760$ mm $= 0.760$ m, $d = 13.6$ g/cm^3 $= 13\,600$ kg/m^3 (the density of mercury) and $g = 9.81$ N/kg in

$$p = hdg$$
$$= 0.760 \text{ m} \times 13\,600 \text{ kg/m}^3 \times 9.81 \text{ N/kg}$$
$$= 101\,000 \text{ Pa} = 101 \text{ kPa}$$

(ii) **Aneroid barometer.** An aneroid (from Greek words meaning 'no liquid') barometer consists of a thin-walled sealed metal box with corrugated sides (to increase its strength) containing air at low pressure (Fig. 7.16(*a*)). The box is prevented from collapsing by a strong spring. If the atmospheric pressure increases, the box caves in slightly; if it decreases the spring pulls it out. A system of levers magnifies this movement and causes a chain to move a pointer over a scale.

Aneroid barometers are used as weather glasses (Fig. 7.16(*b*)), high pressure (anticyclones) being associated with fine weather and low pressure (depressions) with bad weather. Being portable and easy to read they are also

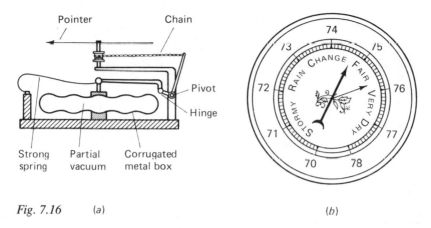

Fig. 7.16   (a)   (b)

useful as *altimeters* to measure height above sea level, since pressure decreases with height. The pressure scale (cm of mercury in Fig. 7.16(b)) is then replaced by an altitude scale marked in metres.

7.8 Pumps and Pressure

Pumps transfer liquids and gases from one place to another. The two described here use atmospheric pressure.

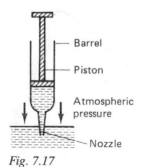

Fig. 7.17

(i) **Syringe** (Fig. 7.17). Syringes of various kinds are used by doctors to give injections and by gardeners to spray plants. A syringe consists of a tight-fitting piston in a barrel, and is filled by putting the nozzle under the liquid and drawing back the piston. This reduces the air pressure in the barrel and atmospheric pressure forces the liquid up into it. Pushing down the piston drives liquid out of the nozzle.

(ii) **Bicycle pump** (Fig. 7.18). When the piston is pushed in, the air between it and the tyre valve is compressed. This pushes the rim of the plastic cup washer

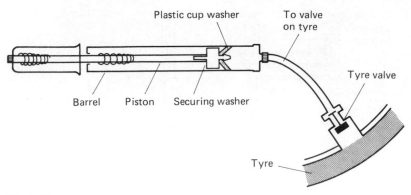

Fig. 7.18

against the wall of the barrel to form an airtight seal. When the pressure of the air between the plastic washer and the valve is greater than the pressure of the air in the tyre, air is forced past the tyre valve into the tyre.

When the piston is drawn back, the tyre valve is closed by the greater pressure in the tyre. Atmospheric pressure then forces air past the plastic washer (which is no longer pressed hard against the wall) into the barrel.

7.9 Archimedes' Principle

A ship floats because it gets support from the water. Any object in a liquid, whether floating or submerged, is acted on by an upward force or *upthrust*. This makes it seem to weigh less than it does in air. The upthrust arises because the liquid pressure, which pushes on all sides of the object, is greatest on the bottom where the liquid is deepest (Fig. 7.19).

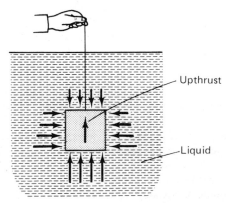

Fig. 7.19

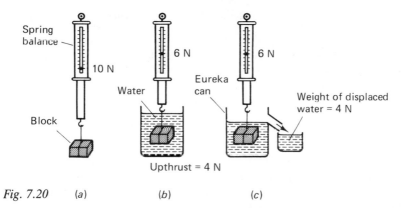

Fig. 7.20   (a)   (b)   (c)

In Fig. 7.20(*a*) the block hanging from the spring balance weighs 10 N in air. When it is completely immersed in water the reading becomes 6 N (Fig. 7.20(*b*)). The loss in weight of the block is $(10 - 6)$ N $= 4$ N; the upthrust of the water on it is therefore 4 N.

If a can like that in Fig. 7.20(*c*) is used, full of water to the level of the spout, the water displaced by the block (the overflow) can be collected and weighed. Its weight here is 4 N, the same as the upthrust. (Its volume is exactly equal to the volume of the block.) Experiments with other liquids and also with gases lead to the general conclusion called Archimedes' principle:

When a body is wholly or partly submerged in a fluid,
the upthrust equals the weight of fluid displaced.

The upthrust thus depends on the *volume* of the object and not on its weight.

7.10 Measuring Relative Densities

In Unit 2.12 we saw that

$$\text{relative density} = \frac{\text{mass of substance}}{\text{mass of same volume of water}}$$

But weight is proportional to mass, that is, if a mass of 1 kg has weight 10 N, a mass of 2 kg has weight 20 N. We can therefore write

$$\text{relative density} = \frac{\text{weight of substance}}{\text{weight of equal volume of water}}$$

(i) **Solids.** A suitable object is chosen of the substance whose relative density is to be measured (such as a glass stopper or an iron bolt) and this is weighed on a suitable balance, first in air and then immersed in water. By Archimedes' principle, the apparent loss in weight equals the weight of water displaced by the object. The volume of this weight of water is the same as the volume of the object. Hence, for a solid object,

$$\text{relative density} = \frac{\text{weight of object}}{\text{apparent loss in weight of object in water}}$$

For example, if the object weighs 10 N in air and 6 N in water, the apparent loss in weight is 4 N and its relative density is 10 N/4 N = 2.5.

The same result would be obtained if masses were measured instead of weights, and the relative density calculated from

$$\text{relative density} = \frac{\text{mass of object}}{\text{apparent loss in mass of object in water}}$$

(ii) **Liquids.** An object is weighed first in water, then dried and weighed in the liquid whose relative density is to be found. As before, the apparent loss in weight of the object equals the weight of liquid having the same volume as the object. Therefore, for a liquid,

$$\text{relative density} = \frac{\text{weight of any volume of liquid}}{\text{weight of an equal volume of water}}$$

$$= \frac{\text{apparent loss in weight of object in liquid}}{\text{apparent loss in weight of object in water}}$$

Again the result could also be found from

$$\text{relative density} = \frac{\text{apparent loss in mass of object in liquid}}{\text{apparent loss in mass of object in water}}$$

Hence if the apparent loss in mass of an object is 8 g in water and 10 g in a liquid X, then the relative density of X is 8 g/10 g = 0.8.

7.11 Floating and Sinking

(i) **Principle of flotation.** A stone held below the surface of water sinks when released; a cork rises, however. The weight of the stone is greater than the upthrust on it (that is, the weight of water displaced) and there is a net or

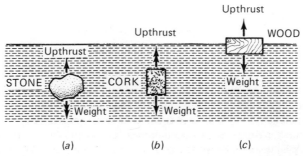

Fig. 7.21 (a) Stone sinks, (b) cork rises, (c) wood floats

resultant downward force on it (Fig. 7.21(a)). If the cork has the same volume as the stone, it will displace the same weight (and volume) of water. The upthrust on it when completely immersed is therefore the same as for the stone, but it is greater than the weight of the cork. The resultant upward force on the cork makes it rise through the water (Fig. 7.21(b)).

When an object such as a wooden block floats in water, the upthrust equals the weight of the object. The net force on the object is zero (Fig. 7.21(c)), and the weight of water displaced equals the weight of the object in air. This is an example of the *principle of flotation:*

A floating object displaces its own weight of fluid.

For example, a block of wood of weight 10 N (mass 1 kg) displaces a volume of water (or any other liquid in which it floats) having weight 10 N (mass 1 kg).

An object sinks in any liquid that has a smaller density than its own; in other liquids it floats, partly or wholly submerged. For example, a piece of glass of relative density 2.5 (density 2.5 g/cm³) sinks in water (density 1.0 g/cm³) but floats in mercury of relative density 13.6 (density 13.6 g/cm³). An iron nail sinks in water, but an iron ship floats because its *average* density is less than that of water.

(ii) **Ships.** A floating ship displaces a weight of water equal to its own weight including that of the cargo. The load lines (called the *Plimsoll mark*) on the side of a ship show the levels to which it can legally be loaded under different

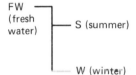

Fig. 7.22

conditions (Fig. 7.22 shows a simplified version). It floats lower in fresh water than in salt water because fresh water is less dense than salt water; similarly, it floats lower in warm water than in cold, because warm water is less dense than cold water.

(iii) **Submarines.** A submarine sinks by taking water into its buoyancy tanks. Once submerged, the upthrust is unchanged but the weight of the submarine increases with the inflow of water and it sinks faster. To surface, compressed air is used to blow water out of the tanks.

(iv) **Balloons and airships.** A balloon filled with hot air or hydrogen weighs less than the weight of cold air it displaces. The upthrust is therefore greater than its weight and the resultant upward force on the balloon causes it to rise. A hot air balloon carries a gas burner beneath it; a quick blast on the burner about every 30 seconds keeps the air inside the balloon hot. Meteorological balloons filled with hydrogen and carrying scientific instruments called

Fig. 7.23

radiosondes are regularly sent into the upper atmosphere; a small radio transmitter sends signals back to earth giving information about the temperature, pressure and humidity.

The airship *Skyship 600* (Fig. 7.23) has a gas bag made of polyurethane-laminated polyester material and filled with helium (a non-inflammable gas that is less dense than air). It is powered by two car engines which drive swivelling propellers that provide vertical thrust for take-off and landing and also horizontal thrust for forward motion. It can climb at about 700 metres a minute, cruises sedately at 80 km per hour and travels 1000 km on just 340 litres of fuel. Its roles include surveying, photographic, advertising, surveillance, cargo and passenger-carrying work.

7.12 Hydrometers

A hydrometer measures the relative density of a liquid quickly though not as accurately as by the methods outlined in Unit 7.10. It consists of a weighted sealed glass tube and scale, which is placed in the liquid and the scale read at the level of the liquid surface (Fig. 7.24(*a*)). The denser the liquid the higher

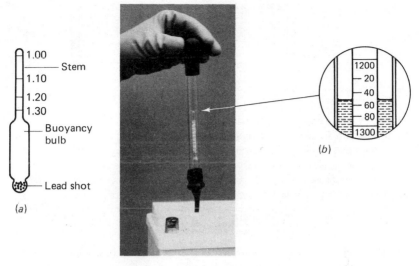

Fig. 7.24

the scale floats, since less liquid has to be displaced to equal its own weight; the numbers on the scale therefore increase downwards.

The large bulb gives the instrument buoyancy and the small weighted bulb makes it float upright. The narrow stem gives greater sensitivity, that is, small density differences produce large differences between the levels where the hydrometer floats.

A hydrometer can be used to check the state of a car battery (Fig. 7.24(*b*)). In a fully charged battery the relative density of the acid should be 1.25, and recharging is required when the reading is less than 1.18. Hydrometers are also used in breweries to measure the relative density of beer; the 'watering down' of milk and wine can also be detected by checking relative densities.

7.13 Bernoulli's Principle

The pressure is the same at all points on the same level in a fluid that is at rest; but this is not so when it is moving.

(i) **Liquids.** A liquid will only flow through a pipe if the pressure at one end of the pipe is higher than that at the other, that is, there is a pressure difference between the ends of the pipe. (In Unit 18.8 you will learn that electric charges will only flow through a wire if there is an electrical pressure difference, called a potential difference, between the ends of the wire.) The pressure at different points in a liquid flowing through (*a*) a uniform pipe and (*b*) a pipe with a narrow part, is shown by the height of the liquid in the vertical manometers in Fig. 7.25(*a*) and (*b*).

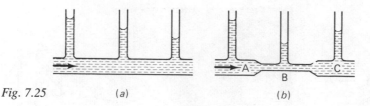

Fig. 7.25   (a)   (b)

In (*a*) the pressure drop along the tube is steady. In (*b*) the pressure falls in the narrow part B but rises again in the wider part C. Since in a certain time the same volume of liquid passes through B as enters A, the liquid must be moving faster in B than in A; the pressure in the liquid thus decreases as the speed of the liquid increases. Conversely an increase of pressure accompanies a fall in speed. This effect, called *Bernoulli's principle*, is stated as follows:

> *When the speed of a fluid increases, the pressure in the fluid decreases and vice versa.*

In Fig. 7.25(*b*) the liquid speeds up as it goes from the wide part A of the tube to the narrower part B, that is, it is accelerated. Therefore, since $F = ma$, the force at A, and so also the pressure at A, must be greater than the force and pressure at B. Between B and C the liquid slows down due to the pressure at C being greater than that at B.

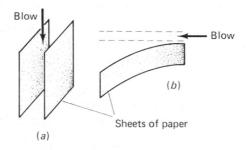

Fig. 7.26   (a)

(ii) **Gases.** Bernoulli effects in air streams can be shown as in Fig. 7.26(*a*) and (*b*), where in both cases the pressure falls in the moving air stream. In (*a*) the two sheets of paper come together when you blow between them and in (*b*) the paper rises when you blow over it.

(iii) **Applications.** As a fluid comes out of a jet its speed increases and its pressure decreases. This fact is used in a Bunsen burner (Fig. 7.27(*a*)); air is drawn into a carburettor by a jet of petrol in a similar manner. A spinning ball takes a curved path because it drags air round with it, thereby increasing the speed of the air flow on one side and reducing it on the other (Fig. 7.27(*b*)).

An aircraft wing, called an *aerofoil*, is shaped so that the air has to travel farther and so faster over the top surface than underneath (Fig. 7.28). The resultant upward force on the wing provides 'lift' for the aircraft.

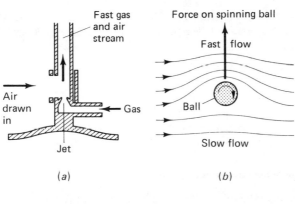

Fig. 7.27   (a)   (b)

Fig. 7.28

A *Venturi* meter contains a horizontal pipe with a constriction in it; as the fluid flows through the constriction the pressure falls, and the rate of flow can be calculated from the size of the pressure drop.

7.14 Worked Examples

1. A piece of metal weighing 6.4 N in air is hung from a thin string and completely immersed in water; its apparent weight is then 5.6 N. When similarly immersed in another liquid its apparent weight is 5.8 N. What are the relative densities of (a) the metal, (b) the liquid?

(a) Relative density of metal $= \dfrac{\text{weight of metal}}{\text{apparent loss in weight of metal in water}}$

$$= \frac{6.4\,\text{N}}{(6.4 - 5.6)\,\text{N}} = \frac{6.4\,\text{N}}{0.8\,\text{N}} = \underline{\underline{8.0}}$$

(b) Relative density of liquid $= \dfrac{\text{apparent loss in weight of metal in liquid}}{\text{apparent loss in weight of metal in water}}$

$$= \frac{(6.4 - 5.8)\,\text{N}}{(6.4 - 5.6)\,\text{N}} = \frac{0.6\,\text{N}}{0.8\,\text{N}} = \underline{\underline{0.75}}$$

2. A block of stone of volume $0.10 \, m^3$ has a density of $2500 \, kg/m^3$. What is (a) its weight, (b) its apparent weight in water of density $1000 \, kg/m^3$? (Take $g = 10 \, N/kg$.)

(a) Since density = mass/volume, we can say

$$\text{mass of stone} = \text{density} \times \text{volume of stone}$$
$$= 2500 \, kg/m^3 \times 0.1 \, m^3$$
$$= 250 \, kg$$
$$\therefore \text{weight of stone} = 250 \, kg \times 10 \, N/kg$$
$$= 2500 \, N$$

(b) By Archimedes' principle,

apparent loss in weight of stone = weight of water displaced

mass of water displaced = vol. of water displaced × density of water

$\therefore$ weight of water displaced = vol. of water displaced
$$\times \text{density of water} \times g$$
$$= \text{vol. of stone} \times \text{density of water} \times g$$
$$= 0.10 \, m^3 \times 1000 \, kg/m^3 \times 10 \, N/kg$$
$$= 1000 \, N$$
$\therefore$ apparent loss in weight = 1000 N
$\therefore$ apparent weight = weight − apparent loss in weight
$$= 2500 \, N - 1000 \, N$$
$$= 1500 \, N$$

3. A balloon of volume $1000 \, m^3$ contains hydrogen of density $0.090 \, kg/m^3$. If the mass of the fabric is 210 kg, what is the greatest load that can be carried? (Take $g = 10 \, N/kg$, and the density of air $= 1.3 \, kg/m^3$.)

Weight of air displaced by balloon = vol. of air displaced × density of air × g
$$= \text{vol. of balloon} \times \text{density of air} \times g$$
$$= 1000 \, m^3 \times 1.3 \, kg/m^3 \times 10 \, N/kg$$
$$= 13\,000 \, N$$
$\therefore$ upthrust on balloon = 13 000 N

If the balloon is just to rise, its *total* weight must be less than 13 000 N.

Weight of fabric of balloon = 210 kg × 10 N/kg
$$= 2100 \, N$$
Weight of hydrogen in balloon = vol. of hydrogen × density of hydrogen × g
$$= 1000 \, m^3 \times 0.090 \, kg/m^3 \times 10 \, N/kg$$
$$= 900 \, N$$
$\therefore$ weight of fabric + hydrogen = 2100 + 900 = 3000 N

$\therefore$ greatest weight that can be lifted by balloon = upthrust − 3000 N
$$= 13\,000 \, N - 3000 \, N$$
$$= 10\,000 \, N \; (1000 \, kg)$$

7.15 Revision Questions

1. What does it mean to say that the pressure acting on a surface is 2 Pa?

2. (a) A girl in stiletto heels is more likely to damage a wooden floor than an elephant is. Why?
   (b) Walnuts can be broken in the hand by squeezing *two* together but not one. Why?

3. State four laws of liquid pressure.

4. Write down an expression for the pressure p at the foot of a column of liquid of density d and height h.

5. (a) State two properties of liquids used in hydraulic machines.
   (b) Name four hydraulic machines.

6. What is the approximate value of atmospheric pressure at sea level in (a) mmHg, (b) Pa, (c) atm?

7. Explain why a liquid can be 'sucked' up a straw.

8. Name two types of pressure gauge.

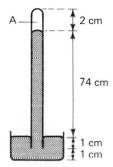

Fig. 7.29

9. A simple mercury barometer is shown in Fig. 7.29.
   (a) What is the region A?
   (b) What keeps the mercury in the tube?
   (c) What is the value of atmospheric pressure shown by the barometer?
   (d) What would be the effect on the *vertical* height of the mercury column of (i) using a narrower tube, (ii) tilting the tube at an angle, (iii) taking the barometer to the top of a mountain?

10. State (a) Archimedes' principle, (b) the principle of flotation.

11. Explain in terms of the forces involved (a) why a submarine sinks when it takes water into its tanks, (b) why a balloon can rise and (c) why a ship floats even though steel is much denser than water.

12. What is a hydrometer used for?

7.16 Problems

Take $g = 10\,\text{N/kg} = 10\,\text{m/s}^2$.

Pressure

1. (*a*) What is the pressure on a surface when a force of 50 N acts on an area of (i) $2.0\,\text{m}^2$, (ii) $100\,\text{m}^2$, (iii) $0.50\,\text{m}^2$?
   (*b*) A pressure of 10 Pa acts on an area of $3.0\,\text{m}^2$. What force acts on the area?

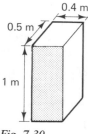

Fig. 7.30

2. (*a*) What is the volume of the block in Fig. 7.30?
   (*b*) What is the mass of the block if its density is $2000\,\text{kg/m}^3$?
   (*c*) What is the weight of the block?
   (*d*) What pressure is exerted on the ground by the block?
   (*e*) If the block is turned so that its shaded side rests on the ground, what effect, if any, will this have on (i) the force exerted by the block on the ground, (ii) the pressure exerted by the block on the ground?

Liquid Pressure

3. What is the liquid pressure 100 m below the surface of sea water of density $1150\,\text{kg/m}^3$?

4. In a hydraulic press a force of 20 N is applied to a piston of area $0.20\,\text{m}^2$. The area of the other piston is $2.0\,\text{m}^2$. What is (*a*) the pressure transmitted through the liquid, (*b*) the force on the other piston?

5. In the ground floor of a block of flats the pressure in a water pipe is 3×10^5 Pa but in a higher floor it is only 1×10^5 Pa. If the density of water is $1 \times 10^3\,\text{kg/m}^3$, what is the vertical height between the two floors?

Atmospheric Pressure

6. What would be the height of a barometer containing water instead of mercury if atmospheric pressure is 1.0×10^5 Pa? (Density of water $= 1.0 \times 10^3\,\text{kg/m}^3$.)

7. The manometer in Fig. 7.31 is connected to a gas cylinder. If atmospheric pressure is 760 mmHg, what is the pressure of the gas in the cylinder?

8. By how much does the mercury level fall in a barometer when it is taken to a height of 2 km? Take the average density of air to be $1.3\,\text{kg/m}^3$ and the density of mercury to be $1.3 \times 10^4\,\text{kg/m}^3$.

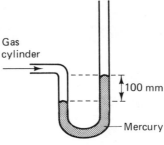

Gas
cylinder

100 mm

Mercury

Fig. 7.31

Archimedes' Principle

9. A metal block is weighed (*a*) in air, (*b*) half-submerged in water, (*c*) fully submerged in water, (*d*) fully submerged in a strong salt solution.

   The readings obtained were 5 N, 8 N, 10 N and 6 N (not necessarily in that order). Which reading was obtained for each weighing?

10. A block of density 2400 kg/m^3 has a volume of 0.20 m^3.
    (*a*) What is its weight?
    (*b*) What is its apparent weight when completely immersed in a liquid of density 800 kg/m^3?

11. An object weighs 12 N in air, 7 N when completely immersed in water and 8 N when completely immersed in another liquid. What is the relative density of (*a*) the object, (*b*) the liquid?

Floating

12. A block of wood of mass 1.0 kg floats in water.
    (*a*) What is the weight of the block?
    (*b*) What is the upthrust on it?
    (*c*) What weight of water does it displace?
    (*d*) What mass of water does it displace?
    (*e*) What volume of water does it displace if the density of water is 1000 kg/m^3?
    (*f*) If it floats in denser salt water, how is the level at which it floats affected?

13. A hot air balloon weighs 3000 N, including its basket, and contains hot air weighing 17 000 N. If it displaces cold air of weight 25 000 N, what is the maximum load it can lift?

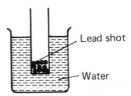

Lead shot

Water

Fig. 7.32

14. The weighted tube in Fig. 7.32 has a uniform cross-sectional area of 2 cm^2 and floats with 8 cm of its length under water of density 1 g/cm^3. What length is under the surface if it floats in a liquid of density 0.8 g/cm^3?

Part Three
Molecules and Heat

Molecules and Matter

8.1 Evidence for Atoms and Molecules

There is a great deal of evidence to support the view that matter is made up of tiny particles which are in continuous rapid motion. Each of the hundred or so elements that form the building blocks for everything else has its own particular kind of *atom*, with a typical diameter of the order of 0.1 nm (10^{-10} m). When atoms join together they form *molecules* (see Unit 1.1(i)).

Fig. 8.1

Atoms and molecules are much too small for us to see them directly, but they can be 'seen' by scientific 'eyes'. One of these is the *field ion microscope* and Fig. 8.1 is a photograph taken with such an instrument of the tip of a metal needle, looking towards the point. The white dots are spots of light each of which *represents* an atom in the metal. Other evidence that we have for the existence of atoms and molecules is less direct but, as we will see shortly, it can be obtained with much simpler apparatus.

8.2 Kinetic Theory of Matter

The kinetic theory is a scientific model which enables us to understand why matter in bulk behaves as it does, in terms of the properties of molecules. It assumes that as well as being in constant motion, molecules also exert strong electrical forces on one another when they are close together (since they themselves are made up of even smaller, electrically charged particles—see Unit 23).

The electrical forces are both attractive and repulsive; the attractive forces hold the molecules together and the repulsive forces, which act only at very short range, cause them to resist being squeezed any further. Molecules thus have both *kinetic energy* because of their motion and *potential energy* because of the 'spring-like' forces that are trying to pull them together.

The kinetic theory can explain the existence of the solid, liquid and gaseous states.

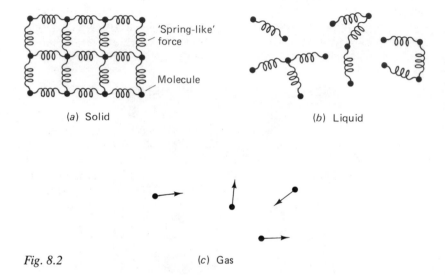

(a) Solid   (b) Liquid

Fig. 8.2   (c) Gas

(i) **Solids.** The molecules are close together and the attractive and repulsive forces between neighbouring molecules balance. Each molecule vibrates to and fro about one position. Solids therefore have a regular, repeating molecular structure (that is, they are *crystalline*) and their shape is definite (Fig. 8.2(a)).

(ii) **Liquids.** The molecules are usually slightly farther apart than in solids. As well as vibrating, they can at the same time move rapidly over short distances, although they are never near each other for long enough to get trapped in a regular structure (Fig. 8.2(b)). Thus a liquid has no fixed shape and can flow.

(iii) **Gases.** The molecules are much farther apart than in solids or liquids (about ten times). They have enough energy to dash around at very high speed (500 m/s for air molecules) in all the space available (Fig. 8.2(c)). The molecular forces can act only during the brief spells when they collide with other molecules or with the walls of the container.

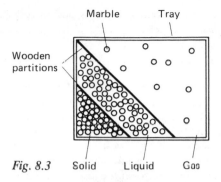

Fig. 8.3   Solid   Liquid   Gas

A model illustrating the states of matter is shown in Fig. 8.3. When the tray is rotated to and fro on a table, the motions of the marbles in the three sections represent molecular motion in the three states of matter.

8.3 Brownian Motion

In 1827, the Scottish botanist, Robert Brown, discovered that fine pollen grains suspended in water were always on the move, covering short zig-zag paths but never stopping. The effect, now called *Brownian motion*, was explained some time later as being due to the irregular bombardment of the pollen grains by the vibrating water molecules. It offers strong evidence in support of the kinetic theory.

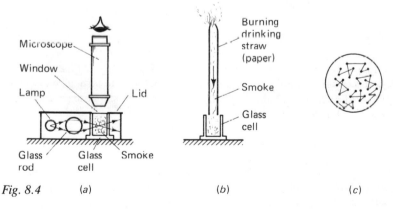

Fig. 8.4   (a)   (b)   (c)

Brownian motion is also observed with small particles floating in gases, using for example, an arrangement like that in Fig. 8.4(a). The glass cell is first filled with smoke from a burning, waxed-paper drinking straw (Fig. 8.4(b)). A bright beam of light is focused by the glass rod (acting as a lens) on the smoke. When correctly adjusted, the microscope should reveal bright specks dancing around haphazardly (Fig. 8.4(c)). The specks are smoke particles seen by reflected light, and their random motion is due to collision with the fast-moving air molecules in the cell.

8.4 Diffusion

Smells, pleasant or otherwise, travel quickly and are caused by rapidly moving molecules. This is an example of the spreading out of a substance of its own accord, which is called *diffusion* and is due to molecular motion.

Diffusion of gases can be shown using brown nitrogen dioxide gas, which is made by pouring a mixture of equal volumes of concentrated nitric acid and water on to copper turnings in a gas jar. When the action has stopped a second gas jar, containing air, is inverted over the jar of nitrogen dioxide (Fig. 8.5(*a*)). The brown colour spreads into the upper jar showing that nitrogen dioxide molecules diffuse upwards against gravity. Air molecules also diffuse into the lower jar.

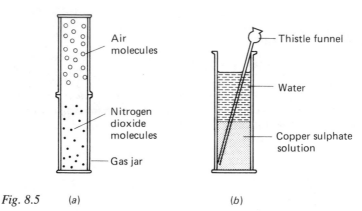

Fig. 8.5   (*a*)   (*b*)

Diffusion in liquids can be demonstrated as in Fig. 8.5(*b*). Copper sulphate solution is poured carefully down the thistle funnel so as to form a layer at the bottom of the cylinder. After 24 hours the blue copper sulphate solution will have diffused upwards into the water.

8.5 Estimate of the Size of a Molecule

Some molecules are considerably larger than others. A rough estimate of the size of an olive oil molecule can be made using the apparatus shown in Figs. 8.6(*a*) and (*b*).

(i) **Method.** Water is poured into a waxed tray till it is overbrimming. The surface is then *lightly* sprinkled with lycopodium powder.

A drop of olive oil is taken up on a V-shaped loop of thin wire by dipping the end into the oil and *quickly* removing it. The wire loop is fixed in a holder with a $\frac{1}{2}$ mm scale and the drop and scale viewed through a hand lens. If the

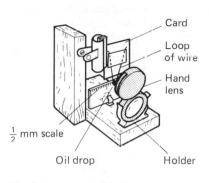 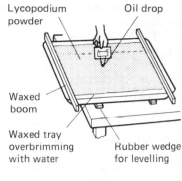

Fig. 8.6   (a)   (b)

diameter of the drop is not about ½ mm, it is discarded and another one taken up.

The loop is removed from the holder and the end dipped into the centre of the water in the tray. The oil spreads outwards, pushing the powder before it and forming a clear circular film whose diameter is measured.

If the water surface is cleaned by drawing two waxed booms across it from the middle of the tray, the experiment can be repeated with several more ½ mm diameter drops.

(ii) **Calculation.** If we assume that the drop is a sphere of diameter d then, from the formula in Unit 2.7,

$$\text{volume of drop} = \frac{4}{3} \pi \left(\frac{d}{2} \right)^3 = \frac{\pi d^3}{6}$$

If D is the diameter of the circular film, assumed to be a flat cylinder of height h then

$$\text{volume of film} = \pi \left(\frac{D}{2} \right)^2 h = \frac{\pi D^2 h}{4}$$

But volume of film = volume of drop

$$\therefore \frac{\pi D^2 h}{4} = \frac{\pi d^3}{6}$$

$$\therefore h = \frac{2 d^3}{3 D^2}$$

Substituting $d = 0.5$ mm $= 0.5 \times 10^{-3}$ m $= 5 \times 10^{-4}$ m, we get

$$h = \frac{2(5 \times 10^{-4})^3}{3 D^2}$$

$$= \frac{250 \times 10^{-12}}{3 D^2}$$

Hence h can be calculated if the average value of D is inserted in this equation. Assuming that the oil spreads out till it is just one molecule thick, the thickness h of the film equals the size of one molecule. The experiment usually gives a result of roughly 2×10^{-9} m = 2 nanometres (2 nm), which means that a row of 500 million olive oil molecules arranged side by side would be 1 metre long. This may be compared with the size of a single atom, which is typically of the order of 0.1 nm.

8.6 Surface Tension

A needle, though made of steel which is denser than water, will float on a *clean* water surface. If a film is formed by dipping an inverted funnel in a detergent solution, it *rises up* the funnel (Fig. 8.7(*a*)). When the film inside the cotton loop in Fig. 8.7(*b*) is broken, the loop forms a circle (Fig. 8.7(*c*)).

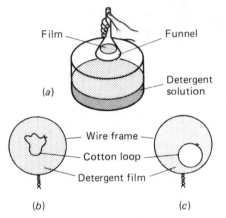

Fig. 8.7   (*b*)   (*c*)

These facts suggest that the surface of a liquid (in a vessel or on a film) behaves as if covered with an elastic skin that is trying to shrink. The effect is called *surface tension*. It is reduced if the liquid is 'contaminated' by, for example, detergent; a needle floating in water sinks if a drop of detergent is added.

Surface tension is due to the molecules in a liquid surface being slightly farther apart than normal (like those in a stretched wire). This is because the molecules in the vapour are more widely separated than those in the liquid, and the increase in separation takes place gradually *through* the surface.

8.7 Adhesion and Cohesion

The force of attraction between molecules of the same substance is known as *cohesion*; that between molecules of different substances is *adhesion*. The adhesion of water to glass is greater than the cohesion of water; this is why

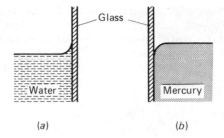

Fig. 8.8   (a)   (b)

water spilt on clean glass wets it by spreading to a thin film. It is also why water has an upward-curved surface or *meniscus* where it touches glass (Fig. 8.8(a)).

By contrast, mercury on glass forms drops—spherical if small and flattened if large—because cohesion of mercury is stronger than its adhesion to glass. For the same reason, mercury in contact with glass forms a downward-curved meniscus (Fig. 8.8(b)).

The cleaning action of detergents depends on their ability to weaken the cohesion of water. Instead of forming drops on greasy clothes, the water penetrates the fabric and releases dirt.

8.8 Capillarity

If a very narrow glass tube (a *capillary tube*) is dipped into water, the water rises up inside the tube to a height of a few centimetres (Fig. 8.9(a)); the narrower the tube, the greater the rise. Adhesion between water and glass exceeds cohesion between water molecules and the water is pulled up.

The action of blotting paper is due to capillary rise in the narrow air spaces between its fibres. Oil rises up a lamp wick in the same way. The damp course in a house is a layer of non-porous material (plastic, felt and bitumen) in the walls just above ground level but below the floor; it prevents water rising up the pores in the bricks by capillary action from the ground and causing dampness within the building.

Unlike water, mercury is depressed in a capillary tube (Fig. 8.9(b)); the narrower the tube, the farther it falls below the level of the surrounding mercury.

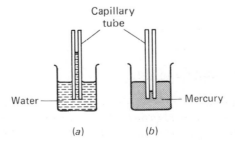

Fig. 8.9   (a)   (b)

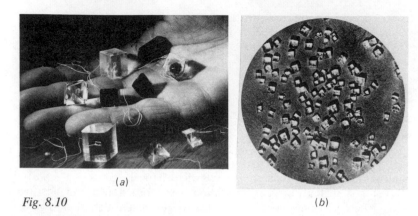

Fig. 8.10   (b)

8.9 Crystals

Crystals have hard, smooth faces and straight edges. Their shapes and sizes vary but whatever their size, crystals of the same substance usually have the same shape. The crystals in Fig. 8.10(a) are of different substances and are differently shaped, while those in Fig. 8.10(b) are all of salt and are all cube-shaped, but of different sizes.

These facts about crystals can be explained by assuming that they consist of particles (such as atoms or molecules) arranged in an orderly way according to a definite plan. If crystal models are built using polystyrene balls to represent 'particles', different shapes can be made as in Fig. 8.11(a) (for crystals of different substances) and different sizes 'grown' as in Fig. 8.11(b) (for crystals of the same substance). This suggests that the regularity of a crystal's outward appearance may be due to the regular arrangement of the atoms or molecules that make it up.

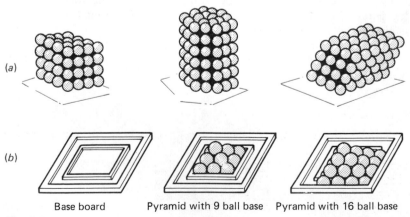

Base board   Pyramid with 9 ball base   Pyramid with 16 ball base

Fig. 8.11

Crystals are much more common than appears at first sight. In fact, all solids are crystalline but most solids consist of thousands of very small crystals joined together in a haphazard arrangement.

8.10 Revision Questions

1. (a) State two main assumptions of the kinetic theory of matter.
   (b) What forms of energy do molecules have?

2. (a) Describe how a molecule moves in (i) a solid, (ii) a liquid, (iii) a gas.
   (b) Why are gases more easily squeezed than liquids or solids are?

3. (a) If you use a microscope to view illuminated smoke floating in air in a glass cell, what do you see?
   (b) What is the effect called? Explain it.
   (c) Name one other effect which supports your explanation.

4. Explain why (a) diffusion occurs more quickly in a gas than in a liquid, (b) diffusion is still quite slow even in a gas.

5. (a) 'Liquids exhibit surface tension.' What does this mean?
   (b) Give three examples of the effects of surface tension.

6. (a) Explain the terms adhesion and cohesion as applied to liquids.
   (b) Why does water 'wet' glass but mercury doesn't?

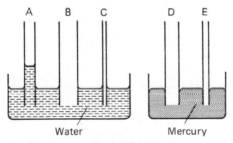

Fig. 8.12

7. (a) Name the effect shown in tube A of Fig. 8.12.
   (b) Copy the diagram and mark the water levels in B and C and the mercury levels in D and E.
   (c) State two uses of this effect.

8. What is a damp-course and what is its purpose?

9. Why do the properties of crystals support the view that matter is made up of particles?

8.11 Problems

1. A tray is 50 cm long and 40 cm wide and has 2.0×10^3 cm^3 of water poured into it. What is the depth of water?

2. A drop of oil of volume 6.0×10^{-11} m^3 spreads out on a clean water surface to a film of area 3.0×10^{-3} m^2. Calculate the size of an oil molecule, stating any assumption you make.

3. A drop of oil of volume 6×10^{-10} m^3 is allowed to fall on some clean water and it spreads to form a circle of diameter 0.2 m. Estimate the upper limit of the size of an oil molecule. (Take $\pi = 3$.)

Effects of Heating

9.1 Temperature

The temperature of an object tells us how hot it is and is measured by a thermometer, usually in degrees Celsius (°C). The kinetic theory (see Unit 8.2) regards the temperature of an object as a measure of the average kinetic energy of its molecules: the greater this is, the faster the molecules move and the higher the temperature of the object.

(i) **Scale of temperature.** A scale and a unit of temperature are obtained by choosing two temperatures, called *fixed points*, and dividing the range between them into a number of equal divisions or degrees. On the Celsius scale (named after the Swedish scientist who suggested it), the fixed points are defined as follows:

    1. The *lower fixed point* is the temperature of pure melting ice and is taken as 0 °C. (If the ice is impure its melting-point is lowered—see Unit 10.7.)

    2. The *upper fixed point* is the temperature of the steam above water boiling at standard atmospheric pressure of 760 mmHg and is taken as 100 °C. (The temperature of the boiling water itself is not used because any impurities in the water raise its boiling-point, but the temperature of the steam is not affected; also the measurement must be made at standard atmospheric pressure, since the boiling-point is affected by pressure changes. See Unit 10.12(i).)

The fixed points can be found for an unmarked mercury-in-glass thermometer (see Unit 9.3(i)) as shown in Figs. 9.1(a) and (b). When they have been marked on the thermometer, the distance between them is divided into 100 equal degrees (Fig. 9.1(c)). This calibrates the thermometer. The scale can be extended for temperatures above 100 °C and below 0 °C.

(ii) **Absolute zero and the Kelvin scale.** As the temperature of a body falls, its molecules move more slowly and their average kinetic energy decreases. At a temperature of −273 °C, called *absolute zero*, the molecules have their lowest possible kinetic energy. (We believe they must always have some energy, otherwise they would stop moving.)

    Absolute zero is the lowest temperature attainable and is taken as the zero of the absolute or Kelvin scale of temperature, which is the most used in science. Its divisions are the same as those on the Celsius scale, that is, 1 °C = 1 kelvin = 1 K (not °K) and since −273 °C = 0 K, then

$$0\,°C = 273\,K$$
$$15\,°C = 273 + 15 = 288\,K$$
$$100\,°C = 273 + 100 = 373\,K$$

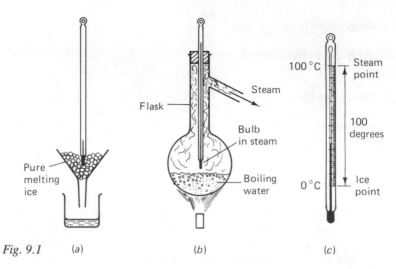

Fig. 9.1   (a)   (b)   (c)

In general, temperatures on the Kelvin scale are denoted by T and those on the Celsius scale by the Greek letter θ (*theta*). Therefore

$$T = 273 + \theta$$

9.2   Heat and Temperature

It is important not to confuse the temperature of a body with the *heat energy* that it can give out. For example, a red-hot spark from a fire is at a higher temperature than that of boiling water in a saucepan but the latter has much more heat and would burn you more severely if you spilt it over yourself.

Heat is also called *thermal* or *internal energy* since it is the energy a body has because of the kinetic energy *and* the potential energy of its molecules. Increasing the temperature of a body increases its heat energy due to the k.e. of its molecules increasing. But as we will see later (in Unit 10.5), the heat energy of a body can also be increased by increasing the p.e. of its molecules. The molecules in the pan of boiling water have less kinetic energy per molecule than those in the spark, but since there are many more water molecules their total energy is greater.

Heat passes from a body at a higher temperature to one at a lower temperature. This is due to the average k.e. (and speed) of the molecules in the 'hot' body falling as a result of having collisions with molecules of the 'cold' body whose average k.e., and therefore temperature, increases. When the average k.e. of the molecules is the same in both bodies, they are at the same temperature.

In a solid k.e. and p.e. are present in roughly equal amounts. In a gas, where the intermolecular forces are weak, the molecules have much more k.e. than p.e.

9.3 Thermometers

Thermometers use the fact that the property of matter on which they are based changes with temperature.

(i) **Liquid-in-glass thermometers.** In this type, the liquid in a glass bulb expands along a capillary tube when the bulb is heated. The liquid must be seen easily, and must expand (or contract) over a wide range of temperatures. The narrower the capillary tube, the more sensitive is the thermometer, that is, the farther the liquid moves along the tube for a given temperature change. The most commonly used liquids are mercury and coloured alcohol.

The advantages of *mercury* are that it does not stick to the inside of the tube (and give a low reading when the temperature is falling), that it is easy to see and that it responds quickly to temperature changes. It has the disadvantage of freezing at the not very low temperature of $-39\,°C$, and it is also expensive.

The advantages of *alcohol* are a low freezing-point ($-115\,°C$) and greater expansion for a given temperature change. On the other hand it sticks to the tube, has a low boiling-point ($78\,°C$) and the liquid 'thread' tends to break.

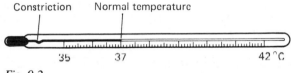

Constriction   Normal temperature

3b   37   42 °C

Fig. 9.2

(ii) **Clinical thermometer.** This is a special kind of thermometer used by doctors and nurses (Fig. 9.2). Its scale covers only a few degrees on either side of the normal human body temperature of $37\,°C$.

The tube has a constriction (that is, a narrower part) just beyond the bulb. When the thermometer is placed under the patient's tongue the mercury expands, forcing its way past the constriction. When the thermometer is removed (after 1 minute or so) from the mouth, the mercury in the bulb cools and contracts, breaking the mercury thread at the constriction. The mercury beyond the constriction stays in the tube and allows the body temperature to be read. After the reading has been taken the mercury is returned to the bulb by shaking the thermometer.

(iii) **Thermocouple thermometer.** A thermocouple consists of two wires of different materials, such as copper and iron, joined together (Fig. 9.3). When one junction is at a higher temperature than the other, an electric current flows and produces a reading on a sensitive current meter or *galvanometer* (with a scale marked in °C), which depends on the temperature difference between the junctions. Thermocouple thermometers are used in industry to measure oven and furnace temperatures up to about $1500\,°C$. They are suitable for observing rapidly changing temperatures, because the wire junction is small

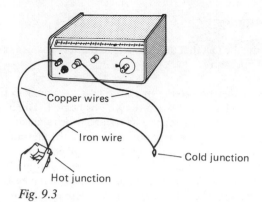

Fig. 9.3

and needs very little heat to warm it up and the instrument therefore responds rapidly to any temperature variation.

(iv) **Other thermometers.** The *platinum resistance thermometer* uses the fact that the electrical resistance (see Unit 19.4) of a platinum wire increases with temperature; it covers a wide range (-200 to $1200\,°C$) and is very accurate, but it is unsuitable for rapidly changing temperatures. It is best for measuring small temperature differences.

The *pyrometer* is the only thermometer for measuring temperatures above $1500\,°C$. The *disappearing filament* type is used to measure temperatures such as that of a glowing furnace. A filament lamp (see Unit 20.5) is placed in front of the hot source and the light from both is viewed through a red filter, which transmits red light only. Both source and filament appear red. The current through the lamp is adjusted until the lamp seems as bright as the background light from the source, that is, until it disappears. An ammeter measures the lamp current, and its scale is calibrated in $°C$ so that the temperature can be read off directly.

9.4 Expansion of Solids

Most solids expand when heated and contract when cooled, but only by a very small amount. Nevertheless large forces are created, which are in some circumstances useful and in others a nuisance.

The kinetic theory's explanation is that the molecules of a solid vibrate more vigorously when heated, forcing each other a little farther apart. Expansion in all directions results. Cooling reduces the vibrations, the forces of attraction between molecules bring them closer together and the solid contracts slightly.

(i) **Demonstrations.** The *ball and ring* in Fig. 9.4(*a*) can be used to show the expansion of a solid. When the ball and ring are both cold, the ball just passes through the ring. If the ball is heated over a burner its diameter increases in all

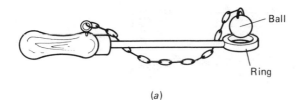

(a)

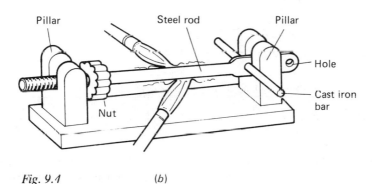

Fig. 9.1   (b)

directions, by only a tiny amount but enough to stop it going through the ring.

The *bar breaker* experiment in Fig. 9.4(*b*) shows the large forces of expansion and contraction in metals. The nut is first tightened so that there is no room for expansion. Heating the steel rod with one or more burners eventually makes the cast iron bar snap. When the nut and cast iron bar are fitted on the other sides of the pillars and the nut tightened *after* the steel rod has been heated, the bar breaks as the rod cools.

(ii) **Uses of expansion.** In *shrink fitting*, an axle is made just too large for the hole in a gear or other wheel, and then cooled to about −200 °C in liquid nitrogen. It then fits into the wheel and as it regains normal temperature it expands to give a very tight fit.

A *bimetal strip* is made of equal lengths of two different metals, such as brass and invar (an iron–nickel alloy with a very small expansion—the name is taken from the word 'invariable'), fixed together so that they cannot move separately (Fig. 9.5(*a*)). When heated, brass expands more than invar and to allow this, the strip bends with brass on the outside (Fig. 9.5(*b*)).

Bimetal strips are used as *thermostats* to keep the temperature of a room or appliance about constant. Fig. 9.5(*c*) shows how one is used in the electrical heating circuit of an electric iron. When the iron reaches the required temperature the strip bends down, breaks the circuit at the contacts and switches off the heater. After cooling a little the strip straightens, remakes contact and turns the heater on again. A near-steady temperature results. If the control knob is screwed down, the strip has to bend more to break the heating circuit and must reach a higher temperature to bend sufficiently.

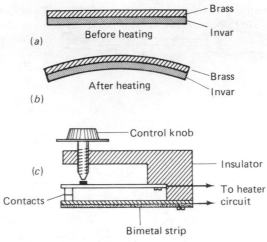

Fig. 9.5

The *flashing direction indicators* in a car also use a small bimetal strip which is warmed by an electric heating coil wound round it.

(iii) Precautions against expansion. Steel and concrete beams used in constructing *bridges* must be able to expand when the temperature rises, or the bridge will be damaged. The ends of bridges are therefore set on rollers and an expansion gap left, as in Fig. 9.6.

Steel *railway lines* were previously laid with gaps between the lengths of rail to allow for expansion in hot weather. They caused a 'clickety-click' sound as the train passed over them. Today the rails are welded into lengths of about

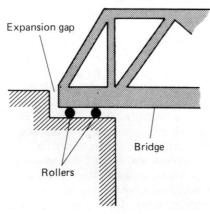

Fig. 9.6

1 km and are held by concrete sleepers (lying in stone chippings) that can withstand the large forces created without buckling. Also, at the joints the ends are tapered and overlap, giving rail passengers a smoother journey and allowing some expansion near the ends of each length of rail.

9.5 Linear Expansivity

Although a solid expands in all directions, often it is only the linear (lengthways) expansion which is important in practice.

(i) **Definition.** An engineer can calculate the linear expansion of a bridge if he knows (*a*) the length of the bridge, (*b*) the range of temperature it will experience and (*c*) the linear expansivity (symbol α) of the material to be used.

The linear expansivity of a material is the increase in length
of unit length per degree rise in temperature.

The value of α is found by experiment. For steel it is 0.000 012 per °C (or per K). This means that when the temperature rises by 1 °C,

1 m of steel increases in length by 0.000 012 m,
2 m of steel increases in length by 2 ×0.000 012 m.

We can say this because a 2 m length may be thought of as two 1 m lengths joined end to end. Hence a steel bridge 100 m long will expand by 0.000 012 ×100 m for each 1 °C rise. If the maximum temperature change expected is 50 °C (from −15 °C to +35 °C, say), the expansion will be 0.000 012 × 100 ×50 =0.060 m (6.0 cm). In general,

expansion (or contraction)
=linear expansivity ×original length ×temperature change

or, in symbols,

$$\Delta l = \alpha \times l \times \Delta\theta$$

where Δ (the Greek capital letter D, pronounced 'delta') stands for a 'change in'.

(ii) **Measurement.** Rewriting the above expression gives

$$\alpha = \frac{\Delta l}{l \times \Delta\theta}$$

To find the linear expansivity of a material we must measure the expansion Δl of a known length l for a known temperature rise $\Delta\theta$.

One form of apparatus is shown in Fig. 9.7. The original length of a rod of the material (about 50 cm) is measured with a metre rule. It is placed in the steam jacket with one end against the stop. The micrometer is adjusted until it just touches the other end, and the reading is taken; the temperature of the rod is recorded.

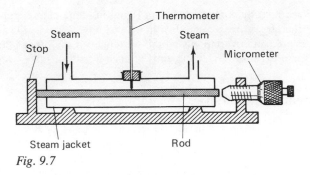

Fig. 9.7

The micrometer is unscrewed and steam is passed through the jacket for several minutes. It is screwed up again and the new reading noted. The procedure is repeated shortly afterwards, to ensure that the reading has not changed, showing that the rod is at the steam temperature—which is also taken. The difference in the micrometer readings equals the expansion of the rod, Δl, and the difference between the first and the final thermometer readings gives $\Delta \theta$; the linear expansivity can then be calculated.

The change in length for a given temperature rise of a material of known linear expansivity can be calculated from the equation in (i), which is true for decreases as well as increases in temperature. The change in length is obtained in the same unit as the original length.

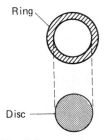

Fig. 9.8

It is useful to realize that a hole expands by the same amount as the material round it. Therefore if the ring and disc in Fig. 9.8 are of the same material and just fit at one temperature, they will at any other.

9.6 Expansion of Liquids

When liquids are heated they expand much more than solids do, and we have to consider volume changes rather than linear expansions. The expansion of a

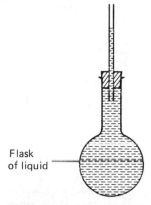

Flask
of liquid

Fig. 9.9

liquid can be shown by placing a flask like that in Fig. 9.9 in hot water. Initially the level of the liquid in the tube falls slightly due to the flask expanding before the liquid is warmed. Eventually the liquid expands and rises up the tube.

(i) Unusual behaviour of water. When water is cooled to 4 °C it contracts, as we would expect, but as it cools from 4 °C to 0 °C it expands, surprisingly. Water therefore has a maximum density at 4 °C.

At 0 °C, where water freezes, a considerable expansion occurs and every 100 cm³ of water becomes 109 cm³ of ice; this accounts for the bursting of water pipes in very cold weather. Further cooling of the ice causes it to contract. The unusual behaviour of water is represented by the volume–temperature graph in Fig. 9.10.

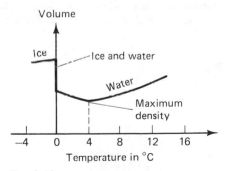

Fig. 9.10

The expansion of water between 4 °C and 0 °C is due to the fact that above 4 °C water molecules form into groups which break up when the temperature drops below 4 °C. The new arrangement occupies a larger volume and this more than cancels out the contraction due to the fall in temperature.

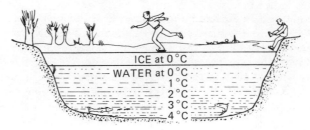

Fig. 9.11

(ii) **Freezing of ponds.** The behaviour of water between 4 °C and 0 °C explains why fish survive in a frozen pond. The water at the top of the pond cools first, contracts and being denser sinks to the bottom. Warmer, less dense water rises to the surface to be cooled. When all the water is at 4 °C the circulation stops. If the temperature of the surface water falls below 4 °C, it becomes less dense and remains at the top, eventually forming a layer of ice at 0 °C. Temperatures in the pond are then as shown in Fig. 9.11.

9.7 Effect of Heat on Gases: the Gas Laws

When a gas is heated, as air is in a jet engine, its pressure as well as its volume may change. Three factors—volume, pressure and temperature—are involved; to find the laws relating them, one of the three has to be kept fixed while the relation between the other two is investigated. This is done in the three experiments described below, each of which studies the behaviour of a fixed mass of dry air.

(i) **Charles' law: relation between volume and temperature at constant pressure.** The apparatus is arranged as in Fig. 9.12. The index of concentrated

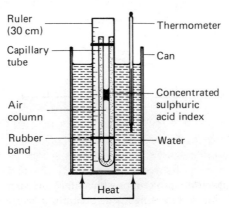

Fig. 9.12

sulphuric acid traps the air column to be investigated and also dries it. The pressure of (and on) the air column is constant and equals atmospheric pressure plus the pressure due to the weight of the acid index.

The capillary tube is adjusted so that the bottom of the air column is opposite a convenient mark on the ruler, and the water is slowly heated. The length of the air column (to the lower end of the index) is noted at different temperatures; before taking each reading the heating is stopped and the water stirred to make sure that the air in the tube has reached the temperature of the water. The length of the air column is proportional to the volume of air if the capillary tube is of constant width.

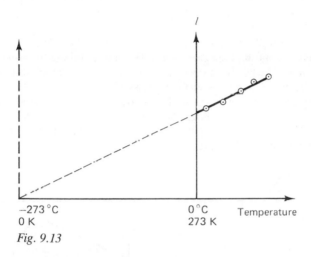

Fig. 9.13

Plotting the length of the air column *l* against temperature in °C gives a straight-line graph like that in Fig. 9.13. When extended backwards it should cut the temperature axis at −273 °C, that is, at absolute zero. Therefore if we take 0 K as the origin of the graph then, since it is a straight line passing through the origin, we can say that the volume *V* is directly proportional to the *absolute temperature T*, so that doubling *T* doubles *V*, and so on. In symbols,

$$V \propto T \text{ or } V = \text{constant} \times T$$

$$\text{or } \frac{V}{T} = \text{constant}$$

1

This is *Charles' law*, which is stated as follows:

> *The volume of a fixed mass of gas is directly proportional*
> *to its absolute temperature if the pressure is kept constant.*

(ii) **Pressure law: relation between pressure and temperature at constant volume.** The apparatus in Fig. 9.14 allows a Bourdon gauge to measure the pressure at different temperatures of the air in the flask, the volume of which

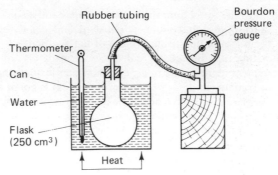

Fig. 9.14

does not change during the experiment. The rubber tubing from the flask to the gauge should be as short as possible, because the air in the tubing is not at the same temperature as the air in the flask.

The temperature of the air in the flask is gradually increased by heating the water. Before taking a reading, the heating should be stopped and time allowed for the gauge reading to become steady; the air in the flask will then be at the temperature of the water.

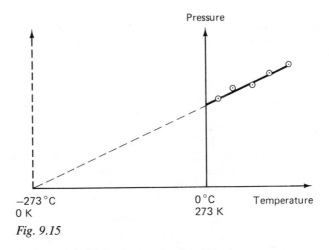

Fig. 9.15

The graph of pressure against temperature (Fig. 9.15) obtained from this experiment is similar to the volume–temperature graph of Fig. 9.13. It passes through absolute zero when extended; the pressure p is thus directly proportional to the absolute temperature T. In symbols,

$$p \propto T \text{ or } p = \text{constant} \times T$$

$$\text{or } \frac{p}{T} = \text{constant}$$

2

This is the *pressure law*, which is stated as follows:

*The pressure of a fixed mass of gas is directly proportional
to its absolute temperature if the volume is kept constant.*

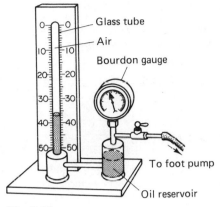

Fig. 9.16

(iii) **Boyle's law: relation between pressure and volume at constant
temperature.** This may be investigated using the apparatus in Fig. 9.16. The
volume V of air trapped in the glass tube is read off on the scale behind. The
pressure is changed by pumping air from a foot pump into the space above the
oil reservoir. As a result, more oil is forced into the glass tube and increases the
pressure p on the air in it. The air pressure above the oil reservoir, which is
measured by the Bourdon gauge, is transmitted through the oil and equals the
pressure p of the trapped air.

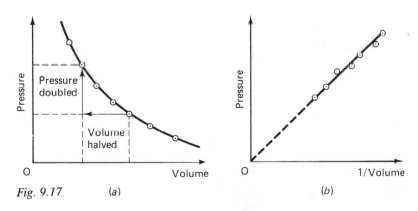

Fig. 9.17   (a)   (b)

A graph of pressure against volume is a curve like that in Fig. 9.17(a). Close
examination of it shows that if p is doubled, V is halved—that is, that p is
inversely proportional to V. In symbols,

$$p \propto \frac{1}{V} \text{ or } p = \text{constant} \times \frac{1}{V}$$

$$\therefore pV = \text{constant} \qquad\qquad 3$$

This is *Boyle's law*, which is stated as follows:

> *The pressure of a fixed mass of gas is inversely proportional to its volume if its temperature is kept constant.*

Since p is *inversely* proportional to V, it must be directly proportional to $1/V$; a graph of p against $1/V$ is therefore a straight line through the origin (Fig. 9.17(b)).

9.8 General Gas Equation

The gas laws give three relations between p, V and T, which can be expressed as one equation called the *general gas equation*. We have

$$\frac{V}{T} = \text{constant} \qquad \text{(Charles' law)}$$

$$\frac{p}{T} = \text{constant} \qquad \text{(pressure law)}$$

$$pV = \text{constant} \qquad \text{(Boyle's law)}$$

These combine to give

$$\frac{pV}{T} = \text{constant}$$

This equation is useful for predicting what happens in cases where p, V and T all change from, say, p_1, V_1, T_1 to p_2, V_2, T_2. So long as the mass of gas remains constant, we can then write

$$\frac{p_1 V_1}{T_1} = \frac{p_2 V_2}{T_2} \qquad\qquad 4$$

If $p_1 = p_2$ (that is, if the pressure remains constant), we get $V_1/T_1 = V_2/T_2$, which is Charles' law.

If $V_1 = V_2$ (the volume remains constant), we get $p_1/T_1 = p_2/T_2$, which is the pressure law.

If $T_1 = T_2$ (the temperature remains constant), we get $p_1 V_1 = p_2 V_2$, which is Boyle's law.

There are three points to notice when using equation 4.

1. The temperatures T_1 and T_2 must be in K.
2. Any units can be used for p and V, so long as they are the same on both sides of the equation.

3. In some calculations the volume of the gas has to be found at s.t.p. (standard temperature and pressure), that is, $0\,°C$ and $760\,mmHg$ pressure.

Most gases obey the gas laws at low and medium pressures and at normal temperatures. At high pressures, the size of the molecules becomes an appreciable fraction of the volume available for motion and so the actual volume is less than the measured value. Near the liquefying temperature of a gas, the attractions between its molecules make the pressure smaller than the gas laws predict.

An *ideal gas* would obey the gas laws exactly under all conditions. Such a gas does not exist in practice, but it is often useful to compare the behaviour of real gases with one.

9.9 Worked Examples

1. A bicycle pump contains $50\,cm^3$ of air at $17\,°C$ and a pressure of 1.0 atmosphere. Find the pressure when the air is compressed to $10\,cm^3$ and its temperature rises to $27\,°C$.

We have

$$p_1 = 1.0 \text{ atmosphere} \qquad p_2 = ?$$
$$V_1 = 50\,cm^3 \qquad\qquad V_2 = 10\,cm^3$$
$$T_1 = 273 + 17 = 290\,K \qquad T_2 = 273 + 27 = 300\,K$$

Rearranging equation 4 gives

$$p_2 = p_1 \times \frac{V_1}{V_2} \times \frac{T_2}{T_1}$$

Substituting values,

$$p_2 = 1.0 \text{ atmosphere} \times \frac{50\,cm^3}{10\,cm^3} \times \frac{300\,K}{290\,K}$$

$$= 5.2 \text{ atmospheres}$$

2. A diver at the bottom of a lake releases an air bubble of volume $2.0\,cm^3$. As the bubble rises its temperature remains constant but its volume increases until it is $4.0\,cm^3$ at the surface. How deep is the lake, if atmospheric pressure equals $10\,m$ of water?

Let x = depth of lake in metres. We are given

p_1 = pressure at bottom of lake
    = atmospheric pressure + pressure due to x metres of water
    = $10\,m$ of water + $x\,m$ of water
    = $(10 + x)\,m$ of water
$V_1 = 2.0\,cm^3$

$$p_2 = \text{pressure at surface of lake}$$
$$= \text{atmospheric pressure}$$
$$= 10 \text{ m of water}$$
$$V_2 = 4.0 \text{ cm}^3$$
$$T_1 = T_2$$

Rearranging equation 4 and cancelling T_1 and T_2 gives

$$p_1 = \frac{p_2 V_2}{V_1}$$

Substituting, $(10 + x)$ m of water $= 10$ m of water $\times \dfrac{4 \text{ cm}^3}{2 \text{ cm}^3}$

$$\therefore \ 10 + x = 20$$
$$x = 20 - 10 = 10 \text{ m}$$
$$\text{Depth of lake} = \underline{\underline{10 \text{ m}}}$$

9.10 Gases and the Kinetic Theory

One of the aims of physics is to explain the behaviour of matter in bulk, in terms of the properties of atoms and molecules—that is, to relate macroscopic (large-scale) effects to microscopic (small-scale) causes. In Unit 8.2 we saw how the kinetic theory could account for the existence of the three states or phases of matter on the assumptions (*a*) that molecules are in continuous rapid motion ('kinetic' means 'due to motion'), and (*b*) that molecules exert forces on each other.

The kinetic theory can also make sense of the properties of gases and the laws they obey.

(i) **Pressure.** The pressure exerted by a gas is due to the molecules bombarding the walls of its container. The molecules are in rapid motion, with a wide range of speeds, and hit the walls of the container in huge numbers every second. The average force and therefore the pressure they exert on the walls is constant (since pressure is force per unit area).

(ii) **Temperature.** When a gas is heated and its temperature rises, the average speed and kinetic energy of its molecules increases.

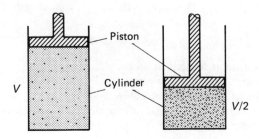

Fig. 9.18

(iii) **Boyle's law.** If the volume of a fixed mass of gas is halved by halving the volume of the container (Fig. 9.18), the number of molecules per cm^3 will be doubled. There will therefore be twice as many collisions per second with the walls, that is, the pressure is doubled.

(iv) **Charles' law.** If the pressure of a gas is to remain constant when its temperature increases, the volume must increase so that the number of molecular collisions with the walls of the container does not change.

(v) **Pressure law.** If the volume of a gas is to stay constant when the temperature rises, its pressure must increase since the molecules collide with the walls of the container more frequently and more violently.

9.11 Revision Questions

1. Name two physical properties which may be used as the basis for measuring temperature.

2. (a) Define (i) the lower fixed point and (ii) the upper fixed point, on the Celsius scale.
   (b) How would you calibrate an unmarked mercury-in-glass thermometer?

3. How does the kinetic theory explain a rise in temperature?

4. Explain the term *absolute zero*. What is its value on the Celsius scale?

5. Which one of the following helps a liquid-in-glass thermometer to record a change of temperature rapidly?

   A a long stem   B a large bulb
   C a narrow stem   D a thick-walled bulb
   E a thin-walled bulb

6. (a) State three advantages and one disadvantage of a mercury thermometer.
   (b) State one advantage and one disadvantage of an alcohol thermometer.

7. Explain why a clinical thermometer (a) covers a small temperature range, (b) has a constriction above the bulb, (c) has a tube with a very narrow bore.

8. Describe how the following work, and state one use for each: (a) a thermocouple thermometer, (b) a platinum resistance thermometer, (c) a disappearing filament pyrometer.

9. Explain why (a) the metal lid on a glass jam jar can be unscrewed more easily if the jar is inverted for a few seconds with the lid in very hot water, (b) furniture may creak at night after a warm day, (c) concrete roads are laid in sections with pitch between them.

10. A bimetallic strip is made from metals A and B. When heated it bends as shown in Fig. 9.19.
    (a) Which metal expands more for the same rise in temperature?
    (b) Draw a diagram to show how the bimetallic strip would appear if it were cooled below room temperature.

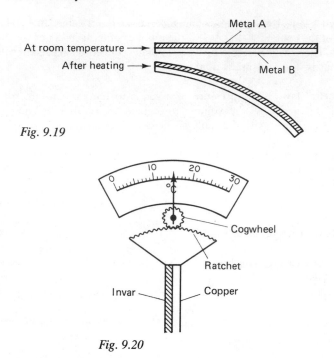

Fig. 9.19

Fig. 9.20

11. How does the bimetallic thermometer in Fig. 9.20 work?

12. Give two examples of problems caused by expanding solids, and state how they are overcome.

13. Define *linear expansivity* and write down an expression for it in symbol form. What is its unit?

14. (*a*) How is the behaviour of water different from that of most other liquids when it is cooled?
    (*b*) Why does a pond freeze first at the top?

15. (*a*) State (i) Charles' law, (ii) the pressure law, (iii) Boyle's law.
    (*b*) Write an equation which combines all three gas laws.
    (*c*) What is an ideal gas?

9.12 Problems

Temperature

1. (*a*) Temperatures are sometimes stated in degrees Fahrenheit (°F) as well as in °C (in weather forecasts, for instance). A quick but rough way of converting °C to °F is to 'double the temperature in °C and add 30'. Using this rule convert to °F: (i) 10 °C, (ii) 15 °C, (iii) 20 °C, (iv) 25 °C.
    (*b*) Write down a rough rule for changing °F to °C. Use it to convert to °C: (i) 40 °F, (ii) 56 °F, (iii) 68 °F, (iv) 90 °F.

2. (a) Change the following temperatures into kelvin: (i) $-273\,°C$, (ii) $0\,°C$, (iii) $17\,°C$, (iv) $100\,°C$.
   (b) Change the following temperatures into $°C$: (i) $873\,K$, (ii) $546\,K$, (iii) $223\,K$, (iv) $73\,K$.

Linear Expansivity

3. The linear expansivity of copper is $0.000\,02/K$. Calculate the change in length of (a) a copper rod 1 m long when its temperature rises by $1\,°C$, (b) a copper rod 1 cm long when its temperature falls by $1\,°C$, (c) a copper rod 5 cm long when its temperature rises from $0\,°C$ to $100\,°C$.

4. The linear expansivities of some common materials are given below:

Aluminium	0.000 03/K	Glass	0.000 009/K
Concrete	0.000 01/K	Platinum	0.000 009/K
Copper	0.000 02/K	Steel	0.000 01/K

   (a) Three rods of aluminium, copper and steel respectively are the same length at $0\,°C$. Which will be the longest at $300\,°C$?
   (b) If the aluminium rod is 1 m long at $0\,°C$, what will be its length at $300\,°C$?
   (c) Why is steel a suitable material for reinforcing concrete?
   (d) Which of the substances listed above would be most suitable for carrying a current of electricity through the walls of a glass vessel?

5. Using the values for linear expansivities in Question 4, calculate the expansion of (a) 100 m of copper pipe heated through $50\,°C$, (b) 50 cm of steel pipe heated through $80\,°C$, (c) 200 m of aluminium pipe heated from $10\,°C$ to $60\,°C$.

6. What is the linear expansivity of the material of a rod which is 1 m long at $20\,°C$ and 1.0016 m long at $100\,°C$?

Gas Laws

7. A gas of volume $200\,m^3$ at $27.0\,°C$ is heated to $327\,°C$ at constant pressure. What is its new volume?

8. To what temperature must a gas in a container at $0\,°C$ be cooled so that its pressure is reduced to one-third of its value at $0\,°C$? Assume the container does not contract.

9. At a pressure of 1.00 atmosphere and a temperature of $27.0\,°C$ a mass of gas has a volume of $200\,cm^3$. What is its volume when the pressure is 1.50 atmosphere and the temperature $127\,°C$?

10. Calculate the volume at the surface of a bubble which has a volume of $3.0\,cm^3$ when released at a depth of 30 m in water. Assume its temperature is constant and that atmospheric pressure is 10 m of water.

Measuring Heat

10.1 Specific Heat Capacity

(i) **Definition.** If 1 kg of water and 1 kg of paraffin are heated in turn for the same time by the same heater, the temperature rise of the paraffin is about *twice* that of the water. Since the heater gives equal amounts of heat energy to each liquid, it follows that different substances require different amounts of heat to cause the same temperature rise in the same mass.

The 'thirst' of a substance for heat is measured by its *specific heat capacity* (symbol c).

> *The specific heat capacity of a substance is the amount of heat required to produce a 1 K (1 °C) rise in temperature in a mass of 1 kg.*

Heat, like other forms of energy, is measured in joules (J) and the unit of specific heat capacity is the *joule per kilogram kelvin* (J/(kg K) or J/(kg °C)).

In physics the word 'specific' indicates that unit mass is being considered.

(ii) **The 'specific heat equation'.** If a substance has a specific heat capacity of 1000 J/(kg K),

$$1000 \text{ J raise the temperature of 1 kg by 1 K,}$$
$$2 \times 1000 \text{ J raise the temperature of 2 kg by 1 K,}$$
$$3 \times 2 \times 1000 \text{ J raise the temperature of 2 kg by 3 K,}$$

that is, 6000 J will raise the temperature of 2 kg of this substance by 3 K. We have obtained this answer by multiplying together:

the *mass* in kg,
the *temperature rise* in K (or °C), and
the *specific heat capacity* in J/(kg K).

If the temperature of 2 kg of the substance fell by 3 K, the heat given out would also be 6000 J. In general, we can write the 'specific heat equation'

heat taken in or given out
$$= \text{mass} \times \text{specific heat capacity} \times \text{temperature change}$$

In symbols,

$$E_h = mc\,\Delta\theta$$

where $\Delta\theta$ is the temperature change in K or °C.

For example, if the temperature of a 5 kg mass of copper, for which $c = 400$ J/(kg K), rises from 15 °C to 25 °C the heat taken in (E_h) is given by

M shc   ∂int∪p

$$E_h = 5\,kg \times 400\,J/(kg\,K) \times (25-15)\,°C = 5 \times 400 \times 10\,J = \underline{\underline{20\,000\,J}}$$

(iii) **Measuring specific heat capacity.** An experiment for measuring the specific heat capacity of water is shown in Fig. 10.1. The pan contains a known mass m of water, the electric heater of known power P is switched on for a known time t and the temperature rise $\Delta\theta$ (in °C) is noted. (A 40 W heater running in 1 kg of water for 5 minutes can be expected to give a reasonable result—a heater must *not* be used if its seal is cracked.) If the power P of the heater is not known it can be found by immersing the heater in water, connecting it to a 12 V d.c. supply and measuring the current I taken and the voltage V across it. Then $P = IV$.

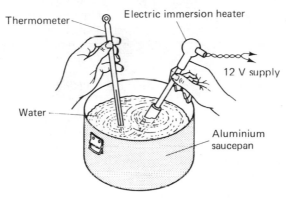

Thermometer

Electric immersion heater

12 V supply

Water

Aluminium saucepan

Fig. 10.1

Assuming that

heat supplied by heater = heat taken in by water

then, from the 'specific heat equation',

$$Pt = mc\,\Delta\theta$$

$$\therefore c = \frac{Pt}{m\,\Delta\theta}$$

Only an approximate value is obtained for c since no account is taken either of the heat loss to the surroundings during the experiment or of the heat used to raise the temperature of the pan.

The specific heat capacity of a metal, such as aluminium, can be found in the same way using a block of the material having holes to take the electric heater and a thermometer (Fig. 10.2).

(iv) **Heat capacity.** The heat capacity (symbol C) of an object is *the heat required to raise its temperature by 1 K* and is measured in J/K. Therefore if an object requires 1000 J to raise its temperature by 2 K, its heat capacity is 1000 J/2 K = 500 J/K. In symbols,

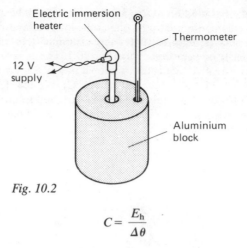

Fig. 10.2

$$C = \frac{E_h}{\Delta \theta}$$

where E_h is the heat supplied and $\Delta \theta$ is the temperature rise.

10.2 Worked Examples

1. A tank holding 60 kg of water is heated by a 3.0 kW electric immersion heater. If the specific heat capacity of water is 4200 J/(kg K), estimate the time needed for the temperature to rise from 10 °C to 60 °C.

A 3.0 kW (3000 W) heater supplies 3000 J of heat energy per second. Let t = time taken in seconds to raise the temperature of the water by $(60 - 10) = 50$ °C,

$$\therefore \text{ heat supplied to water in time } t = E_h = (3000 \times t) \text{ J}$$

From the 'specific heat equation' we can say

$$\begin{aligned} \text{heat taken in by water} &= mc\Delta\theta \\ &= 60 \text{ kg} \times 4200 \text{ J/(kg K)} \times 50 \text{ °C} \\ &= 60 \times 4200 \times 50 \text{ J} \end{aligned}$$

Assuming heat supplied = heat taken in,

$$E_h = mc\Delta\theta$$
$$3000 \times t = 60 \times 4200 \times 50$$

$$\therefore t = \frac{60 \times 4200 \times 50}{3000}$$

$$= 4200 \text{ s (70 min)}$$

2. A piece of aluminium of mass 0.50 kg is heated to 1000 °C and then placed in 0.40 kg of water at 10 °C. If the resulting temperature of the mixture is 30 °C, what is the specific heat capacity of aluminium if that of water is 4200 J/(kg K)?

When two substances at different temperatures are mixed, heat flows from the one at the higher temperature to the one at the lower temperature until both are at the same temperature—the temperature of the mixture. In this example, if there is no heat loss,

> heat given out by aluminium = heat taken in by water

If c is the specific heat capacity of aluminium in J/(kg K) then, using the 'specific heat equation',

$$\text{heat given out} = 0.50 \times c \times (100 - 30) \text{ J}$$
$$\text{heat taken in} = 0.40 \times 4200 \times (30 - 10) \text{ J}$$
$$0.50 \times c \times 70 = 0.40 \times 4200 \times 20$$

$$\therefore c = \frac{4200 \times 8}{35}$$

$$= 960 \text{ J/(kg K)}$$

10.3 Importance of Specific Heat Capacity

(i) **Climate.** The specific heat capacity of water is 4200 J/(kg K) and that of soil is about 800 J/(kg K). A certain mass of water thus needs five times more heat for its temperature to rise by 1 °C than does the same mass of soil. Water also has to give out more heat for its temperature to fall 1 °C. As a result, the temperature of the sea rises and falls more slowly than that of the land and islands, being surrounded by water, experience smaller changes of temperature from summer to winter than do large land masses such as Central Asia.

(ii) **Cooling and heating systems.** The high specific heat capacity of water (as well as its cheapness and availability) makes it useful for storing and carrying heat energy. This accounts for its uses to cool car engines (Fig. 10.3) and in the radiators of central heating systems (see Unit 11.4(ii)).

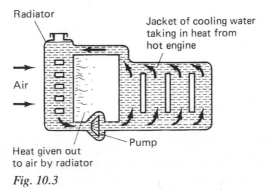

Fig. 10.3

(iii) **Night storage heaters.** The heavy blocks used in night storage heaters have a lower specific heat capacity than water but a greater density so that the same mass occupies less space. Electric heating elements warm up the blocks during the night when electrical energy is cheaper. During the following day the hot blocks cool down, releasing their heat energy.

10.4 Principle of Conservation of Energy

As mentioned in Unit 6.3(ii), energy is conserved (that is, not lost) in all changes from one form to another. Here we shall consider three cases, all involving heat.

(i) **Potential energy (p.e.) to heat.** The p.e. of water at the top of a waterfall becomes k.e. as the water falls, and when it strikes the ground, heat (and sound) are produced. The temperature of the water at the bottom is higher than that at the top. If we assume all the p.e. becomes heat, the temperature rise can be calculated.

Suppose 1.0 kg of water falls a vertical distance of 105 m. We have, taking $g = 10$ N/kg,

$$\text{p.e. of water} = E_p = mgh = 1.0 \times 10 \times 105 \text{ J}$$

Using the 'specific heat equation' and taking the specific heat capacity of water as 4200 J/(kg K),

$$\text{heat produced} = E_h = mc\Delta\theta = 1.0 \times 4200 \times \Delta\theta \text{ J}$$

where $\Delta\theta$ is the temperature rise of the water in K.

Assuming $E_h = E_p$,

$$4200 \ \Delta\theta = 1050$$
$$\therefore \ \Delta\theta = 1050/4200 = 0.25 \,°\text{C}$$

(ii) **Kinetic energy (k.e.) to heat.** When a car is brought to rest by the brakes, k.e. ($= \frac{1}{2}mv^2$) becomes heat energy and the temperature of the brake linings or disc pads rises.

(iii) **Electrical energy to heat.** This is a familiar example of energy conversion, which is used in electrical heating appliances (see Unit 20.4) as well as in the experiments in Unit 10.1(iii), and which was illustrated in the first example in Unit 10.2.

10.5 Latent Heat of Fusion

(i) **Introduction.** Heating a solid does not always increase its temperature. It may melt and change its state or *phase* from solid to liquid without any temperature rise. For example, the temperature of a well-stirred ice–water mixture remains at 0 °C until all the ice is melted.

Heat which is absorbed by a solid during melting is called *latent heat of fusion*. *Latent* means 'hidden' and *fusion* means 'melting'. Latent heat does not cause a temperature rise but must be gained by a solid if it is to become a liquid. Conversely, latent heat of fusion must be lost by a liquid if it is to change to a solid.

The kinetic theory explains latent heat of fusion as being the energy which enables the molecules of a solid to move slightly farther apart and change their vibratory motion about a fixed position to the freer movement they have as molecules of a liquid. Their p.e. increases but their average k.e. does not, in contrast to what happens when heating causes a temperature rise (see Unit 9.2).

(ii) **Specific latent heat of fusion.** The greater the mass of a solid, the more heat energy it requires to change to liquid.

The specific latent heat of fusion of a substance is the amount of heat required to change 1 kg from solid to liquid without temperature change.

It is measured in J/kg and denoted by l_f. In symbols, the 'latent heat equation' is

$$E_h = ml_f$$

where E_h is the heat required (in J) to melt a mass m (in kg) of a solid having specific latent heat of fusion l_f (in J/kg).

For ice, $l_f = 334\,000$ J/kg $= 334$ kJ/kg, which means it requires 334 000 J of heat to change 1 kg of ice at 0 °C to water at 0 °C—almost as much as is needed to heat 1 kg of water from 0 °C to its boiling-point at 100 °C (see the first worked example in Unit 10.6).

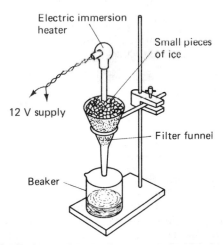

Electric immersion heater

Small pieces of ice

12 V supply

Filter funnel

Beaker

Fig. 10.4

(iii) **Measuring l_f for ice.** The apparatus is shown in Fig. 10.4. The electric immersion heater of known power P is placed in a filter funnel packed with small pieces of ice and switched on for a known time t—a 40 W (40 J/s) heater allowed to run for 3 minutes (180 s) is suitable; do *not* use a heater with a cracked seal. The mass m (in kg) of ice which melts is found by measuring the mass of water collected in the beaker. Assuming that heat supplied by heater = heat used to melt ice,

$$Pt = ml_f$$

$$\therefore l_f = \frac{Pt}{m}$$

The result is only approximate for various reasons. For example, heat gained from the surroundings is not allowed for in the calculation; also not all the ice melted drains into the beaker, so that the measured value of m will be too low.

10.6 Worked Examples

The following values are required:

>   Specific latent heat of fusion of ice = 330 000 J/kg
>   Specific heat capacity of water = 4200 J/(kg K)
>   Specific heat capacity of aluminium = 910 J/(kg K)
>   Specific heat capacity of ice = 2100 J/(kg K)

1. How much heat is needed to change 2.0 kg of ice at 0 °C to water at 100 °C?

There are two stages in the change: (*a*) melting the ice, and (*b*) heating up the water produced.

(*a*) Using the 'latent heat equation',

>   heat to change 2.0 kg ice at 0 °C to water at 0 °C = ml_f
>   = 2.0 kg × 330 000 J/kg
>   = 660 000 J

(*b*) Using the 'specific heat equation',
heat to change 2.0 kg water at 0 °C to water at 100 °C = $mc\Delta\theta$
>   = 2.0 kg × 4200 J/(kg K) × (100 − 0) °C
>   = 840 000 J

$\therefore$ Total heat needed = 660 000 + 840 000 J
>   = 1 500 000 J
>   = 1.5 MJ

2. An aluminium can of mass 0.10 kg contains 0.20 kg of water. Both, initially at 15 °C, are placed in a refrigerator at −5 °C. Calculate the quantity of heat that has to be removed from the water and the can for their temperatures to fall to −5 °C.

(a) Using the 'specific heat equation',

heat lost by can falling from 15 °C to -5 °C $= mc\Delta\theta$
$= 0.10$ kg $\times 910$ J/(kg K) $\times [15 - (-5)]$ °C
$= 0.10 \times 910 \times 20 = 1820$ J

heat lost by water falling from 15 °C to 0 °C $= mc\Delta\theta$
$= 0.20$ kg $\times 4200$ J/(kg K) $\times (15 - 0)$ °C
$= 0.20 \times 4200 \times 15 = 12\,600$ J

(b) Using the 'latent heat equation',

heat lost by water at 0 °C freezing to ice at 0 °C $= ml_f$
$= 0.20$ kg $\times 330\,000$ J/kg
$= 66\,000$ J

(c) Using the 'specific heat equation',

heat lost by ice falling from 0 °C to -5 °C $= mc\Delta\theta$
$= 0.20$ kg $\times 2100$ J/(kg K) $\times [0 - (-5)]$ °C
$= 0.20 \times 2100 \times 5 = 2100$ J

$\therefore$ Total heat removed
$= 1820 + 12\,600 + 66\,000 + 2100$
$= 82\,520 = 83\,000$ J
$= 83$ kJ

10.7 Melting- and Freezing-points

A pure substance melts at a definite temperature, called its *melting-point*. The melted substance solidifies at the same temperature, the freezing-point, which is usually referred to as the melting-point as well.

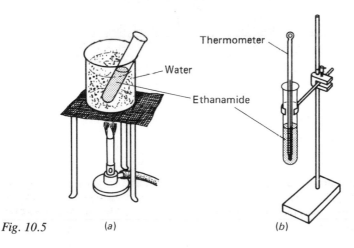

Fig. 10.5   (a)   (b)

(i) **Cooling curve.** An experiment to find the melting-point of ethanamide (acetamide) from its cooling curve is shown in Fig. 10.5. A test-tube half-full of ethanamide is heated in a beaker of water until it has all melted. The test-tube is then removed and the temperature of the ethanamide recorded every minute as it cools (to about 70 °C).

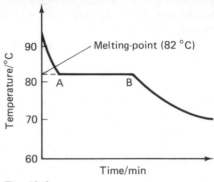

Fig. 10.6

If a graph of temperature against time is plotted, a curve like that in Fig. 10.6 is obtained. It shows that the temperature of liquid ethanamide falls until at A it starts to solidify at its melting-point of 82 °C. It carries on losing heat, latent heat, along AB until it has all solidified but its temperature does not change— this is because the molecules are losing p.e. (but not k.e.) as they move closer together into the fixed average positions of the solid state. At B, the ethanamide is entirely solid and its temperature begins to fall again.

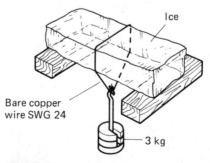

Fig. 10.7

(ii) **Effect of pressure.** The melting-point of a substance changes slightly if pressure is applied to it. For example, increasing the pressure on ice lowers its melting-point, and this may be demonstrated as in Fig. 10.7, in which a weighted copper wire passes through a block of ice without cutting it in two.

A large pressure acts on the ice below the wire. Its melting-point is lowered and the ice, being at 0 °C, melts since its temperature is now above its new melting-point. The wire sinks through the water thus formed; the water is therefore no longer under pressure and its melting-point returns to 0 °C, and it at once refreezes *above* the wire. In refreezing the water gives out latent heat of fusion and this is conducted down through the wire to enable the ice below it to melt. The effect is called *regelation* ('refreezing'); it is the reason why snow 'binds' together when a snowball is made.

The actual depression of the melting-point of ice is only 0.0075 °C for each atmosphere increase in pressure.

(iii) **Effect of impurities.** The melting-point of a substance is also affected by impurities. For example, when an 'impurity' such as salt is added to an ice water mixture, its temperature may fall to about −20 °C.

The salt lowers the melting-point of the ice and the ice, being still at 0 °C (that is, above its new melting-point), therefore melts. In doing so it absorbs latent heat from the mixture, whose temperature falls till it freezes at the new melting-point. The freezing mixture so formed can be used for cooling purposes.

This effect explains the action of antifreeze in car radiators and also why brine and sea sand are spread on icy roads. The 'impurity' lowers the freezing-point of the mixture and may prevent it from freezing.

10.8 Latent Heat of Vaporization

(i) **Introduction.** Just as latent heat is needed to change a solid into a liquid, it is also needed to change a liquid into a vapour. The reading of a thermometer in boiling water remains constant at 100 °C even though heat is still being absorbed by the water from the source heating it. This heat is called *latent heat of vaporization*. When steam condenses to form water, latent heat is given out. This is why a scald from steam may be more serious than one from boiling water.

Before the molecules in a liquid can overcome the forces holding them together and gain the freedom to move around independently in the form of a gas, they need a large amount of energy to increase their separation. They receive this as latent heat of vaporization which, like latent heat of fusion, increases the p.e. of the molecules but not their k.e. since there is no temperature change. It also gives the molecules the energy required to 'push back' the surrounding atmosphere in the large expansion that occurs when a liquid vaporizes.

(ii) **Specific latent heat of vaporization** is defined as follows:

The specific latent heat of vaporization of a substance is the amount of heat required to change 1 kg from liquid to vapour without temperature change.

It is measured in J/kg and denoted by l_v. If E_h is the heat required (in J) to vaporize a mass m (in kg) of a liquid having specific latent heat of vaporization l_v (in J/kg), then the 'latent heat equation' is similar to that for fusion:

$$E_h = ml_v$$

For water, $l_v = 2\,260\,000\,\text{J/kg} = 2.26\,\text{MJ/kg}$, which means it requires $2\,260\,000\,\text{J}$ of heat to change 1 kg of water at $100\,°\text{C}$ to steam at $100\,°\text{C}$.

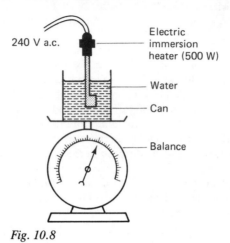

240 V a.c.

Electric immersion heater (500 W)

Water

Can

Balance

Fig. 10.8

(iii) **Measuring l_v for water.** An estimate can be made using the apparatus in Fig. 10.8. The mains-operated immersion heater of power P is clamped so that it is well covered by the water in the can. When the water is boiling briskly the reading on the balance is noted and a stop clock started. The time t for a mass m of water (say 50 g, or 0.05 kg) to be boiled off, is found. Assuming that heat supplied by heater = heat used to boil off water,

$$Pt = ml_v$$

$$\therefore l_v = \frac{Pt}{m}$$

The result is only approximate because the calculation takes no account of heat loss from the can and water to the surroundings.

10.9 Worked Examples

Specific heat capacity of water $= c = 4200\,\text{J/(kg K)}$
Specific latent heat of vaporization of water $= l_v = 2\,300\,000\,\text{J/kg}$

1. How much heat is needed to change 2.0 kg of water at $50\,°\text{C}$ into steam at $100\,°\text{C}$?

There are two stages in the change: (a) the heating up of the water, and (b) its vaporization.

(a) Using the 'specific heat equation',

heat to change 2.0 kg of water at 50 °C to water at 100 °C $= mc\Delta\theta$
$$= 2.0 \text{ kg} \times 4200 \text{ J/(kg K)} \times (100 - 50) \text{ °C}$$
$$= 2.0 \times 4200 \times 50 \text{ J}$$
$$= 420\,000 \text{ J}$$

(b) Using the 'latent heat equation',

heat to change 2.0 kg of water at 100 °C to steam at 100 °C $= ml_v$
$$= 2.0 \text{ kg} \times 2\,300\,000 \text{ J/kg}$$
$$= 4\,600\,000 \text{ J}$$

∴ Total heat needed $= 420\,000 + 4\,600\,000$
$$= 5\,020\,000 \text{ J}$$
$$= 5.0 \text{ MJ}$$

2. An electric kettle with a heating element rated at 2.3 kW contains boiling water. What mass of steam does it produce in 5 minutes?

Power of heating element $= 2.3 \text{ kW} = 2300 \text{ W}$
∴ Heat produced per second by element $= 2300 \text{ J}$
E_h = heat produced in 300 seconds (5 min) $= 2300 \times 300 \text{ J}$

From the 'latent heat equation' $E_h = ml_v$, where m is the mass of steam produced, we get

$$m = \frac{E_h}{l_v} = \frac{2300 \times 300}{2\,300\,000} = \frac{300}{1000}$$
$$= 0.3 \text{ kg}$$

10.10 Evaporation

In evaporation a liquid changes to a vapour or gas without ever reaching its boiling-point, though the nearer it is to boiling the faster it changes its state. Evaporation is the process by which pools of water in the road disappear and wet clothes dry. It happens because the molecules of a liquid have a range of speeds: the faster molecules have enough energy to overcome the attractions of the rest, and are able to escape from the liquid surface.

(i) **Factors affecting evaporation.** The rate of evaporation is increased by:

1. *increasing the temperature* of the liquid, thereby making the molecules move faster and enabling more to escape;

2. *increasing the surface area* of the liquid, so that more molecules have a chance to escape since more are near the surface; and

3. *blowing air across the surface*, which makes it easier for more molecules to escape by removing those already existing as vapour above the liquid.

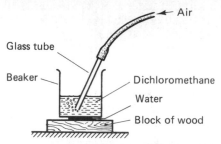

Fig. 10.9 This experiment should be done in a fume-cupboard

(ii) **Cooling by evaporation.** A liquid needs latent heat of vaporization to evaporate which, if the liquid is not being heated, is obtained from the surroundings. This can be shown by pumping air through a beaker of dichloromethane, arranged as in Fig. 10.9. Dichloromethane is a *volatile* liquid, that is, it evaporates readily at room temperature because of its low boiling-point. Latent heat is taken from the dichloromethane itself, the beaker and the film of water between the beaker and the piece of wood. The water soon freezes causing the wood and the beaker to stick together. (**Note. Dichloromethane is harmful, particularly to the eyes, and this experiment *should* be performed in a fume-cupboard.**)

Volatile liquids, such as methylated spirits, feel cold when spilt on the hand. Some are used as perfumes.

Water evaporates from the skin when we sweat. This is the body's way of using unwanted heat and keeping a constant temperature. After vigorous exercise there is a risk of the body being overcooled, especially in a draught; it is then thought to be less able to resist infection.

(iii) **Cooling and the kinetic theory.** During evaporation it is the faster molecules which escape from the liquid surface. The average speed, and therefore the average k.e. of the molecules left behind decreases, that is, the temperature of the liquid falls.

10.11 Applications of Evaporation

(i) **Refrigerator.** In a refrigerator heat is taken in at one place and given out at another by the refrigerating substance as it is pumped round a circuit (Fig. 10.10).

The coiled pipe round the *freezer* at the top of the refrigerator contains a volatile liquid (called *Freon*). This evaporates and takes latent heat from its

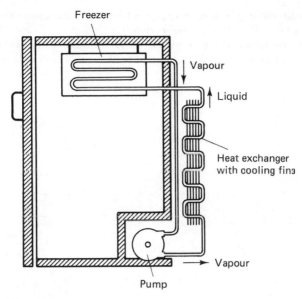

Fig. 10.10

surroundings, so causing cooling. The pump, which is electrically driven, removes the vapour (so reducing the pressure, lowering the boiling-point—see Unit 10.12—and encouraging evaporation or even boiling) and forces it into the *heat exchanger* (a set of pipes with cooling fins outside the rear of the refrigerator). Here the vapour is compressed and liquefies, giving out latent heat of vaporization to the surroundings. The liquid is returned to the coil round the freezer and the cycle is repeated.

An adjustable thermostat switches the pump on and off, controlling the rate of evaporation and so the temperature in the refrigerator.

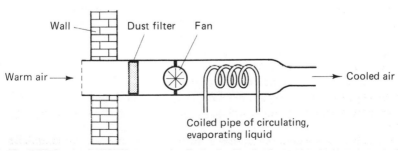

Fig. 10.11

(ii) **Air-conditioning.** Cooling by evaporation is also used in an air-conditioning unit. The principle is shown in Fig. 10.11. Warm air is pulled in through a dust filter by a fan and cooled by supplying latent heat to the liquid evaporating in the coiled pipe.

10.12 Boiling

Boiling is very fast evaporation which occurs at a definite temperature, the *boiling-point*; vapour bubbles form in the body of the boiling liquid and expand, rise to the surface and burst.

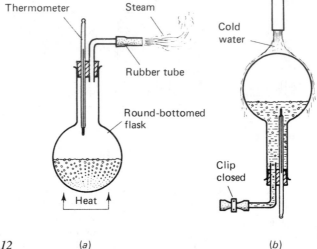

Fig. 10.12   (a)   (b)

(i) **Effect of pressure.** The boiling-point of water rises when the pressure above it is raised. This can be demonstrated using the apparatus in Fig. 10.12(a), in which the pressure can be increased by pinching the rubber tube for *just long enough* to see that the thermometer reading rises.

The same apparatus can be used to show that decreasing the pressure lowers the boiling-point. The water should first be boiled for a few minutes so that the steam sweeps out most of the air. The heating is then stopped and the clip closed. Cold water is run over the inverted flask (Fig. 10.12(b)), so condensing the water vapour inside it and reducing the pressure above the water. The water starts to boil and if the cooling continues in this way it may go on boiling until below 50 °C.

In a pressure cooker, the pressure of the steam above the water can rise to twice the normal atmospheric value and the water then boils at about 120 °C, thus cooking the food more quickly than usual.

(ii) **Effect of impurities.** An 'impurity' such as salt when added to water raises its boiling-point.

10.13 Revision Questions

1. What is the meaning of the statement that 'copper has a specific heat capacity of 400 J/(kg K)'?

2. Write down the 'specific heat equation', stating what each symbol stands for.

3. If the heat capacity of an object is 100 J/K, what does this mean?

4. State two ways in which the high specific heat capacity of water is useful.

5. Use the kinetic theory to explain why heat is needed to change a solid into a liquid.

6. (a) What is the meaning of the statement that 'the specific latent heat of fusion of ice is 334 000 J/kg'?
   (b) Write down the 'latent heat equation' for fusion, stating what each symbol stands for.

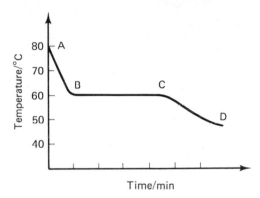

Fig. 10.13

7. The cooling curve in Fig. 10.13 is for a pure substance.
   (a) What is its melting-point?
   (b) Which part of the curve refers to (i) solid only, (ii) liquid only, (iii) solid and liquid?

8. What is the effect on the melting-point of ice of (a) increasing the pressure on the ice, (b) adding salt to the ice?

9. Use the kinetic theory to explain why heat is needed to change a liquid into a gas or vapour.

10. What is meant by the statement that the specific latent heat of vaporization of water is 2 260 000 J/kg?

11. State three ways in which a liquid can be made to evaporate more quickly.

12. (a) Give two applications of 'cooling by evaporation'.
    (b) Explain 'cooling by evaporation' in terms of the kinetic theory.

13. State two ways in which (a) boiling differs from evaporation, (b) the boiling-point of a liquid can be raised.

14. Explain the following:
    (a) On a very cold day good snowballs cannot be made.
    (b) When you walk on snow it 'cakes' and sticks to the soles of your shoes.
    (c) A good cup of tea cannot be brewed on a high mountain.
    (d) A bottle of milk keeps better when it stands in water in a porous earthenware pot in a draught.

10.14 Problems

Specific Heat Capacity
Specific heat capacity of water $=4200\,J/(kg\,K)$.

1. How much heat is needed to raise the temperature by $10\,°C$ of $5\,kg$ of a substance of specific heat capacity $300\,J/(kg\,K)$?

2. The same quantity of heat is given to different masses of three substances A, B and C. The temperature rise in each case is shown in the table. Calculate the specific heat capacities of A, B and C.

Substance	Mass (kg)	Heat given (J)	Temp. rise (°C)
A	1.0	2000	1.0
B	2.0	2000	5.0
C	0.5	2000	4.0

3. How much heat is given out when an iron ball of mass $2.0\,kg$ and specific heat capacity $440\,J/(kg\,K)$ cools from $300\,°C$ to $200\,°C$?

4. How many joules of heat energy are supplied by a $2.0\,kW$ heater in (a) $10\,s$, (b) 1 minute?

5. A $40\,W$ immersion heater raises the temperature of $1.0\,kg$ of water in a vessel at an initial rate of $0.50\,°C$ every minute.
    (a) How much heat is supplied by the heater every minute?
    (b) What value do these results give for the approximate specific heat capacity of water?

6. An electric heater raises the temperature of $0.50\,kg$ of water by $30\,°C$ every minute. Assuming no heat is lost, what is the power of the heater?

7. What mass of cold water at $10\,°C$ must be added to $60\,kg$ of hot water at $80\,°C$ by someone who wants to have a bath at $50\,°C$? Neglect heat losses.

Latent Heat of Fusion
Specific latent heat of fusion of ice $=330\,000\,J/kg$.

8. (a) How much heat will change $3.0\,kg$ of ice at $0\,°C$ to water at $0\,°C$?
    (b) What quantity of heat must be removed from $5.0\,kg$ of water at $0\,°C$ to change it to ice at $0\,°C$?

9. (a) How much heat is needed to change 0.50 kg of ice at 0 °C to water at 50 °C?
   (b) If a refrigerator cools 0.20 kg of water from 20 °C to its freezing-point in 10 minutes, how much heat is removed per minute from the water?

10. How long will it take a 50 W heater to melt 0.10 kg of ice at 0 °C?

11. Some small aluminium rivets of total mass 0.11 kg and at 100 °C are emptied into a hole in a large block of ice at 0 °C.
    (a) What will be the final temperature of the rivets?
    (b) How much ice will melt? (Assume specific heat capacity of aluminium = 900 J/(kg K).)

Latent Heat of Vaporization

Specific latent heat of vaporization of water = 2 300 000 J/kg.

12. (a) How much heat is needed to change 10 kg of water at 100 °C to steam at 100 °C?
    (b) Find the heat given out when 0.10 kg of steam at 100 °C condenses and cools to water at 0 °C.

13. A 3.0 kW kettle is left on for 230 seconds after the water starts to boil. What mass of water is boiled off in this time?

14. A piece of copper of mass 0.10 kg is heated in a flame to a temperature of 700 °C and when it is transferred to a boiling liquid, 0.01 kg of the liquid vaporizes. If the specific heat capacity of copper is 400 J/(kg K) and the boiling-point of the liquid is 100 °C, find its specific latent heat of vaporization.

Unit Eleven

How Heat Travels

A knowledge of the three ways in which heat travels is useful for many practical purposes. For example, it is necessary for the design of buildings and houses that can be kept at a comfortable temperature, economically and efficiently, in winter and summer.

11.1 Conduction

The handle of a metal spoon held in a hot drink soon gets warm. Heat passes along the spoon by conduction.

Conduction is the flow of heat through matter from places of higher to places of lower temperature without movement of the matter as a whole.

(i) **Good and bad conductors.** A simple demonstration of the different conducting powers of various metals is shown in Fig. 11.1. A matchstick is attached to one end of each rod with a little Vaseline or melted wax. The other ends of the rods are heated by a burner. When the temperatures of the far ends reach the melting-point of the Vaseline or wax, the matches drop off. The match on copper falls first showing it is the best conductor, followed by aluminium, brass and iron.

Most metals are good conductors of heat; materials such as wood, glass,

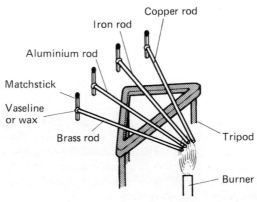

Fig. 11.1

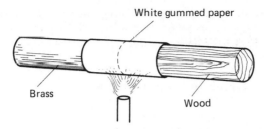

White gummed paper

Brass

Wood

Fig. 11.2

cork, plastics and fabrics are bad conductors. The apparatus in Fig. 11.2 can be used to show the difference between brass and wood as conductors. If the rod is passed through a flame several times, the paper over the wood scorches but not that over the brass. The brass conducts the heat away from the paper quickly and prevents it from reaching the temperature at which it burns. The wood conducts heat away only slowly.

Metal objects below body temperature feel colder than those made of bad conductors, because they carry heat away faster from the hand—even though the different objects are at the same temperature.

Liquids and gases also conduct heat, but very slowly. Water is a poor conductor, as may be demonstrated by the experiment shown in Fig. 11.3. The water at the top of the tube can be boiled before the ice at the bottom melts.

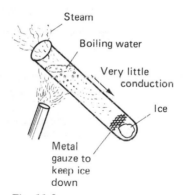

Steam

Boiling water

Very little conduction

Ice

Metal gauze to keep ice down

Fig. 11.3

(ii) **How materials conduct.** Two processes occur in metals. They have a large number of 'free' electrons (see Unit 24.1) which wander about inside them. When one part of a metal object is heated, the electrons there move faster (that is, their k.e. increases) and farther. As a result they 'jostle' atoms in cooler parts, so passing on some of their energy and raising the temperature of these parts. This process occurs quickly.

In the second process, which is much slower, the atoms at the hot part themselves make 'colder' neighbouring atoms vibrate more vigorously. This process is less important in metals, but is the only way conduction occurs in non-metals since they do not have 'free' electrons.

11.2 Uses of Good and Bad Conductors

(i) **Good conductors.** These are used whenever heat is required to travel quickly through something. Kettles, saucepans, boilers and radiators are made of metals such as aluminium, iron and copper.

(ii) **Bad conductors (insulators).** The handles of teapots, kettles and saucepans are made of wood or plastic. Cork is used for table mats.

Air is one of the worst conductors (that is, one of the best insulators). This is why houses keep warmer in winter and cooler in summer if they have cavity walls, which consist of two walls separated by an air space, and double-glazed windows.

Materials which trap air, such as wool, felt, fur, feathers, polystyrene foam and glass fibres, are also very bad conductors. Some are used as 'lagging' to insulate water pipes, hot water cylinders, ovens, refrigerators and the roofs (and walls) of houses. Others make warm winter clothes.

11.3 Convection in Liquids

Convection is the usual method by which heat travels through fluids (liquids and gases). It can be shown in water by dropping a few crystals of potassium permanganate, which is an intense purple colour, down a tube to the bottom of a flask of water. When the tube is removed and the flask heated just below the crystals by a *small* flame (Fig. 11.4), purple streaks of water rise upwards and fan outwards.

Streams of warm moving fluids are called *convection currents*. They arise

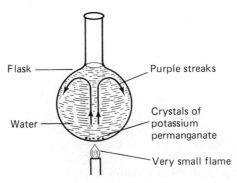

Fig. 11.4

when a fluid is heated because it expands, becomes less dense and is forced upwards by surrounding cooler, denser fluid which moves under it. We say 'hot water (or hot air) rises'. Warm fluid behaves like a cork released under water: being less dense than its surroundings, it bobs up. In convection, however, a fluid floats in a fluid, not a solid in a fluid.

> *Convection is the flow of heat through a fluid from places of higher to places of lower temperature by movement of the fluid itself.*

11.4 House Hot Water and Central Heating Systems

(i) **Hot water system.** One is shown in Fig. 11.5. A convection current of hot water from the *top* of the boiler rises up pipe A to the *top* of the hot water cylinder, and cold water flows down pipe B from the *bottom* of the cylinder to the *bottom* of the boiler. Hot water is drawn off from the *top* of the cylinder and is replaced by cold water from the cold water tank which enters the *bottom* of the cylinder by pipe C.

Water is supplied from the mains to the cold tank through a ballcock. The expansion pipe D allows the escape of dissolved air which comes out of the water when it is heated, which might otherwise cause air-locks in the pipes. It also allows the escape of steam if the water boils, which without an outlet could cause an explosion.

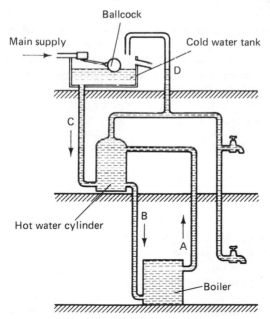

Fig. 11.5

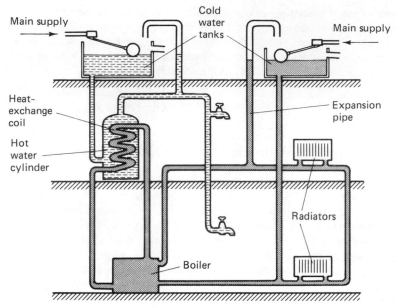

Fig. 11.6

(ii) **Combined hot water and central heating system** (Fig. 11.6). Here the water in the central heating part of the system is quite separate from the water in the hot water part. The latter is similar to Fig. 11.6, except that the hot water cylinder is heated indirectly by a heat-exchange coil in the cylinder: the temperature of the central heating water in the boiler and radiators is therefore hardly affected when hot water is drawn off. A second small cold water tank keeps the boiler and radiators topped up.

Modern systems use narrow pipes and the water is pumped round them.

11.5 Convection in Air

Black marks often appear on the wall or ceiling above a lamp or a radiator. They are caused by dust being carried upwards in air convection currents produced by the hot lamp or radiator.

(i) **Demonstration.** A laboratory demonstration of convection currents in air can be given using the apparatus of Fig. 11.7. The direction of the convection current created by the candle is made visible by the smoke from the touch paper (made by soaking brown paper in strong potassium nitrate solution and drying it).

Convection currents set up by electric, gas and oil heaters help to warm our homes. Many so-called 'radiators' are really convector heaters.

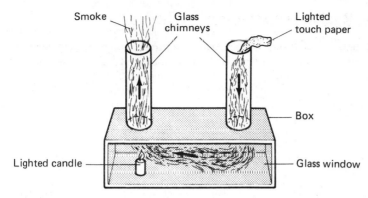

Fig. 11.7

(ii) **Coastal breezes.** During the day the temperature of the land increases more quickly than that of the sea (because the specific heat capacity of the land is much smaller—see Unit 10.1). The hot air above the land rises and is replaced by colder air from the sea. A breeze from the sea results (Fig. 11.8(*a*)).

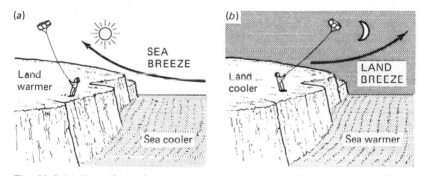

Fig. 11.8 (a) Day, (b) night

At night the opposite happens. The sea has more heat to lose and cools more slowly. The air above the sea is warmer than that over the land and a breeze blows from the land (Fig. 11.8(*b*)).

(iii) **Gliding.** Gliders, including 'hang-gliders', depend on hot air currents called *thermals*. By flying from one thermal to another gliders can stay airborne for several hours.

11.6 Radiation

Radiation is a third way in which heat can travel but whereas conduction and convection both need matter to be present, radiation can occur in a vacuum. It is the way by which heat reaches us from the sun.

Radiation has all the properties of electromagnetic waves (see Unit 16.8); for example, it travels at the speed of radio waves and gives interference effects. When it falls on an object, it is partly reflected, partly transmitted and partly absorbed; the absorbed part raises the temperature of the object.

*Radiation is the flow of heat from one place to another
by means of electromagnetic waves.*

Radiation is emitted by all bodies above absolute zero and consists mostly of infrared radiation (Unit 16.9(i)) but light and ultraviolet radiation are also emitted by very hot bodies, such as the sun.

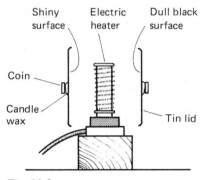

Fig. 11.9

(i) **Good and bad absorbers.** Some surfaces absorb radiation better than others, and this may be shown using the apparatus in Fig. 11.9. The inside surface of one lid is shiny and that of the other is dull black. The coins are stuck on the outside of each lid with candle wax. If the heater is midway between the lids they must each receive the same amount of radiation. After a few minutes the wax on the black lid melts and the coin falls off, while the shiny lid stays cool and the wax on it unmelted.

Dull black surfaces are better *absorbers* of radiation than white shiny surfaces—the latter are good *reflectors* of radiation. This is why buildings in hot countries are often painted white and why light-coloured clothes are cooler than dark ones in summer. Also, reflectors on electric fires are made of polished metal because of their good reflecting properties.

(ii) **Good and bad emitters.** The cooling fins on the heat exchanger of a refrigerator (see Unit 10.11(i)) are painted black so that they lose heat more quickly. On the other hand, teapots and kettles which are polished are poor emitters and keep their heat well.

In general, *surfaces that are good absorbers of radiation are good emitters when hot.*

Some surfaces also emit radiation better than others when they are hot. If you hold the backs of your hands on either side of a hot copper sheet which has one side polished and the other blackened (Fig. 11.10), you will soon find that the dull black surface is a better emitter of radiation than the shiny one.

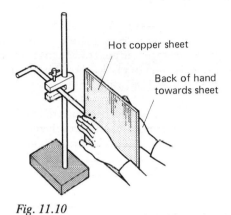

Hot copper sheet

Back of hand towards sheet

Fig. 11.10

11.7 Vacuum Flask

A vacuum or Thermos flask (Fig. 11.11) keeps hot liquids hot or cold liquids cold. It is very difficult for heat to travel into or out of the flask.

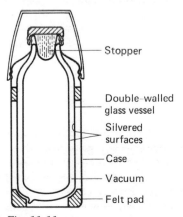

Stopper

Double-walled glass vessel

Silvered surfaces

Case

Vacuum

Felt pad

Fig. 11.11

Heat losses by conduction and convection are minimized because the flask has double glass walls with a vacuum between the walls. Radiation is reduced by silvering both walls on the vacuum side, so that if, for example, a hot liquid is stored, the small amount of radiation from the hot inside wall is reflected back across the vacuum by the silvering on the outer wall. The slight heat loss which does occur takes place by conduction up the walls and through the stopper.

11.8 Greenhouse Effect

The warmth from the sun is not cut off by a sheet of glass but that from a red-hot fire is. The radiation from a very hot body like the sun is mostly in the form of light and short-wavelength infrared radiation (see Unit 16.9(i)) which can pass through glass, unlike that from a less hot object such as a fire, which is largely long-wavelength infrared radiation.

(i) **Greenhouse.** Light and short-wavelength infrared radiation from the sun penetrate the glass of a greenhouse and are absorbed by the soil and plants inside it, raising their temperature. They in turn emit infrared radiation but, because of their relatively low temperature, this has a long wavelength and cannot pass through the glass. The greenhouse thus acts as a 'heat-trap' and its temperature rises.

(ii) **Thermal pollution.** Water vapour and carbon dioxide in the lower layers of the atmosphere exhibit the same 'selective absorption' effect as a greenhouse window, and prevent infrared radiation emitted by the earth from escaping. It has been estimated that if the combustion of fossil fuels and the resulting increase of carbon dioxide in the atmosphere should lead to a rise in the earth's average temperature of only 3.5 °C, both geographical features and climates worldwide could alter dramatically. Some scientists believe that 'thermal pollution' is as great a threat as any other form.

11.9 Solar Panels

A solar water-heating system contains one or more panels, usually on the roof of a house or building, which are designed to produce warm water. The unit in Fig. 11.12(a) contains copper tubes partly embedded in a copper plate, which is mounted on a good thermal insulator in a metal frame, as in Fig. 11.12(b). Solar radiation falls on the tubes and plate through a glass window and the water in the tubes is warmed and stored in an insulated tank.

The tubes and plate have blackened surfaces so that they act as good radiation absorbers. They are made of copper because copper is an excellent thermal conductor and therefore readily passes the heat absorbed to the water, and the tubes have thin walls so that they do not keep much of it themselves

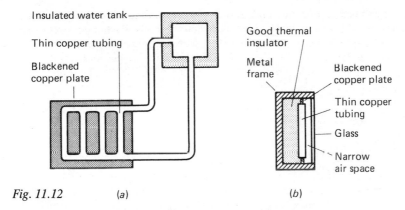

Fig. 11.12   (a)   (b)

(that is, so that they have a small heat capacity). The glass plate and narrow air space lessen energy losses to the atmosphere from the tubes and plate, while convection is reduced and radiation loss stopped by the 'greenhouse effect'.

11.10 Revision Questions and Problems

1. Explain the following:
    (a) A newspaper wrapping keeps hot fish and chips hot, and ice cream cold.
    (b) Fur coats would keep their owners warmer if they were worn inside out.
    (c) A glass milk bottle is likely to crack if boiling water is poured into it.
    (d) A wire gauze is often placed over a Bunsen burner.
    (e) A piece of metal feels colder than a piece of wood, even though both are at the same temperature.

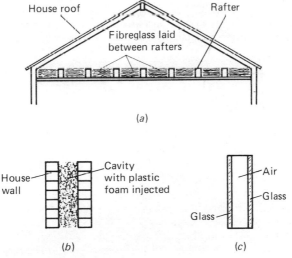

Fig. 11.13 (a) Roof insulation, (b) cavity wall insulation, (c) double glazing

2. As fuels become more expensive, more people are finding it worthwhile to reduce heat losses from their homes. Fig. 11.13 illustrates three ways of doing this.
   (i)   As far as you can, explain how each of the three methods reduces heat losses. Draw diagrams where they will help your explanations.
   (ii) Why are fibreglass and plastic foam good substances to use?
   (iii) Air is one of the worst conductors of heat. What is the point of replacing it by the plastic foam in (b)?
   (iv) A vacuum is an even better heat insulator than air. Suggest one scientific reason why the double glazing should not have a vacuum between the sheets of glass.

3. Using Fig. 11.5, explain (a) what happens when hot water is drawn off from a tap, (b) why an expansion pipe is required.

4. Convection occurs

   A only in gases   B only in liquids
   C in solids and gases   D in solids only
   E in liquids and gases

5. (a) What is the advantage of placing an electric immersion heater (i) near the top, (ii) near the bottom, of a tank of water?
   (b) Why is the freezer placed at the top of a refrigerator?

6. What causes coastal breezes to blow in from the sea on a hot summer's day? Why do they blow out to sea at night?

7. We feel the heat from a coal fire by

   A convection   B conduction   C regelation
   D radiation   E diffusion

8. Three cans have the same size and shape. One is painted matt black, one is dull white and one is shiny white. The cans are filled with boiling water. In which one does the water cool down most quickly? Give a reason.

9. The door canopy in Fig. 11.14 shows in a striking way the difference between white and black surfaces when radiation falls on them. Explain why.

Fig. 11.14

10. (a) The earth has been warmed by the radiation from the sun for millions of years yet we think its average temperature has remained fairly steady. Why is this?

(b) Why is frost less likely on a cloudy night than on a clear one?

11. A vacuum flask has a silver layer on its thin glass walls to reduce loss of heat by

        A conduction   **B** radiation
        C convection   **D** evaporation

12. Solar radiation consists of

        A infrared radiation only   **B** light only
        C infrared, light and ultraviolet radiation
        D light and infrared radiation only

Unit Twelve

Heat Engines

A heat engine is a machine which changes heat energy, obtained by burning a fuel, to kinetic energy. In an *internal combustion engine*, such as petrol, diesel or jet engines, the fuel is burnt in the cylinder or chamber where the energy change occurs. This is not so in other engines, such as the steam turbine.

12.1 Petrol Engines

Petrol engines all depend on the use of the rapid expansion of heated gases to force a piston to move inside the cylinder or chamber.

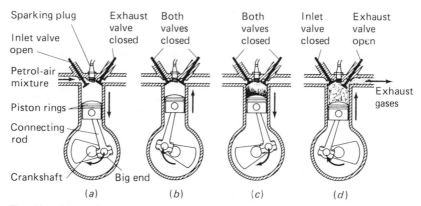

Fig. 12.1 (a) Intake, (b) compression, (c) power, (d) exhaust

(i) **Four-stroke engine.** Fig. 12.1 shows the action.

On the *intake stroke*, the piston is moved down (by the starter motor in a car or the kickstart in a motor cycle turning the crankshaft), so reducing the pressure inside the cylinder. The inlet valve opens and the petrol–air mixture from the carburettor is forced into the cylinder by atmospheric pressure.

On the *compression stroke*, both valves are closed and the piston moves up, compressing the mixture.

On the *power stroke*, a spark jumps across the points of the sparking plug and explodes the mixture, forcing the piston down.

On the *exhaust stroke*, the outlet valve opens and the piston rises, pushing the exhaust gases out of the cylinder.

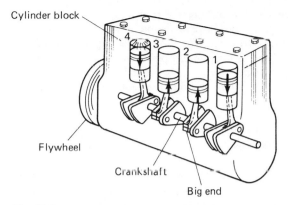

Cylinder block

Flywheel

Crankshaft

Big end

Fig. 12.2

The crankshaft turns a flywheel (a heavy wheel), whose momentum keeps the piston moving between one power stroke and the next.

Most cars have at least four cylinders on the same crankshaft (Fig. 12.2). Each cylinder 'fires' in turn, in the order 1–3–4–2, giving a power stroke every half-revolution of the crankshaft. Smoother running results.

(ii) **Two-stroke engine.** This is used in mopeds, lawn-mowers and small boats. Valves are replaced by ports on the side of the cylinder which are opened and closed by the piston as it moves.

In Fig. 12.3(*a*), the piston is at the top of the cylinder and the mixture above it is compressed. The exhaust and transfer ports are closed but fresh mixture enters the crankcase by the inlet port. When the spark ignites the compressed mixture, the piston is driven down on its power stroke, closing the inlet port and compressing the mixture in the crankcase.

In Fig. 12.3(*b*), the piston is near the bottom of the power stroke and the

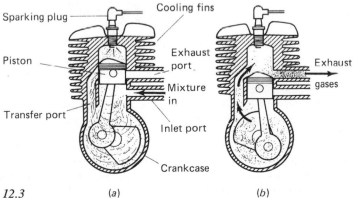

Sparking plug

Cooling fins

Piston

Exhaust port

Mixture in

Transfer port

Inlet port

Crankcase

Exhaust gases

Fig. 12.3   (*a*)   (*b*)

mixture below it passes through the transfer port into the cylinder above the piston. The exhaust port is now open and the burnt gases are pushed out as the piston moves up again. The shape of the piston helps to stop fresh fuel and burnt gases mixing. The cycle of operations is completed in two strokes.

The efficiency of petrol engines is about 30 per cent, which means that only 30 per cent of the heat energy supplied becomes kinetic energy; much of the rest is lost with the exhaust gases.

12.2 Diesel Engines

The operation of two- and four-stroke diesel engines is similar to that of the corresponding petrol-driven engines. Fuel oil is used instead of petrol, however, there is no sparking plug and the carburettor is replaced by a fuel injector.

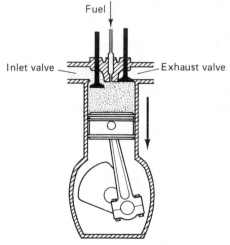

Fig. 12.4

Air is drawn into the cylinder on the downstroke of the piston (Fig. 12.4), and on the upstroke it is compressed to about one-sixteenth of its original volume (which is twice the compression in a petrol engine). This very high compression increases the temperature of the air considerably (mechanical energy is changed to heat—just as the air in a bicycle pump gets hot when it is squeezed). Thus when, at the end of the compression stroke, fuel is pumped into the cylinder by the fuel injector, it ignites automatically. The resulting explosion drives the piston down on its power stroke.

Diesel engines, sometimes called *compression ignition* (C.I.) engines, though heavier than petrol engines, are reliable and economical. Their efficiency of about 40 per cent is higher than that of any other heat engine.

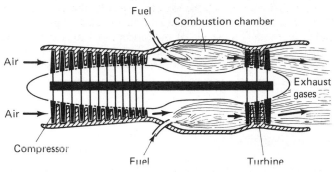

Fig. 12.5

12.3 Jet Engines (Gas Turbines)

There are several kinds of jet engine; Fig. 12.5 is a simplified diagram of a *turbo-jet*.

To start the engine, an electric motor sets the compressor rotating. The compressor is a kind of fan; its blades draw in and compress air at the front of the engine. Compression raises the temperature of the air before it reaches the combustion chamber. Here kerosene (paraffin) fuel is injected and burns to produce a high-speed stream of hot gas which escapes from the rear of the engine, so thrusting it forward (as explained in Unit 5.12, where we considered momentum). The exhaust gas also drives a turbine (another fan) which is on the same shaft as the compressor and which keeps it turning once the engine is started.

Turbo-jet engines have a high power-to-weight ratio (they produce large power for their weight) and are ideal for use in aircraft. They are also being tried in ships, trains and cars.

12.4 Rockets

Rockets, like jet engines, obtain their thrust from the hot gases they eject when they burn a fuel. They can travel where there is no air, however, since they carry the oxygen needed for burning the fuel instead of taking it from the atmosphere as a jet engine does.

Space rockets use oxygen in liquid form (at −183 °C). Common fuels are kerosene and liquid hydrogen (at −253 °C), but solid fuels are also used. Fig. 12.6 (overleaf) is a simplified drawing of a rocket.

12.5 Steam Turbines

Steam turbines are used in power stations and in ocean liners such as *Queen Elizabeth 2*. They have efficiencies of about 30 per cent.

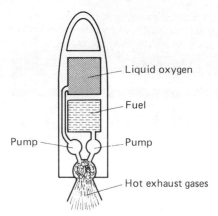

Fig. 12.6

The action of a steam turbine resembles that of a water wheel but moving steam causes the motion, not moving water. Steam produced in a separate boiler enters the turbine and is directed by the *stator* (sets of fixed blades) on to the *rotor* (sets of blades on a shaft that can rotate). The rotor revolves and drives whatever is coupled to it—for example, an electrical generator or a ship's propeller. The steam expands as it passes through the turbine and the size of the blades increases along the turbine to allow for this.

Rotary engines like the steam turbine run more smoothly than piston (*reciprocating*) engines do.

12.6 Revision Questions and Problems

1. Most car engines are four-stroke petrol engines.
    (*a*) Name the four strokes, in the correct sequence.
    (*b*) How many times does the crankshaft revolve during the four strokes?

2. (*a*) Fig. 12.7 shows the cylinder of a four-stroke petrol engine. If the spark plug has just fired, what is wrong with the diagram? Explain why the engine would not work very well with this fault.
    (*b*) What are the basic differences between four-stroke and two-stroke engines?

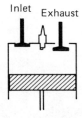

Fig. 12.7

3. In a motor car engine, chemical energy is converted into mechanical energy. What other forms of energy are produced? Some of the mechanical energy is not usefully employed. What happens to it? Describe the energy changes involved when the brakes are applied.

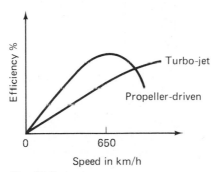

Fig. 12.8

4. (*a*) Explain the actions of (i) a compressor, (ii) a turbine, in a jet engine.
   (*b*) Draw a labelled diagram of a jet engine, showing the positions of the compressor and the turbine.
   (*c*) The graphs in Fig. 12.8 compare the performance of a propeller-driven aircraft with that of a turbo-jet. Explain what the graphs show.

5. (*a*) Explain how a rocket engine obtains its forward thrust.
   (*b*) Draw a labelled diagram of a typical rocket engine.
   (*c*) What fuels are used in modern rockets?
   (*d*) Why does a rocket work better outside the atmosphere?

Part Four

Light and Sound: Waves

Reflection and Mirrors

13.1 About Light

Light carries energy from one place to another and has a speed of about 3×10^8 m/s (300 000 km/s) in air.

(i) **Luminous and non-luminous objects.** You can see an object only if light from it enters your eyes. Some objects such as the sun, electric lamps and candles make their own light. They are *luminous* objects.

Most things you see do not make their own light but reflect light that comes from a luminous object. They are *non-luminous* objects. This page, you and the moon are examples.

Luminous sources radiate light when their atoms become 'excited' as a result of receiving energy. In a light bulb, for example, the energy comes from electricity. The 'excited' atoms give off their light haphazardly in most luminous sources.

A light source that works differently is the *laser*, invented in 1960. In it, 'excited' atoms act together and emit a narrow, very bright beam of light. Lasers now have many uses in industry (the road surface profilometer in Fig. 13.1 contains a laser) and medicine, and also in communications where they are used to send information as light pulses along very thin glass fibre cables.

Fig. 13.1

(ii) **Rays and beams.** The sight of sunbeams streaming through trees suggests that *light travels in straight lines*. The beams are visible because dust particles in the air reflect light into our eyes.

The direction of the path in which light is travelling is called a *ray* and is represented in diagrams by a straight line with an arrow on it. A *beam* is a stream of light and is shown by a number of rays; it may be parallel, diverging (spreading out) or converging (getting narrower) (Fig. 13.2).

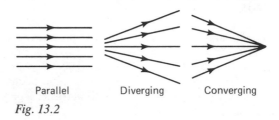

Parallel   Diverging   Converging

Fig. 13.2

13.2 Shadows

Shadows are formed because light travels in straight lines. A very small source of light, called a *point* source, gives a sharp shadow which is equally dark all over. This may be shown as in Fig. 13.3(*a*), where the small hole in the card acts as a point source.

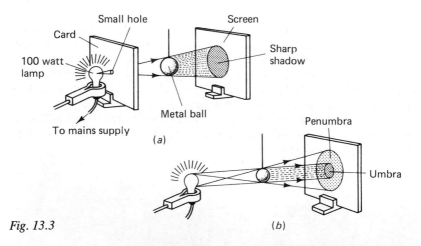

Fig. 13.3

If the card is removed the lamp acts as a large or *extended* source (Fig. 13.3(*b*)). The shadow is then larger and has a central dark region, the *umbra*, surrounded by a ring of partial shadow, the *penumbra*. You can see by the rays that some light reaches the penumbra but none reaches the umbra.

13.3 Eclipses

(i) **Solar eclipse.** There is an eclipse of the sun by the moon when the sun, moon and earth are in a straight line. The sun is an extended source (like the lamp in Fig. 13.3(*b*)). People on the earth who are in the umbra of the moon's shadow, at B in Fig. 13.4(*a*)), see a *total* eclipse of the sun (that is, they can't see the sun at all during the eclipse). Those in the penumbra, at A, see a *partial* eclipse (part of the sun is still visible).

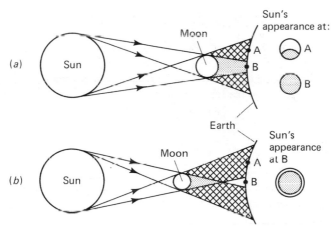

Fig. 13.4

Sometimes, however, the moon is so far from the earth (it does not go round the earth in a perfect circle) that the tip of the umbra does not reach the earth (Fig. 13.4(*b*)). When this happens people at A still see a partial eclipse, but those at B see an *annular* eclipse (the word means 'ring-shaped'—the central region of the sun is hidden but not its outer parts). (Note that the eclipse diagrams in this Unit are *not* drawn to scale.)

A total eclipse seen from one place may last for up to seven minutes. During this time, although it is day, the sky is dark, stars are visible, the temperature falls and birds stop singing.

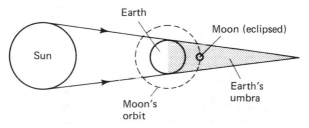

Fig. 13.5

(ii) **Lunar eclipse.** A lunar eclipse occurs when the moon passes into the earth's shadow and the light it reflects from the sun is cut off (Fig. 13.5). It happens only infrequently, and then only at full moon, but can last for up to $1\frac{3}{4}$ hours because the moon is much smaller than the earth. During a total lunar eclipse some light reaches the moon (due to refraction by the earth's atmosphere—see Unit 14.1) and makes it look a coppery colour.

13.4 Pinhole Camera

This consists of a box with a pinhole at one end and a greaseproof paper screen at the other (Fig. 13.6). If a luminous object, such as a lamp or a candle, is placed in front of the pinhole an inverted (upside-down) *image* of it is produced on the screen. An image is a likeness of an object and need not be an exact copy; in this case the image is smaller and less bright than the object. In Fig. 13.7 two rays, from the top and bottom of the object respectively, show how the image is formed.

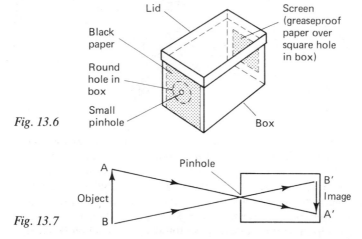

Fig. 13.6

Fig. 13.7

If the pinhole is made bigger the image becomes brighter—because more light gets through—but it becomes blurred as well. In fact, a large pinhole behaves like a number of small pinholes each giving an image in a slightly different position.

A photograph can be taken with a pinhole camera if the screen is replaced by a photographic film; an exposure of several minutes is needed, however.

13.5 Reflection of Light

If we know how light behaves when it is reflected, we can use mirrors to change the direction in which it is travelling; the principle is used in a periscope (described in (iii) below).

An ordinary mirror is made by depositing a thin layer of metal, often silver, on one side of a piece of glass; this is then protected with paint. The silver at the back of the glass acts as the reflecting surface.

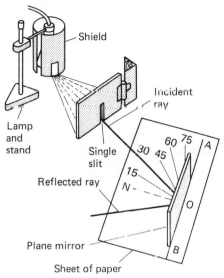

Fig. 13.8

(i) Investigating reflection by a plane mirror. A line AOB is drawn on a sheet of paper and angles marked on it using a protractor at the point O (Fig. 13.8). The angles are measured from the perpendicular ON, which is at right angles to AOB. A plane (flat) mirror is set up with its *reflecting* (back) surface on AOB.

A narrow ray of light is shone along say the 30° line, on to the mirror (this is called the *incident ray*) and the position of the reflected ray marked. The mirror is removed and the angle measured between the reflected ray and ON. The procedure is repeated for incident rays at other angles. A simple relation between the angles should be evident.

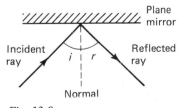

Fig. 13.9

(ii) Laws of reflection. Terms used in connection with reflection are shown in Fig. 13.9. The perpendicular to the mirror at the point where the incident ray strikes it is called the *normal*. The angle of incidence *i* is the angle between the incident ray and the normal; similarly, the angle of reflection *r* is the angle between the reflected ray and the normal. There are two laws of reflection:

1. *The angle of incidence equals the angle of reflection.*
2. *The incident ray, the reflected ray and the normal all lie in the same plane.*
(This means that they can all be drawn on a flat sheet of paper.)

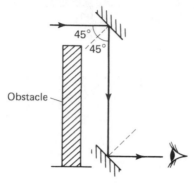

Fig. 13.10

(iii) **Periscope.** A simple periscope consists of a tube containing two plane mirrors, fixed parallel to and facing one another (Fig. 13.10). Each makes an angle of 45° with the line joining them. Light entering the periscope from an object is turned through 90° at each reflection, and an observer is thus able to see over the heads of a crowd or the top of an obstacle.

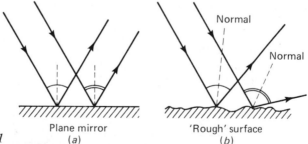

Fig. 13.11   Plane mirror   'Rough' surface
                    (a)   (b)

(iv) **Regular and diffuse reflection.** If a parallel beam of light falls on a plane mirror it is reflected as a parallel beam at the same angle (Fig. 13.11(*a*)). *Regular* reflection is said to occur. Most surfaces reflect light irregularly, however, and the rays in an incident parallel beam are reflected in many directions (Fig. 13.11(*b*)), giving *irregular* or *diffuse* reflection.

Diffuse reflection is due to the reflecting surface not being perfectly smooth like a mirror. At each point on the surface the laws of reflection are obeyed but the angle of incidence (and so the angle of reflection) varies from point to point. The reflected rays are scattered haphazardly. Most objects, being rough, are seen by diffuse reflection.

13.6 Image in a Plane Mirror

(i) **How an image is formed.** When you look at yourself in a mirror you see a reflection behind the mirror or (as it is called in physics) an image. In Fig. 13.12, for simplicity, just two rays OA and OB are shown falling on a plane

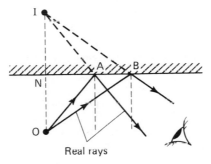

Fig. 13.12

mirror from a small lamp O. The reflected rays both seem to come from the point I behind the mirror where the eye imagines the rays intersect when produced backwards.

The image is said to be *virtual* because light rays do not pass through it as they do for a *real* image such as that formed in the pinhole camera. IA and IB are construction lines and are shown as broken lines in the diagram. A real image can be obtained on a screen; a virtual image cannot.

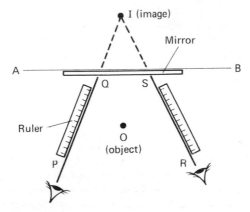

Fig. 13.13

(ii) **Finding the image position.** A simple method is shown in Fig. 13.13. The object is a pin O stuck upright about 10 cm in front of the mirror, which stands on a sheet of paper with its reflecting surface (usually the back one) on a line AB.

A ruler is placed as shown so that its edge is lined up with the image of the pin. A line PQ is then drawn along it on the paper. Line RS is obtained similarly. If PQ and RS are extended, the point I where they meet is the position of the image of O.

As a check, if a second pin is placed at I, the image of O (seen in the mirror) should line up with the top of the second pin (seen above the mirror). Furthermore when you move your head sideways the two should stay in line. There is then said to be *no parallax* (that is, no apparent movement—see Unit 2.3) between the second pin and the image.

Measurement of the *perpendicular* distances of O and I from AB should show they are equal.

(iii) **Lateral inversion.** If you look into a plane mirror and close your left eye, your image in the mirror seems to close the right eye. In a mirror image, left and right are interchanged and the image is said to be *laterally inverted*. The effect occurs whenever an image is formed by one reflection and is evident if print is viewed in a mirror.

(iv) **Summary.** The image in a plane mirror is:
1. as far behind the mirror as the object is in front and the line joining them is perpendicular to the mirror,
2. the same size as the object,
3. virtual (that is, imaginary),
4. laterally inverted but the right way up.

13.7 Curved Mirrors

For some purposes mirrors with curved surfaces are more useful than plane mirrors. You can see the images they form by looking into both sides of a polished spoon. A *concave* mirror curves inwards like a cave (Fig. 13.14(*a*)); a *convex* one curves outwards (Fig. 13.14(*b*)).

(i) **Spherical mirrors.** Many curved mirrors have spherical surfaces. The *principal axis* of a spherical mirror is the line joining the *pole* P or centre of the mirror to the *centre of curvature* C. The point C is the centre of the sphere of which the mirror is a part; it is in front of a concave mirror and behind a convex one. The distance CP is the *radius of curvature* r of the mirror.

When a beam of light parallel to the principal axis is reflected from a concave mirror, the laws of reflection hold and the reflected beam converges to a point on the axis called the *principal focus* F. Since light passes through it, it is a real focus and can be obtained on a screen. A convex mirror has a virtual principal

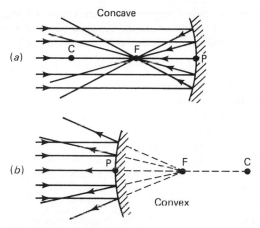

Fig. 13.14

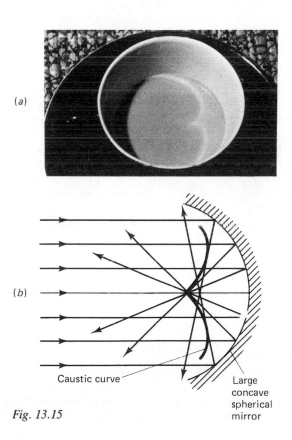

Fig. 13.15

focus behind the mirror, from which the reflected beam appears to diverge.

The *focal length* f of the mirror is the distance FP, and experiment and theory show that FP = CP/2 or $f = r/2$, that is,

focal length = half the radius of curvature

The formation of a point focus by a parallel beam (and the fact that $f = r/2$) is seen only on reflection either by a *small* mirror or by a large mirror *if the beam is close to its axis*. If a wide parallel beam falls on a large concave spherical mirror, the reflected rays do not all come to a focus at one point on its axis but form a curve of light, known as a *caustic curve*. You can often see one on the surface of tea in a cup (Fig. 13.15(a)). It is due to rays farther out from the principal axis being reflected by the inside of the cup so that they pass nearer to the mirror than do the rays close to the axis (Fig. 13.15(b)).

(ii) **Parabolic mirrors.** If a cone is sliced parallel to one of its sides as in Fig. 13.16(a), a parabolic shape is obtained. A concave parabolic mirror has the very useful property of focusing all the rays in a *wide* parallel beam to a point focus F on its principal axis (Fig. 13.16(b)).

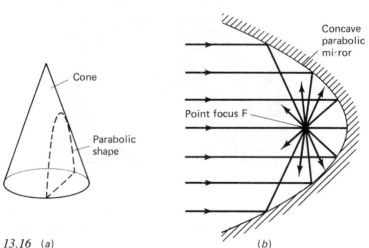

Fig. 13.16 (a)   (b)

13.8 Images in Curved Mirrors

(i) **Ray diagrams.** The nature, position and size of the image formed by a spherical mirror depend on the distance of the object from the mirror, and can be found either by experiment or by drawing a ray diagram using two of the following rays:

1. *A ray parallel to the principal axis which is reflected through or as if it came from the principal focus F* (Fig. 13.17(a));

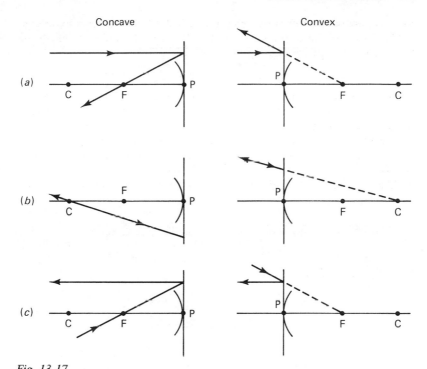

Concave   Convex

Fig. 13.17

2. *a ray through the centre of curvature C which, since it hits the mirror normally, is reflected back along its own path* (Fig. 13.17(*b*)) (the radius of a sphere is perpendicular to the surface where it meets it);

3. *a ray through the principal focus F which is reflected parallel to the principal axis* (Fig. 13.17(*c*)).

When accurate ray diagrams have to be drawn, for example in numerical problems, two points should be noted. First, a curved mirror is shown as a *straight* line. This in effect represents only the centre part of the mirror and allows us to draw a good-sized object and to regard the rays from it as forming a point focus, that is, the mirror behaves as a small one. Second, the vertical scale used for object and image heights need not be the same as the horizontal scale for object and image distances (see the worked example in Unit 13.9).

(ii) **Concave mirror.** The ray diagrams in Fig. 13.18(*a*), (*b*), (*c*) and (*d*) show the images for four object positions. In each case two rays are drawn from the top A of an object OA and the point where they intersect after reflection gives the top B of the image IB. The foot I of each image is on the axis since ray OP hits the mirror normally and is reflected back along the axis. In (*d*) the dotted rays and the image are virtual (not real).

(a) *Object* beyond C

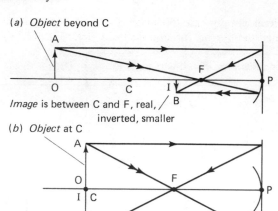

Image is between C and F, real, inverted, smaller

(b) *Object* at C

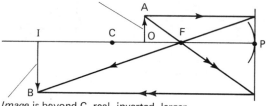

Image is at C, real, inverted, same size

(c) *Object* between C and F

Image is beyond C, real, inverted, larger

(d) *Object* between F and P

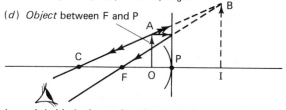

Image is behind mirror, virtual, erect, larger

(e) *Object* in any position

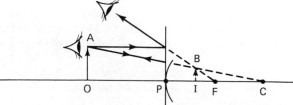

Image behind mirror, virtual, erect, smaller

Fig. 13.18

(iii) **Convex mirror.** In this case the image is virtual, erect, smaller than the object and behind the mirror, for *all* object distances (Fig. 13.18(*e*)).

(iv) **Linear magnification.** The linear magnification *m* is given by

$$m = \frac{\text{height of image}}{\text{height of object}}$$

It can be shown that *m* is also given by

$$m = \frac{\text{distance of image from mirror}}{\text{distance of object from mirror}}$$

13.9 Worked Example

An object 8.0 cm high and at right angles to the principal axis of a concave mirror of radius of curvature 40 cm is 48 cm from the pole. Find the position, size and nature of the image.

Focal length = half radius of curvature, that is,

$$f = r/2 = 40/2 = 20 \text{ cm}$$

Take vertical scale of 1 cm to represent 4 cm:

∴ Height of object is represented by AO = 2.0 cm

Take horizontal scale of 1 cm to represent 8 cm:

∴ *f* is represented by FP = 2.5 cm, *r* by CP = 5.0 cm and object distance by OP = 6.0 cm

Two construction rays AQ and AR are drawn from the top A of the object, as

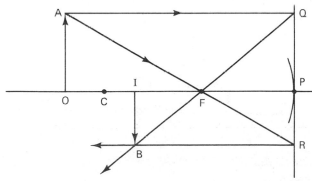

Fig. 13.19

shown in Fig. 13.19. The reflected rays QB and RB intersect at B so the position of the image IB is located. From the diagram,

IP $=4.2$ cm, $\therefore$ true distance of object from pole P $=4.2\times8=34$ cm

IB $=1.4$ cm $\therefore$ true height of image $=1.4\times4=5.6$ cm

Since rays QB and RB pass through the image, it is real.

13.10 Measuring f of a Concave Mirror

(i) **Rough method.** We use the fact that the rays from a point on an object that is very distant (*at infinity*) are nearly parallel (Fig. 13.20(*a*)). The mirror is arranged as in Fig. 13.20(*b*) and moved until a *sharp* image of a window at the other side of the room is obtained on a white screen. The distance between the mirror and the screen is f roughly, since the approximately parallel rays from the window form an image at the principal focus of the mirror.

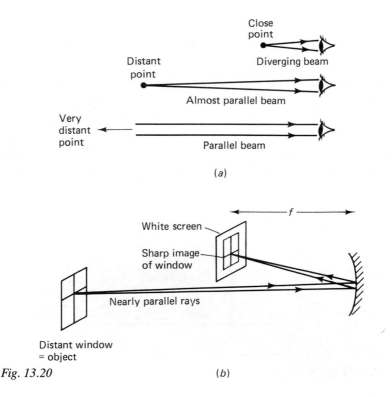

Fig. 13.20   (*b*)

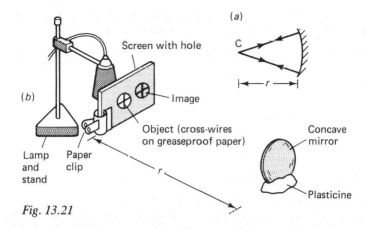

Fig. 13.21

(ii) **Radius of curvature method.** When an object is placed at the centre of curvature C of a concave mirror, a real image is formed also at C (Fig. 13.21(a)). The mirror, arranged as in Fig. 13.21(b), is moved until a *sharp* image of the cross-wire is obtained on the screen. The distance from screen to mirror is the radius of curvature r, hence f ($= r/2$) can be calculated.

13.11 Uses of Mirrors

(i) **Plane mirrors.** Apart from their everyday use, plane mirrors can improve the accuracy of measurements made with meters.

In a *pointer instrument* (such as an ammeter for measuring electric current) a reading is correct only if your eye is directly over the pointer. In any other position there is an error, called the 'parallax' error (see Unit 2.3). If a plane mirror is fitted in the scale, the correct position is found by moving your head until the image of the pointer in the mirror is hidden behind the pointer (Fig. 13.22).

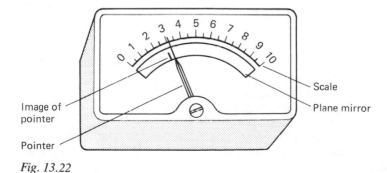

Fig. 13.22

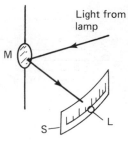

Light from
lamp

M

S—   L

Fig. 13.23

In a *light-beam galvanometer* (which detects very small electric currents) a tiny mirror M is attached to the coil of wire which rotates when current passes through it. A beam of light from a lamp falls on M and the reflected beam, which acts as a 'pointer', produces a spot of light L on a scale S (Fig. 13.23). A very small rotation of M causes appreciable movement of L if the 'pointer' is long.

(ii) **Concave mirrors** are often used as shaving and make-up mirrors, and form a magnified, virtual, erect image of the face if it is between the points F and P in Fig. 13.18(*d*). They are used in reflecting telescopes (see Unit 15.8(ii)) instead of lenses.

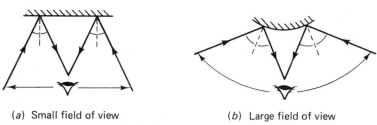

(*a*) Small field of view   (*b*) Large field of view

Fig. 13.24

(iii) **Convex mirrors.** A convex mirror gives a wider field of view than does a plane mirror of the same size (Fig. 13.24(*a*) and (*b*)). For this reason and because it always gives an erect (though smaller) image, it is used as a car driving mirror.

(iv) **Parabolic mirrors.** A concave parabolic mirror can bring a wide parallel beam to a point focus and conversely can produce a wide parallel beam from a small source of light at its principal focus. The first property is used by 'dish' aerials to collect and bring to a focus microwave signals (which obey the same laws of reflection that light does) from communication satellites. The second property explains the use of the parabolic mirror as a car headlight reflector (Fig. 13.25).

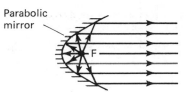

Parabolic
mirror

F

Fig. 13.25

13.12 Revision Questions

1. Name (*a*) three luminous objects, (*b*) three non-luminous objects.

2. How does the shadow from an extended source of light differ from that from a point source?

3. What are the relative positions of the sun, earth and moon during (*a*) a lunar eclipse, (*b*) a solar eclipse?

4. How would the size and brightness of the image formed by a pinhole camera change (*a*) if the camera was made longer, (*b*) if the object was moved farther away from the camera?

5. What changes would occur in the image if the single pinhole in a camera was replaced by (*a*) four pinholes close together, (*b*) a hole 1 cm wide?

6. State the laws of reflection of light.

7. Name a surface which gives (*a*) regular reflection, (*b*) diffuse reflection.

8. How does a real image differ from a virtual one?

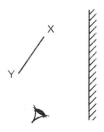

X

Y

Fig. 13.26

9. Copy and complete Fig. 13.26 to show how the image of XY is formed. Do it by drawing two rays from both X and Y which after reflection enter the eye.

10. State four properties of the image in a plane mirror.

11. Draw diagrams to represent (*a*) a convex mirror, (*b*) a concave mirror. Mark on

each the principal axis, the principal focus F and the centre of curvature C if the focal length of (a) is 3 cm and that of (b) is 4 cm.

12. Copy and complete the following table for a concave mirror.

Object position	Image			
	Position	Real/virtual	Larger/smaller	Erect/inverted
Between F and P				
Between F and C				
At C				
Beyond C				

13. Describe how you would find the focal length of a concave mirror (a) roughly, (b) exactly.

14. (a) State two scientific uses of a plane mirror.
(b) What property of a concave mirror makes it useful as a shaving or make-up mirror?
(c) Why is a convex mirror used as a driving mirror?
(d) Why is a concave parabolic mirror used as a car headlamp reflector?

13.13 Problems

Reflection of Light
1. What is the angle of reflection of a ray which falls on a plane mirror at an angle of 60° to the mirror surface?

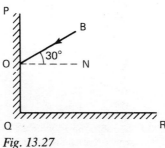

Fig. 13.27

2. In Fig. 13.27 PQ and QR are two mirrors at right angles to each other. BO is a ray of light and NO is a normal to PQ.

(a) What is the angle of reflection of BO from PQ?

(b) Copy the diagram and continue the ray BO to show how it is reflected from QR.

(c) What is the angle of reflection at QR?

3. A ray of light falls on a plane mirror at an angle of incidence of 50° and is reflected on to a second mirror which is at an angle of 60° with the first mirror.

Draw a ray diagram and from it find the angle of reflection at the second mirror.

Image in a Plane Mirror

4. A girl stands 5 m away from a large plane mirror. How far must she walk to be 2 m away from her image?

5. By how far does the distance between a boy and his image decrease if he walks from a position where he is 10 m away from a mirror to one where he is 3.0 m away?

Fig. 13.28

6. If a watch with dots instead of numbers is held up in front of a mirror at 11.15 (Fig. 13.28), what will the time appear to be on the image of the watch?

Curved Mirrors

7. An object 1.0 cm high is placed 20 cm from a concave mirror of focal length 8.0 cm. Draw a ray diagram to a suitable scale, and find the position, size and nature of the image.

8 Find, by means of ray diagrams drawn to suitable scales, the size, nature and position of the image of an object 3.0 cm high which is placed (a) 50 cm, (b) 10 cm in front of a concave mirror of focal length 15 cm. The object is perpendicular to, and has one end on, the axis of the mirror.

9. An object is placed 5.0 cm in front of a concave mirror. A real image is produced 15 cm from the mirror. What is the linear magnification produced by the mirror?

Unit Fourteen

Refraction and Lenses

14.1 Refraction of Light

(i) **The coin trick.** If you place a coin in an empty cup and move back until you just cannot see it, it surprisingly comes into view when someone pours water into the cup *gently*.

In a transparent material, such as air, light travels in straight lines. But if it passes into a different material, such as water, it changes direction—that is, it is bent—at the boundary between the two. The bending of light when it passes from one material or *medium* to another is called *refraction*. It causes effects like the coin trick.

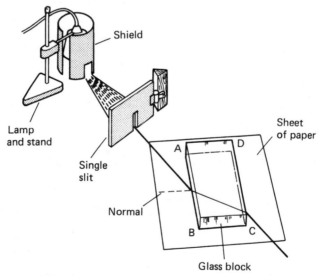

Fig. 14.1

(ii) **Investigating refraction.** Take a glass block which has its lower face painted white or frosted, draw its outline ABCD on a sheet of white paper and shine a narrow ray of light on to it at an angle as in Fig. 14.1. Mark the positions of the rays on the paper; then remove the block and draw normals on the paper at the points where the ray entered AB and where it left CD. Repeat this for rays falling at other angles on AB.

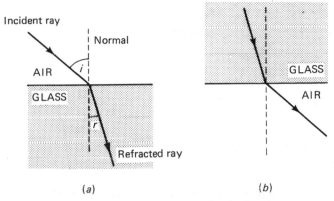

Fig. 14.2 i = angle of incidence; r = angle of refraction

Three aspects of refraction are demonstrated by this experiment.

1. A ray is bent *towards* the normal when it enters an optically denser medium at an angle (Fig. 14.2(a)), and *away from* the normal when it enters an optically less dense medium (Fig. 14.2(b)). (*Optically denser* means having a greater refraction effect; the actual density may or may not be greater.)

2. A ray emerging from a parallel-sided block is parallel to the ray entering, but is displaced sideways.

3. A ray travelling along the normal is not refracted.

Terms used in connection with refraction are illustrated in Fig. 14.2.

(iii) **Laws of refraction.** The angle of refraction (r) increases when the angle of incidence (i) increases, but not in any immediately obvious way. In 1620 the Dutch scientist Snell discovered that sin i divided by sin r always gave the same number for two media (air and glass, for instance) whatever the value of i. There are two laws.

1. *The incident and refracted rays are on opposite sides of the normal and all lie in the same plane.*

2. *The value of sin i/sin r is constant for light passing from one particular medium to another.* This is called *Snell's law* and is illustrated in Fig. 14.3.

Snell's law can be tested for light passing from air to glass using the apparatus in Fig. 14.1 if several measurements of i and r are made and sin i/sin r calculated in each case.

(iv) **Refractive index.** If i is the angle of incidence in air (strictly a vacuum but the difference is negligible) and r is the angle of refraction in a medium, the constant value of sin i/sin r is called the *refractive index* (n) of the medium. For glass and Perspex it is about 1.5 ($\frac{3}{2}$); for water it is 1.3 ($\frac{4}{3}$). The larger n is for a material, the more that material bends light.

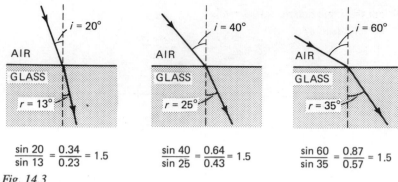

$$\frac{\sin 20}{\sin 13} = \frac{0.34}{0.23} = 1.5$$ $$\frac{\sin 40}{\sin 25} = \frac{0.64}{0.43} = 1.5$$ $$\frac{\sin 60}{\sin 35} = \frac{0.87}{0.57} = 1.5$$

Fig. 14.3

We will see later (in Unit 16.5(ii)) that refraction is due to a change of speed when another medium is entered. It can be shown that

$$n = \frac{\text{speed of light in air}}{\text{speed of light in medium}} = \frac{c_a}{c_m}$$

That is, the more light is slowed down, the more it is bent. In air $c_a = 3 \times 10^8$ m/s; in glass $c_m = 2 \times 10^8$ m/s, giving a value of n for glass of $\frac{3}{2}$.

14.2 Worked Examples

Angle	6°	12°	17°	24°	30°	37°	44°	53°	64°	90°
Sine (approx)	0.1	0.2	0.3	0.4	0.5	0.6	0.7	0.8	0.9	1.0

1. A ray of light travelling from air into glass has an angle of incidence of 37° and an angle of refraction of 24°. What value does this give for the refractive index of glass?

Angle of incidence $= i = 37°$
Angle of refraction $= r = 24°$
Refractive index of glass $= n = ?$

From the table above, $\sin 37 = 0.6$ and $\sin 24 = 0.4$.

$$\therefore n = \frac{\sin i}{\sin r} = \frac{\sin 37}{\sin 24} = \frac{0.6}{0.4} = 1.5$$

2. A ray of light travelling from air into a liquid of refractive index 1.4 has an angle of incidence of 30°. Find the angle of refraction.

Angle of incidence $= i = 30°$
Angle of refraction $= r = ?$
Refractive index $= n = 1.4$

From the table above, sin 30 = 0.5.

$$n = \frac{\sin i}{\sin r}; \quad 1.4 = \frac{\sin 30}{\sin r}$$

$$\therefore \sin r = \frac{\sin 30}{1.4} = \frac{0.5}{1.4} = 0.4 \text{ (approx.)}$$

$$\therefore r = \underline{\underline{24°}} \text{ (to nearest degree)}$$

14.3 Real and Apparent Depth

(i) **Apparent depth of a pool.** Rays of light from a point O on the bottom of a pool are refracted away from the normal at the water surface since they are passing into air, which is a less dense medium (Fig. 14.4). On entering the eye they appear to come from a point I *above* O; I is the virtual image of O formed by refraction. The apparent depth of the pool is less than its real depth.

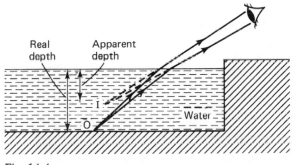

Fig. 14.4

It can be shown that for *perpendicular viewing* of O (that is, where the observer's eyes are close to the normal), that

$$\text{refractive index } (n) = \frac{\text{real depth}}{\text{apparent depth}}$$

For example, if $n = 1.5$, a pond 3 m deep appears to be 2 m deep.

(ii) **Finding n by real and apparent depth.** A pin O is stuck at the end of a glass block (Fig. 14.5) and a second pin I mounted with its point on top of the block. (The mounting can be a cork with three small pins as legs.) O is viewed through the block and at the same time I is moved nearer or farther from O until I and the image of O stay together in the same straight line as the observer's head is moved to the right or left. I then occupies the position of the image of O (that is, there is no parallax between them).

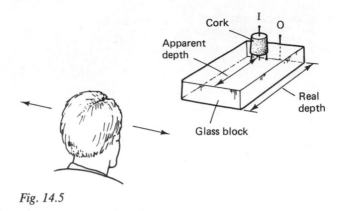

Fig. 14.5

If the real and apparent depths of the block are measured, *n* can be calculated using the equation in (i).

14.4 Total Internal Reflection

(i) **Critical angle.** When light passes at small angles of incidence from a denser to a less dense medium (from glass to air, for example) a strong refracted ray emerges into the less dense medium and at the same time a weak ray is reflected back into the denser medium (Fig. 14.6(*a*)).

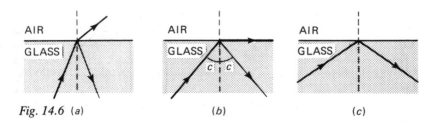

Fig. 14.6 (a)   (b)   (c)

Increasing the angle of incidence increases the angle of refraction. At a certain angle of incidence, called the *critical angle c*, the angle of refraction is 90° (Fig. 14.6(*b*)). For angles of incidence greater than *c*, the refracted ray disappears and all the incident light is reflected inside the denser medium (Fig. 14.6(*c*)). The light does not cross the boundary and is said to suffer *total internal reflection*.

If the direction of the refracted ray in Fig. 14.6(*b*) is reversed (this is possible because light is reversible), then the angle of incidence *i* for light travelling from air to glass is 90° and the angle of refraction *r* in the glass is *c*. Hence

$$\text{refractive index } n = \frac{\sin i}{\sin r} = \frac{\sin 90}{\sin c}$$

$$\therefore n = \frac{1}{\sin c} \text{ (since } \sin 90 = 1)$$

$$\text{or } \sin c = \frac{1}{n}$$

For glass, $n = \frac{3}{2}$, $\sin c = \frac{2}{3}$ giving $c = 42°$.
For water, $n = \frac{4}{3}$, $\sin c = \frac{3}{4}$ giving $c = 49°$.

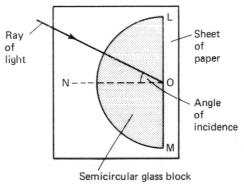

Fig. 14.7

(ii) Measuring c for glass. Take a semicircular glass block which has its lower face whitened or frosted, place it on a sheet of paper (Fig. 14.7) and draw its outline LOMN where O is the centre and ON the normal at O to LOM. Direct a narrow ray of light (at an angle of about 30°) *along a radius towards* O. The ray is not refracted at the curved surface (because it is perpendicular to the surface). There is a refracted ray in the air beyond LOM and also a weak internally reflected ray in the glass.

Now rotate the paper slowly so that the angle of incidence increases, until total internal reflection just occurs. Mark the incident ray, and measure the angle of incidence; this gives the critical angle c.

(iii) Totally reflecting prisms. Total internal reflection occurs when light falls on a glass prism with angles of 45°, 45° and 90°. This is because a ray falling normally on any face of such a prism hits an inside face at 45°, and this is greater than the critical angle of glass (about 42°). In Fig. 14.8(a) the ray is turned through 90° and in Fig. 14.8(b) through 180°. Totally reflecting prisms are used in periscopes (instead of mirrors) and in binoculars.

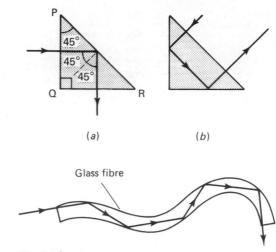

Fig. 14.8   (a)   (b)

Glass fibre

Fig. 14.9

(iv) Light pipes or optical fibres. Light can be trapped by total internal reflection inside a bent glass rod and 'piped' along a curved path (Fig. 14.9). A single, very thin fibre of very pure (optical) glass behaves in the same way. If several thousand such fibres are taped together a flexible *light pipe* is obtained that can be used (by a doctor or an engineer, for example) to light up some awkward spot. If necessary a second bundle of fibres carries back the image for inspection.

A very recent use for optical fibres is in telecommunications, for carrying pulses of light from a laser which represent information such as telephone conversations, television pictures and computer data. An optical fibre has a much greater information-carrying capacity than a copper cable of the same thickness carrying an electric current, as well as being thinner and lighter.

14.5 Lenses

(i) Introduction. Lenses are made of glass or plastic and most have spherical surfaces. They form images like those produced by curved mirrors, but they do so by refracting light rather than reflecting it. A *convex* lens is thickest in the centre and is also called a *converging* lens because it bends light inwards (Fig. 14.10(a)). You may have used one as a magnifying glass (Fig. 14.11(a)) or as a burning glass for concentrating the sun's rays on to one spot. A *concave* or *diverging* lens is thinnest in the centre and spreads light out (Fig. 14.10(b)); it always gives a diminished image (Fig. 14.11(b)).

The centre of a lens is its *optical centre* C; the line through C at right angles to the lens is called the *principal axis*.

The action of a lens can be understood by treating it as a number of glass blocks or prisms. Each block bends the rays towards the normal as they enter it

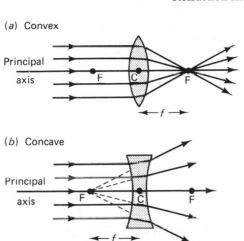

(a) Convex

Principal axis

F   C   F

$\leftarrow f \rightarrow$

(b) Concave

Principal axis

F   C   F

$\leftarrow f \rightarrow$

Fig. 14.10

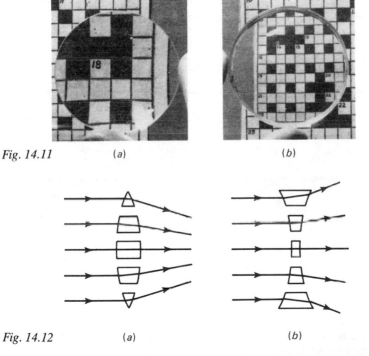

Fig. 14.11   (a)   (b)

Fig. 14.12   (a)   (b)

and away from the normal as they leave (Fig. 14.12(a) and (b)). The central block is parallel-sided and if the lens is thin rays pass straight through it.

(ii) **Principal focus.** When a beam of light parallel to the principal axis of a convex lens passes through the lens, it is refracted so as to converge to a point on the axis called the *principal focus* F. It is a real focus. A concave lens has a virtual principal focus behind the lens, from which the refracted beam seems to diverge.

Since light can fall on both faces of a lens it has two principal foci, one on each side, equidistant from C. The distance CF is the *focal length* (f) of the lens and is an important property of it.

14.6 Images Formed by Lenses

(i) **Ray diagrams.** Information about the images formed by lenses (as with those formed by curved mirrors—see Unit 13.8) can be obtained either experimentally or by drawing ray diagrams using two of the following rays:

1. *a ray parallel to the principal axis which is refracted through the principal focus F* (Fig. 14.13(*a*));
2. *a ray through the optical centre C which is undeviated* (Fig. 14.13(*b*));
3. *a ray through the principal focus F which is refracted parallel to the principal axis* (Fig. 14.13(*c*)).

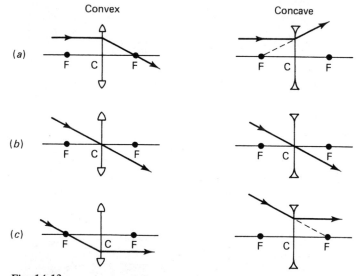

Fig. 14.13

In diagrams a thin lens is represented by a straight line at which all the refraction is considered to occur. Also, as for curved mirrors, the vertical scale in numerical problems need not be the same as the horizontal one.

(ii) **Convex lens.** In the formation of images by lenses two important points on the principal axis are F and 2F. 2F is at a distance of twice the focal length from

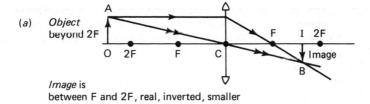

(a)   *Object beyond 2F*

Image is
between F and 2F, real, inverted, smaller

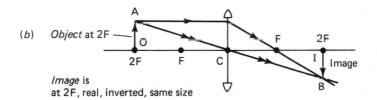

(b)   *Object at 2F*

Image is
at 2F, real, inverted, same size

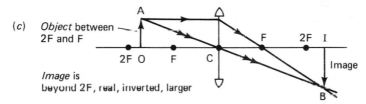

(c)   *Object between 2F and F*

Image is
beyond 2F, real, inverted, larger

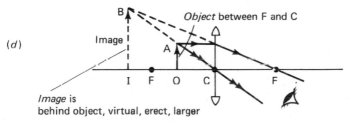

(d)

Object between F and C

Image is
behind object, virtual, erect, larger

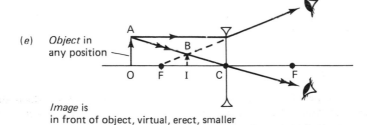

(e)   *Object in any position*

Image is
in front of object, virtual, erect, smaller

Fig. 14.14

C. The nature, position and size of the image depends on the position of the object in relation to F, 2F and C; the ray diagrams in Fig. 14.14(a), (b), (c) and (d) show the images for four object positions. In each case two rays are drawn from the top A of an object OA and the point where they intersect after refraction gives the top B of the image IB. The foot I of each image is on the axis since ray OC passes through the lens undeviated. In (d) the dotted rays and the image are virtual.

(iii) **Concave lens.** This lens behaves like a convex mirror, and gives a virtual, erect, smaller image for *all* object positions (Fig. 14.14(e)).

(iv) **Linear magnification.** The linear magnification m is given by

$$m = \frac{\text{height of image}}{\text{height of object}}$$

For each of the ray diagrams in Fig. 14.14 it can be shown that triangles OAC and BIC are similar, so it follows (as for curved mirrors) that

$$m = \frac{\text{IB}}{\text{OA}} = \frac{\text{IC}}{\text{OC}} = \frac{\text{distance of image from lens}}{\text{distance of object from lens}}$$

14.7 Worked Example

An image is formed by a convex lens at a distance of 10 cm from the lens; the image is erect, and twice the size of the object. Find the focal length of the lens.

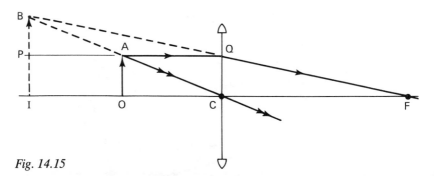

Fig. 14.15

Since the image is erect, it must be virtual and on the same side of the lens as the object. Taking a horizontal scale of 1 cm = 2 cm, draw the image IB 2 cm high at a distance of 5 cm from the lens (Fig. 14.15). Now draw a line PQ, 1 cm from and parallel to the principal axis; this must touch the top of the object (since it is half the size of IB). Join B and C; the line BC must also touch the top of the object (since BC is the undeviated ray through C). The top of the object is therefore at the point A where BC cuts PQ.

A ray AQ parallel to the principal axis is refracted through the principal focus and appears to come from B on the image. Join B and Q, therefore, and produce BQ to cut the principal axis at F, which is the principal focus of the lens.

Since $CF = 5$ cm on the diagram, the actual focal length of the lens $= 5 \times 2 = 10$ cm.

14.8 Measuring f of a Convex Lens

(i) **Distant object method.** This is a rough method which uses the fact that rays from a point on a distant object are nearly parallel (see Unit 13.10(i), Fig. 13.20(a)). The lens is arranged as in Fig. 14.16 and moved until a *sharp* image of a window at the other side of the room is obtained on the screen. The distance between the lens and the screen is approximately equal to f, since the image is formed at the principal focus.

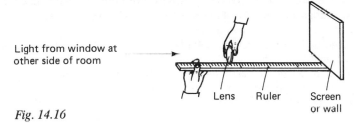

Fig. 14.16

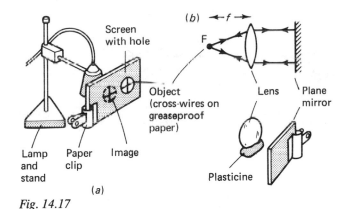

Fig. 14.17

(ii) **Plane mirror method.** Using the arrangement in Fig. 14.17(a), the lens is moved until a *sharp* image of the object (the illuminated cross-wire) is formed on the screen beside the object. When this happens, light from the object must be travelling back along nearly the same path to hit the mirror normally (Fig. 14.17(b)). The object is then at the lens's principal focus F and the focal length f is the distance between the lens and the screen.

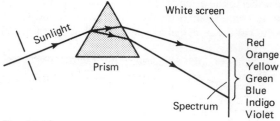

Fig. 14.18

14.9 Dispersion

(i) **Newton's experiments.** The experiment shown in Fig. 14.18 was first performed by Newton in 1666. A narrow beam of sunlight, which is white, falls on a triangular glass prism and produces a band of colours, called a *spectrum*, on a white screen. The effect is known as *dispersion* and Newton concluded that white light is a mixture of many colours of light, which the prism separates out because the refractive index of glass is different for different colours; the refractive index is greatest for violet light (since it is refracted most) and least for red light.

To test this suggestion Newton tried two further experiments, shown in Fig. 14.19(*a*) and (*b*). In (*a*), adding the second prism did not introduce any more colours—the spectrum RV just became wider. In (*b*) only one colour R (red)

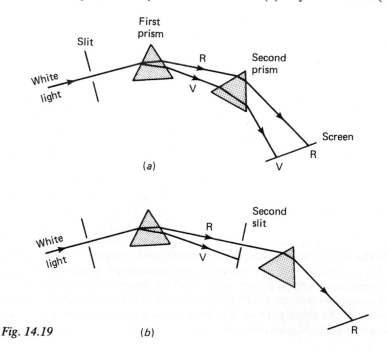

Fig. 14.19   (*b*)

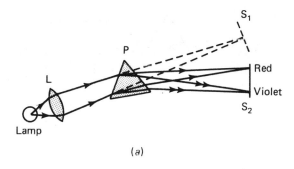

(a)

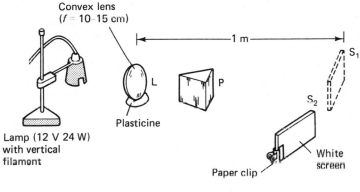

Fig. 14.20   (b)

was allowed to go through the second slit (that is, he used *monochromatic*—literally 'one coloured' light) and again no other colours appeared.

(ii) Producing a pure spectrum. A pure spectrum is one in which the colours do not overlap, as they do when a prism alone is used. A convex lens has to be used to focus each colour, as in Fig. 14.20(a).

A lens L is arranged so that it forms an image of the vertical filament of a lamp on a screen at S_1, 1 m away (Fig. 14.20(b)). The filament acts as a narrow source of white light. A 60° glass prism P is inserted and the screen moved to S_2 (still at the same distance from L) to receive the spectrum. P is rotated until the spectrum is pure.

(iii) Recombining the spectrum. The colours of the spectrum can be recombined to form white light *either* by arranging a second prism so that the light is deviated in the opposite direction (Fig. 14.21(a)) (although recombination is not quite complete and some colour is visible at the edges of the beam), *or* by using an electric motor to rotate at high speed a disc with the spectral colours painted on its sectors (Fig. 14.21(b)). (The whiteness obtained is slightly grey because paints are not pure colours.)

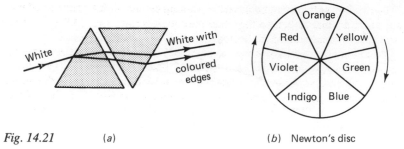

Fig. 14.21   (a)   (b)   Newton's disc

14.10 Colour

(i) **Colour of an object.** The colour of an object depends on the colour of the light falling on it and the colour(s) it transmits or reflects.

1. *Filters.* A filter is made of glass or celluloid and lets through light of certain colours only. For example, a red filter transmits mostly red light and absorbs other colours; it therefore produces red light when white light shines through it.

2. *Opaque objects.* These do not allow light to pass but are seen by the light reflected from them. A white object reflects all colours and appears white in white light, red in red light, blue in blue light, and so on. A blue object appears blue in white light because the red, orange, yellow, green and violet colours in white light are absorbed and only blue reflected. It also looks blue in blue light but in red light it appears black since no light is reflected and blackness indicates the absence of colour.

(ii) **Mixing coloured lights.** In science red, green and blue are called *primary* colours (they are not the artist's primary colours) because none of them can be produced from other colours of light. However, they give other colours when suitably mixed.

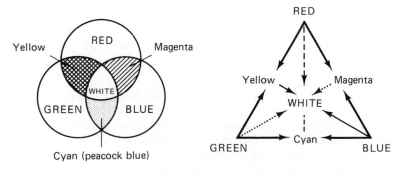

Fig. 14.22   (a)   (b)

The primary colours can be mixed by shining beams of red, green and blue light on to a white screen so that they partially overlap (Fig. 14.22(a)). The results are summarized in the 'colour triangle' of Fig. 14.22(b).

The colours formed by adding two primaries are called *secondary* colours; they are yellow, cyan (turquoise or peacock blue) and magenta. The three primary colours give white light when they are mixed together, as do the three secondaries. A primary colour and the secondary opposite it in the colour triangle—such as blue and yellow—also give white light: any two colours producing white light are called *complementary* colours.

(iii) **Mixing coloured pigments.** Pigments are materials that give colour to paints and dyes by reflecting light of certain colours only and absorbing all other colours. Most pigments are impure, that is, they reflect more than one colour. When they are mixed the colour reflected is the one common to all. For example, stirring blue and yellow paints together gives a green mixture because blue paint reflects indigo and green (its neighbours in the spectrum) as well as blue, while yellow paint reflects green, yellow and orange (Fig. 14.23). Only green is reflected by both.

Mixing coloured pigments is a process of *subtraction*; coloured lights are mixed by *addition*.

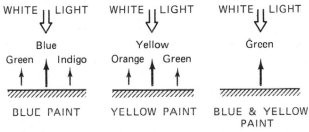

Fig. 14.23

14.11 Revision Questions

1. A ray of light is shown entering a rectangular block of glass in Fig. 14.24.
   (a) Copy the diagram and draw the normal at the point of entry.
   (b) Sketch the approximate path of the ray through the block and out of the other side.

Fig. 14.24

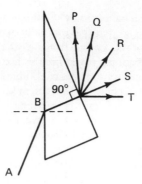

Fig. 14.25

2. Fig. 14.25 shows a ray of light AB striking a glass prism and then passing through it. Which of the rays P, Q, R, S, T correctly represents the emerging ray?

3. State the two laws of refraction.

4. Draw two rays from a point on a fish in a river to show where someone must aim to spear it.

5. Write down three equations for refractive index.

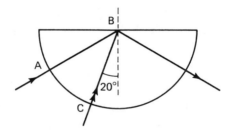

Fig. 14.26

6. Rays of light in a semicircular glass block are shown in Fig. 14.26.
   (a) Why is the ray entering the glass at A not bent?
   (b) Why is the ray AB reflected at B and not refracted?
   (c) Copy the diagram and draw the approximate path of ray CB after it leaves B.

7. Copy Fig. 14.27(a) and (b) and complete the paths of the rays.

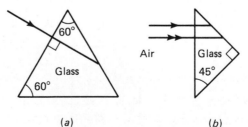

Fig. 14.27   (a)   (b)

8. Write down the relation between refractive index and critical angle.

9. State two uses of total internal reflection.

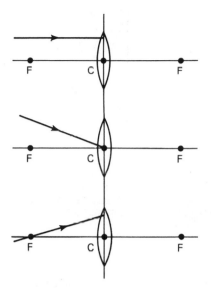

Fig. 14.28

10. (*a*) What kind of lens is shown in Fig. 14.28?
    (*b*) What names are given to (i) C, (ii) F, (iii) CF?
    (*c*) Copy the diagrams and complete them to show the path of the rays after passing through the lens.

11. Copy and complete the following table for a convex lens.

Object position	Image			
	Position	Real/virtual	Larger/smaller	Erect/inverted
Between C and F				
Between F and 2F				
At 2F				
Beyond 2F				

12. How would you find the focal length of a convex lens (*a*) roughly, (*b*) accurately?

13. Explain the term *dispersion*.

14. Copy and complete the diagram in Fig. 14.29 to show what is seen on the screen AB.

15. (*a*) What are the three primary colours in science?
    (*b*) What are the three secondary colours?
    (*c*) What are complementary colours?

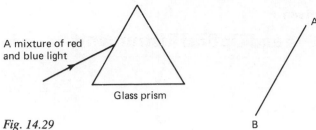

A mixture of red and blue light

Glass prism

Fig. 14.29

(*d*) Draw the colour triangle for mixing coloured lights.

(*e*) What colours are produced (i) if yellow and blue light falls on a white screen, (ii) if yellow and blue paints are mixed? Explain the difference.

(*f*) What colour will a red object appear in (i) magenta light, (ii) blue light?

(*g*) If white light falls on a filter, what colour or colours pass through if the filter is (i) green, (ii) yellow?

14.12 Problems

Where necessary use the sine values given in the table in Unit 14.2, and take the refractive index of glass as $\frac{3}{2}$ and that of water as $\frac{4}{3}$.

Refraction

1. A ray of light travelling from air into another material has an angle of incidence of 30° and an angle of refraction of 24°. What is the refractive index of the material?

2. Light enters water from air at an angle of incidence of (*a*) 24°, (*b*) 53°. What is the angle of refraction in each case?

3. Light entering glass from air has an angle of refraction of 37°. What is the angle of incidence?

4. What is the speed of light in a medium of refractive index 1.2 if its speed in air (and a vacuum) is 300 000 km/s?

5. (*a*) What is the real depth of a pond which appears to be 0.6 m deep when viewed from above?

   (*b*) What is the apparent thickness of a glass block of real depth 9 cm?

Total Internal Reflection

6. If the critical angle for diamond is 24°, calculate its refractive index.

7. Calculate the critical angle of a material of refractive index 2.0.

Lenses

8. An object 1.5 cm high is at right angles to the principal axis of a convex lens and is 8.0 cm from it. If the lens has focal length 5.0 cm, find the distance of the image from the lens and its height. Is it real or virtual?

9. An object 2.0 cm high is 5.0 cm from a convex lens of focal length 10 cm. Find the position, nature and size of the image.

10. A convex lens forms a real image which is three times smaller than an object 20 cm from it. What is the focal length of the lens?

Unit Fifteen

The Eye and Optical Instruments

15.1 The Eye

(i) **Action.** When light from an object reaches the eye (Fig. 15.1), an image is formed on the *retina* by successive refraction at the *cornea*, the *aqueous humour*, the *lens* and the *vitreous humour*. Electrical signals then travel along the *optic nerve* to the brain to be interpreted. In good light, the *yellow spot* (*fovea*) is the part of the retina that is most sensitive to detail and the image is automatically formed there.

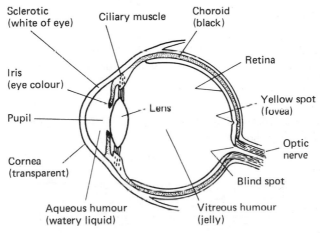

Fig. 15.1

Objects at different distances are focused by the *ciliary muscles* changing the shape and so the focal length of the lens—a process called *accommodation*. The lens flattens when near objects are viewed. The *iris* has a central hole, the *pupil*, whose size it decreases in bright light and increases in dim light.

(ii) **Blind spot.** This is the small area of the retina where the optic nerve leaves the eye. It has no light-sensitive nerve endings and in each eye it is closer to the nose than the yellow spot.

To show its existence, close your left eye and look at the cross in Fig. 15.2. You will also see the black dot. *Slowly* bring the book towards you. At a certain distance the dot disappears; its image has fallen on the blind spot of your right eye.

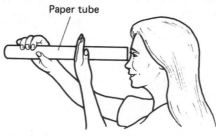

Fig. 15.2

(iii) Binocular vision. Your eyes see an object from slightly different angles, giving two slightly different images which the brain combines to give a three-dimensional impression. This also helps us to judge distances.

Paper tube

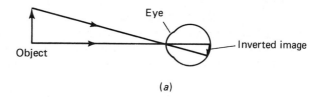

Fig. 15.3

Roll a sheet of paper into a tube and hold it to your right eye with your right hand (Fig. 15.3). Close your left eye and place your left hand halfway along the tube. Open your left eye. Is there a 'hole' in your hand to 'see' through? Explain.

(iv) Image inverted on retina. To show this, make a pinhole in a piece of paper and hold it about 10 cm away from your eyes. Close one eye and look at the hole against the sky or something bright (Fig. 15.4(*a*)). Hold a pin, head

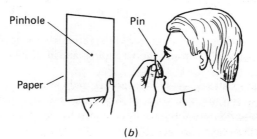

Fig. 15.4   (*b*)

up, very close to your eye (Fig. 15.4(*b*)). Keep looking at the hole and move the pin about slowly until you 'see' it inverted in the hole. Make several pinholes round the first and look again. What do you see?

The pin is too close to the eye for a real image (except a large blur) to be formed on the retina, but a sharp *upright shadow* is produced by light from the pinhole and this falls directly (that is, *still upright*) on the retina. But you 'see' the shadow upside-down; you know therefore that the brain must turn it upside-down. If the brain does that with the shadow, it must do the same with any image falling on the retina. So, as you normally see an upright object as upright, the image must be upside-down on the retina.

15.2 Defects of Vision

The average adult eye can comfortably focus objects from about 25 cm away (the *near point*) to infinity (the *far point*). Your near point may be less than 25 cm from your eye; it gets farther away with age.

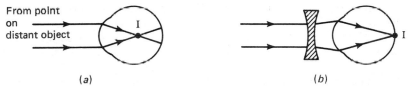

(a)   (b)

Fig. 15.5 Short sight

(i) **Short sight.** A short-sighted person sees near objects clearly but his or her far point is closer than infinity. The image of a distant object is formed *in front of* the retina because the eyeball is too long (Fig. 15.5(*a*)); the object appears blurred. The defect is corrected by a concave spectacle lens which diverges the light before it enters the eye, to give an image *on* the retina (Fig. 15.5(*b*)).

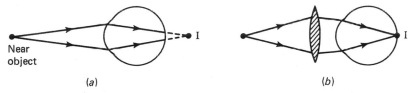

(a)   (b)

Fig. 15.6 Long sight

(ii) **Long sight.** A long-sighted person sees distant objects clearly but his or her near point is more than 25 cm from the eye. The image of a near object is focused *behind* the retina because the eyeball is too short (Fig. 15.6(*a*)). A convex spectacle lens corrects the defect (Fig. 15.6(*b*)).

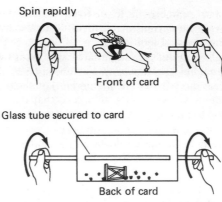

Spin rapidly

Front of card

Glass tube secured to card

Back of card

Fig. 15.7

15.3 Persistence of Vision

An image lasts on the retina for about one-tenth of a second after the object
has disappeared, as can be shown by spinning a card like that in Fig. 15.7. The
effect makes possible the production of motion pictures. Twenty-four separate
pictures, each slightly different from the previous one, are projected on to the
screen per second and give the impression of continuity. In a television
receiver twenty-five complete pictures are produced every second.

15.4 Camera

A camera is a light-tight box in which a convex lens forms a real image on a film
(Fig. 15.8). The film contains chemicals that change on exposure to light; it is
'developed' to give a negative. From the negative a photograph is made by
'printing'.

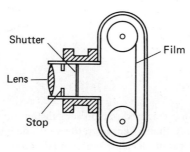

Shutter

Film

Lens

Stop

Fig. 15.8

(i) **Focusing.** In simple cameras the lens is fixed and all distant objects (that is, beyond about 2 metres) are in reasonable focus. Roughly how far from the film will the lens be if its focal length is 5 cm?

In other cameras an object is brought into exact focus by altering the lens position. For near objects it is moved away from the film, the correct setting for a given distance being shown by a scale on the focusing ring.

(ii) **Shutter.** When a photograph is taken, the shutter is opened for a certain time and exposes the film to light entering the camera. In some cameras exposure times can be varied and are given in fractions of a second (1/1000, 1/60, and so forth). Fast-moving objects require short exposures.

(iii) **Stop.** The brightness of the image on the film depends on the amount of light passing through the lens when the shutter is opened, and this is controlled by the size of the hole (*aperture*) in the stop. In some cameras this is fixed but in others it can be altered; it is made larger for a dull scene and smaller for a bright one.

The aperture may be marked in *f-numbers*. The diameter of an aperture with f-number 8, for example, is one-eighth of the focal length of the lens and thus the *larger* the f-number the *smaller* the aperture. The numbers are chosen so that on passing from one to the next higher—from 8 to 11, say—the area of the aperture is halved.

15.5 Projector

A projector forms a real image of an object on a screen: the 'object' is a slide in a slide projector, and a film in a cine-projector. The image is usually so highly magnified that very strong but even illumination of the slide or film is needed if the image is also to be bright. This is achieved by directing light from a small but powerful lamp on to the 'object' by means of a concave mirror and a condenser lens system arranged as in Fig. 15.9. The image is produced by the projection lens which can be moved in and out of its mounting to focus the picture. In many projectors the slide must be placed upside down and laterally inverted, in order to give an erect image the right way round.

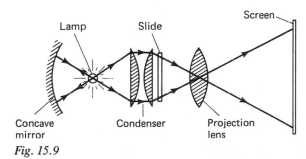

Fig. 15.9

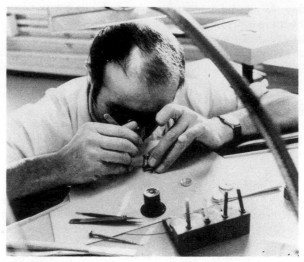

Fig. 15.10

15.6 Magnifying Glass

A watchmaker's magnifying glass is shown in use in Fig. 15.10.

The sleepers on a railway track are all the same length but those nearby seem longer. This is because they enclose a larger angle at your eye than the more distant ones do: as a result their image on the retina is larger so making them appear bigger. This principle is used when a convex lens acts as a magnifying glass. The lens gives an enlarged, upright virtual image of an object placed inside its principal focus F (Fig. 15.11(a)). It acts as a magnifying glass since the angle β made at the eye by the image, which is formed at the near point, is

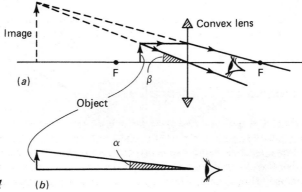

Fig. 15.11   (b)

greater than the angle α made by the object when it is viewed directly at the near point without the magnifying glass (Fig. 15.11(b)).

The fatter (more curved) a convex lens is, the shorter is its focal length and the more it magnifies. A lens with too much curvature produces a distorted image, however.

15.7 Compound Microscope

A compound microscope gives much greater magnification than a magnifying glass and less distortion. In its simplest form it consists of two *short-focus* convex lenses arranged as in Fig. 15.12.

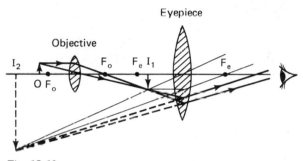

Fig. 15.12

The lens nearer the object, called the *objective*, forms a real, enlarged, inverted image I_1 of a small object O placed just outside its principal focus F_o. I_1 is just inside the principal focus F_e of the second lens, the *eyepiece*, which treats I_1 as an object and acts as a magnifying glass to give a further enlarged, virtual image I_2.

The thicker arrowed lines are actual rays from O, by which the eye sees the top of I_2. The thin lines without arrows are construction lines drawn to find the position of I_2.

In practice, the objective and eyepiece of a microscope are each made of several lenses, as this produces a less distorted image. The object is seen inverted.

15.8 Astronomical Telescopes

(i) **Refracting telescope.** A lens astronomical telescope consists of two convex lenses: a long-focus objective and a short-focus eyepiece. Rays from a point on a distant object, such as a star, are nearly parallel on reaching the telescope. The objective forms a real, inverted, diminished image I_1 of the object at its principal focus F_o (Fig. 15.13). The eyepiece acts as a magnifying glass treating

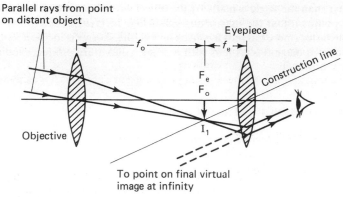

Fig. 15.13

I_1 as an object and forming a magnified, virtual image. Normally the eyepiece is adjusted to give this final image at infinity (that is, a long way off), and so I_1 will be at the principal focus F_e of the eyepiece: F_o and F_e thus coincide. The object is seen inverted.

A telescope magnifies because the final image it forms subtends a much greater angle at the eye than that subtended by the distant object viewed without the telescope. Fig. 15.13 shows that the longer the focal length of the objective, the larger is I_1, and so for greatest magnification the objective should have a long focal length and the eyepiece a short one (like any magnifying glass).

(ii) **Reflecting telescope.** The objective of a telescope must have a large diameter as well as a large focal length. This gives it good light-gathering power so that faint objects can be seen and also enables it to reveal detail.

The largest lens telescope has an objective of diameter 1 metre; a lens any larger than this would sag under its own weight. The biggest astronomical

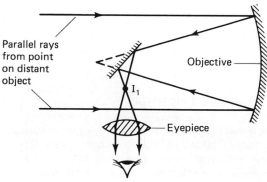

Fig. 15.14

telescopes use long-focus concave mirrors as objectives; they can be supported at the back, to prevent them from sagging and distorting. Fig. 15.14 shows how parallel rays from a distant point object are reflected at the objective and then intercepted by a small plane mirror before they form a real image I_1. This image is magnified by the eyepiece.

The mirror in the Mount Palomar telescope in California has a diameter of 5 metres.

15.9 Revision Questions and Problems

The Eye

1. Name the part of the eye (*a*) which controls how much light enters it, (*b*) on which the image is formed, (*c*) which changes the focal length of the lens.

2. Refraction of light in the eye occurs at

    A the lens only   **B** the iris   **C** the cornea only
    D the pupil   **E** both the cornea and the lens

3. A short-sighted person has a near point of 15 cm and a far point of 40 cm.
    (*a*) Can he see clearly an object at a distance of (i) 5 cm, (ii) 25 cm, (iii) 50 cm?
    (*b*) To see clearly an object at infinity, what kind of spectacle lenses does he need?

4. The near point of a long-sighted person is 50 cm from the eye.
    (*a*) Can he see clearly an object at (i) a distance of 20 cm, (ii) infinity?
    (*b*) To read a book held at a distance of 25 cm, will he need convex or concave spectacle lenses?

Optical Instruments

5. In Fig. 15.15(*a*) a camera is shown focused on an object. In Fig. 15.15(*b*) is it focused on a more distant object or a closer one? Explain your answer.

6. If the amount of light falling on the film in a camera is not to change when the exposure time is decreased, what other change must be made?

7. State two ways in which a camera is similar to the human eye and two ways in which it is different.

8. (*a*) In the diagram of the projector (Fig. 15.9), if the concave mirror has a focal length of 2 cm, how far must it be from the lamp to reflect the light as shown?
    (*b*) If a projector is moved farther away from the screen on which it was giving a sharp image of a slide, state (i) three changes that occur in the image, (ii) how the projection lens must be adjusted to re-focus the image.

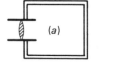

Fig. 15.15

9. (a) Three converging lenses are available having focal lengths of 4 cm, 40 cm and 4 m respectively. Which one would you choose as a magnifying glass?

(b) An object 2 cm high is viewed through a converging lens of focal length 8 cm. The object is 4 cm from the lens. By means of a ray diagram find the position, nature and magnification of the image.

10. The pair of lenses most suitable for a compound microscope is

   A Two concave lenses of focal lengths 4 cm and 2 cm

   B A convex lens of focal length 4 cm and a concave lens of focal length 2 cm

   C Two convex lenses of focal lengths 4 cm and 2 cm

   D Two convex lenses of focal lengths 100 cm and 4 cm

   E Two concave lenses of focal lengths 100 cm and 4 cm.

11. (a) How would the magnification of a telescope be affected by increasing the focal length of (i) the objective, (ii) the eyepiece?

(b) What is the effect in a telescope of increasing the diameter of the objective, if its focal length is kept the same?

(c) How does a reflecting telescope differ from a refracting telescope, and what is its main advantage?

Waves and Light

The idea of a wave is useful for dealing with a wide range of effects in physics involving, for instance, sound, light and radio transmission. A knowledge of wave behaviour is also important to engineers concerned with, for example, harbour or aircraft design.

Waves may be classified as *mechanical* or *electromagnetic*. Mechanical waves are produced by a disturbance (such as a vibrating body) in a material medium which then transmits them. Waves like these can be seen, felt or heard and include waves on a spring, water waves, waves on stretched strings (in musical instruments, for instance) and sound waves, both in air and in other materials.

Electromagnetic waves, as we will see in Unit 16.8, consist of a disturbance in the form of varying electric and magnetic forces. No medium is necessary and they travel more easily in a vacuum than in matter. Radio signals, light and X-rays are examples of this type.

The effects of mechanical and electromagnetic waves can be explained by the same general principles.

16.1 Progressive Transverse Waves

A *progressive* or travelling wave consists of a disturbance moving from a source to surrounding places, as a result of which energy is transferred from one point to another although there is no transfer of matter between the points. There are two types of progressive wave: *transverse*, now to be considered, and *longitudinal*, which we shall discuss in Unit 17.2.

In a transverse wave, the direction associated with the disturbance is at right angles to the direction of travel of the wave. You can send a transverse wave along a rope or a 'Slinky' spring by fixing one end and moving the other end rapidly from side to side as shown in Fig. 16.1(*a*) and (*b*). The disturbance generated by your hand is passed on from one part of the rope or coil of the spring to the next which performs the same motion, but at a slightly later time. The wave travels along the rope or spring, each part of which transmits it by vibrating to and fro transversely about its undisturbed position.

16.2 Describing Waves

(i) **Graphical representation.** A progressive transverse wave can be represented by a *displacement–distance* graph like that in Fig. 16.2. It shows

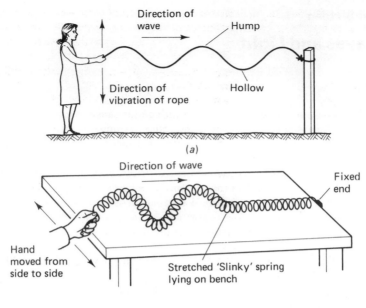

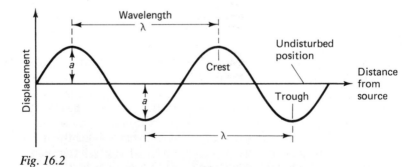

Fig. 16.1   (b)

the displacements from the undisturbed position, *at a certain time*, of the parts vibrating at different distances from the source in the transmitting medium (for example, a rope or spring). The graph helps to explain some of the terms used to describe waves.

Fig. 16.2

(ii) **Wavelength**, represented by the Greek letter λ (lambda), is the distance between successive crests.

(iii) **Frequency** f is the number of complete waves generated per second. If the end of a rope is jerked up and down twice in a second, two waves are produced in this time. The frequency of the wave is 2 vibrations per second or 2 *hertz* (written as 2 Hz, the hertz being the unit of frequency); so too is the frequency of jerking of the end of the rope. That is, the frequencies of the wave and its source are equal.

The frequency of a wave is also the number of crests passing a chosen point per second.

(iv) **Amplitude** *a* is the height of a crest or the depth of a trough measured from the undisturbed position of the rope or spring, or other medium that is carrying the wave. The energy carried by the wave depends on the square of the amplitude.

16.3 The Wave Equation

The faster the end of a rope or spring is waggled, the shorter is the wavelength of the wave produced: that is, the higher the frequency of a wave the smaller is its wavelength. There is a useful equation connecting *f*, λ and the speed of the wave which is true for all types of wave.

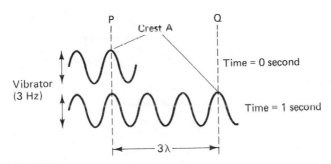

Fig. 16.3

Suppose waves of wavelength λ =20 cm travel on a long rope and three crests pass a certain point P every second. The frequency *f* is therefore 3 Hz. In Fig. 16.3, which represents this wave motion, if crest A is at P at a particular time then 1 second later it will be at Q, a distance from P of three wavelengths, that is, 3 ×20 cm =60 cm.

The speed *v* of the wave is thus 60 cm/s, obtained by multiplying the frequency (*f* =3 Hz) by the wavelength (λ =20 cm). Therefore

wave speed = frequency × wavelength

In symbols,

$$v = f\lambda$$

16.4 Water Waves and the Ripple Tank

The behaviour of progressive transverse waves can be studied using water waves in a ripple tank. This consists of a shallow transparent tray containing water, having a lamp above and a white screen below to receive the image of the waves (Fig. 16.4).

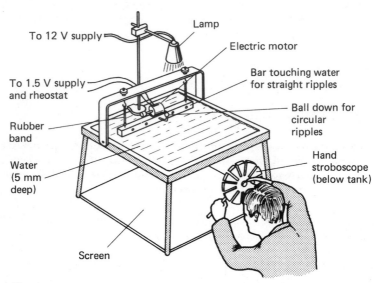

Fig. 16.4

Straight waves, as shown in the drawing, are generated by a bar which just touches the water and which is made to vibrate by an electric motor mounted on it. If the bar is raised and a small ball fitted to it so as to dip into the water, circular waves are obtained when the motor is switched on.

The waves are studied more easily if they are *apparently* stopped ('frozen') by viewing the screen through a stroboscope. This is a disc with equally spaced slits around its edge, which can be spun by hand; if the speed at which it spins is such that the waves have advanced one wavelength each time a slit passes your eye, they do not seem to be moving.

Some wave effects that can be investigated using a ripple tank are described below.

16.5 Reflection and Refraction of Water Waves

(i) **Reflection.** Water waves are reflected from an obstacle in their path according to the same laws of reflection that apply to light (see Unit 13.5), that

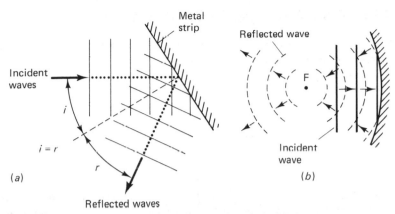

Fig. 16.5

is, the reflected waves bounce off the obstacle at the same angle at which the incident waves fall on it. The wave pattern obtained by allowing straight waves to be reflected from a straight metal strip standing upright in a ripple tank is shown in Fig. 16.5(*a*). The straight lines representing the waves are called *wavefronts* and can be regarded as the crests of the waves. Fig. 16.5(*b*) shows how straight waves are brought to a focus F when they are reflected from a concave surface.

(ii) **Refraction.** If a glass plate is placed in a ripple tank so that the water is about 1 mm deep over it but 5 mm elsewhere, the wavelength of continuous straight waves in the shallow region is found to be shorter than that of the waves in the deeper parts (Fig. 16.6(*a*)). Both sets of waves have the frequency of the vibrating bar and since $v = f\lambda$ then if λ has decreased so has v, since f is fixed. Hence *waves travel more slowly in shallow water*.

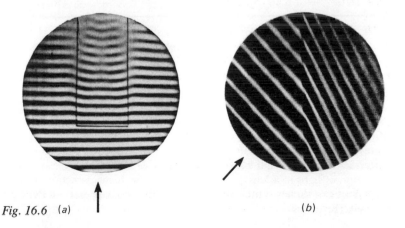

Fig. 16.6 (*a*)   (*b*)

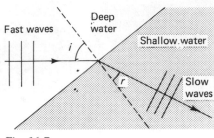

Fig. 16.7

When the plate is at an angle to the waves (Fig. 16.6(*b*)), their direction of travel in the shallow region is bent towards the normal (Fig. 16.7), that is, they are refracted. This refraction, like that of light, is due to a change of speed. To make this clear, consider three people A, B, C marching in line and in step, on a road that approaches a marsh obliquely (Fig. 16.8). On reaching the marsh, A is slowed first and takes shorter paces to keep in step with the others. The line therefore wheels round.

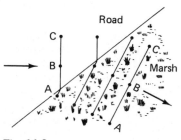

Fig. 16.8

Water waves, like light, are bent towards the normal when speed is lost. It can be shown that, in Fig. 16.7,

$$\frac{\sin i}{\sin r} = \frac{v_1}{v_2} = \frac{\lambda_1}{\lambda_2}$$

where v_1 and v_2 are the speeds of the fast and slow waves and λ_1 and λ_2 are the corresponding wavelengths.

Refraction of a straight water wave at a curved surface (corresponding to refraction of light at a lens) can be shown by the focusing action of a lens-shaped area of shallow water formed by putting a convex piece of Perspex in the tank (Fig. 16.9).

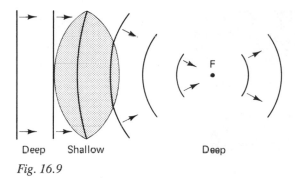

Deep   Shallow   Deep

Fig. 16.9

16.6 Diffraction and Interference of Water Waves

(i) **Diffraction.** In Fig. 16.10(*a*) and (*b*), straight water waves in a ripple tank are falling on gaps formed by obstacles. In (*a*) the gap width is about the same as the wavelength of the waves (1 cm); beyond the gap the waves that have passed through are circular and spread out in all directions. In (*b*) the gap is wide (10 cm) compared with the wavelength and the waves continue straight on; they spread to some extent, but less markedly.

The spreading of waves at the edges of obstacles is called *diffraction*.

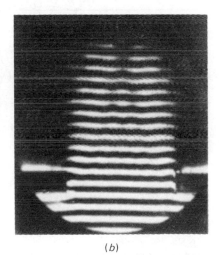

Fig. 16.10   (*a*)   (*b*)

(ii) **Interference.** If two small balls are fitted to the vibrating bar of the ripple tank in Fig. 16.4, both act as wave sources S_1 and S_2, and two sets of circular waves are obtained. If the area where the two sets cross is viewed through a stroboscope, a pattern like that in Fig. 16.11(*a*) is seen.

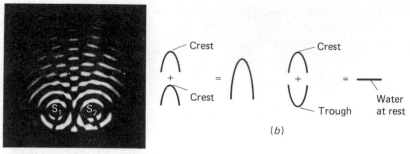

Fig. 16.11   (*a*)

At any point where a crest from $\dot{S}_1$ arrives at the same time as a crest from S_2, a bigger crest is formed and the waves are said to be *in phase*. At any point where a crest and a trough arrive together, they cancel out (if their amplitudes are equal); the waves are exactly *out of phase* (because they have travelled different distances from their sources S_1 and S_2) and the water is undisturbed (Fig. 16.11(*b*)). The dark 'spokes' radiating from S_1 and S_2 join such points.

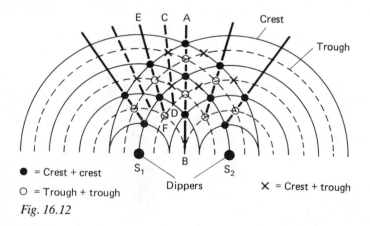

● = Crest + crest

○ = Trough + trough

Dippers

✕ = Crest + trough

Fig. 16.12

Interference or *superposition* is the combination of waves to give either a larger or a smaller wave. Fig. 16.12 shows how the pattern in Fig. 16.11(*a*) is formed. All points on AB are equidistant from S_1 and S_2 and since these vibrate in phase, the crests (or troughs) from S_1 arrive at the same time as crests (or troughs) from S_2. Hence along AB *reinforcement* occurs by superposition and a wave of double amplitude is obtained. Points on CD are half a wavelength nearer to S_1 than to S_2, that is, there is a path difference of half a wavelength. Therefore crests (or troughs) from S_1 arrive simultaneously with troughs (or crests) from S_2 and the waves *cancel*. Along EF the difference of the distances from S_1 and S_2 to any point is one wavelength, making EF a line of reinforcement.

If S_1 and S_2 are moved farther apart, the 'spokes' are closer together. Increasing the frequency of the vibrating sources (that is, reducing the wavelength) has the same effect.

16.7 Light Waves

Although we cannot see how light travels, we can demonstrate that it displays wave properties such as diffraction and interference.

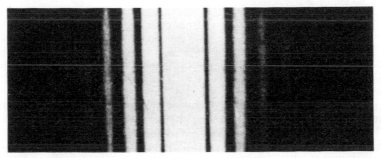

Fig. 16.13

(i) **Diffraction.** Diffraction occurs when light passes the edge of an object, but it is not easy to detect. Fig. 16.13 is the highly magnified diffraction pattern formed by light passing through a very narrow vertical slit (1/100 mm or less) and shows how light has spread into regions that would be in shadow if the rays always travelled exactly in straight lines. Diffraction at slits much wider than this is harder to observe. This suggests that light waves have very small wavelengths, since we saw that diffraction of water waves is most obvious at a gap when its width is comparable with the wavelength of the waves.

(ii) **Interference.** In the ripple tank experiment described in Unit 16.6(ii), a steady interference pattern is obtained because both sets of waves have the same frequency and wavelength and are exactly in phase when they leave the sources S_1 and S_2. They are said to be *coherent*. If we attempt to repeat the experiment using light waves we find it is impossible to obtain a steady interference pattern with two separate lamps; this is because most light sources emit light waves of many wavelengths, in short erratic bursts, each out of phase with the next. The two sets of waves are therefore not coherent.

These difficulties were overcome by Young in 1801 by an experiment in which he allowed light from *one lamp* in a darkened room to fall on two narrow parallel slits very close together (about 0.5 mm separation), as shown in the modern arrangement of Fig. 16.14. A pattern of equally spaced bright and dark bands, called *fringes*, is obtained on a screen (Fig. 16.15(*a*)). The waves leaving the slits are coherent since any phase change in the bursts of light from the lamp affects both sets of waves in the same way at the same time.

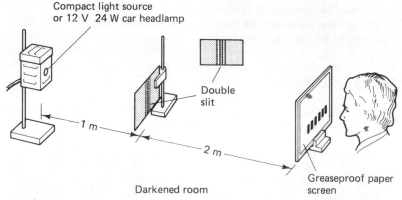

Fig. 16.14

The fringes can be explained by assuming that diffraction occurs at each slit and that interference occurs in the region where the two diffracted beams cross (Fig. 16.15(*b*)). At points on the screen where a 'crest' from one slit arrives at the same time as a 'crest' from the other, the waves are in phase and reinforce

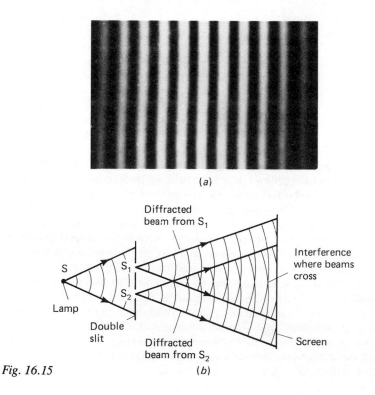

Fig. 16.15   (*b*)

each other, and there are bright bands. Dark bands occur where 'crests' and 'troughs' arrive simultaneously and the waves cancel. At points like these, therefore, we have: light + light = darkness. This makes sense only if we regard light as having a wave nature. Fig. 16.12, which we used to explain the water-wave interference pattern, is also a help when thinking about how light produces interference fringes.

The bright bands are coloured, except for the centre one which is white. If a piece of red celluloid (a filter—see Unit 14.10(i)—which only allows red light to pass) is placed in front of the lamp, the bright bands are red, while with a blue filter they are blue; the red bands are spaced farther apart than the blue ones are (Fig. 16.16(a)). You can check this by looking at the straight filament of a motor car headlamp (2 m away) through a double slit, held *close* to your eye, with the slits *parallel* to the filament and the appropriate filter inserted (Fig. 16.16(b)).

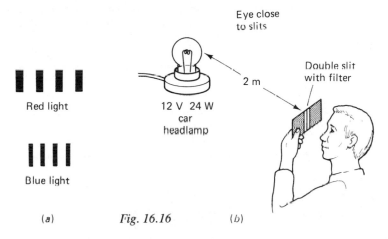

Red light

Blue light

Eye close to slits

2 m

Double slit with filter

12 V 24 W car headlamp

(a)   Fig. 16.16   (b)

(iii) **Colour and wavelength.** In the double slit experiment in Fig. 16.14, if we know the distance between the slits, the distance from the slits to the screen and the fringe separation (that is, the distance from the centre of one bright band to the centre of the next), we can find the wavelength of the light used. Red light, at one end of the spectrum of white light, has the longest wavelength, about 0.0007 mm (7×10^{-7} m = 0.7 μm); violet light, at the other end, has the shortest, about 0.0004 mm (4×10^{-7} m = 0.4 μm). Other colours have intermediate wavelengths.

Monochromatic light is light that is of one colour only and so of one wavelength.

(iv) **Diffraction grating.** A diffraction grating consists of a piece of glass or plastic with a large number of parallel lines marked on it. The lines scatter light and in effect are opaque. The thin clear strips between the lines transmit light and act as slits.

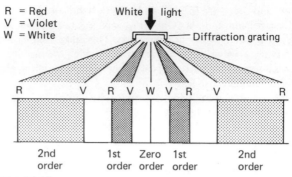

Fig. 16.17

When white light from a straight-filament lamp is viewed through a grating a number of spectra (plural of spectrum) are seen, each like that given by a prism. The spectra are said to be of various *orders*. A 'fine' grating with say 300 lines per mm gives the zero, first and second orders (Fig. 16.17), while a 'coarse' grating, with perhaps 100 lines per mm, gives more orders closer together. The 'coarser' the grating, the more the pattern resembles the two-slits one.

The slits are only a few wavelengths wide and when light falls on them diffraction occurs, causing cylindrical waves to spread out from each one. In certain directions the diffracted waves are in phase and if brought to a focus by a lens or the eye, they reinforce; in other directions they are out of phase to a greater or lesser extent and thus more or less cancel. That is, interference is observed.

16.8 Electromagnetic Waves

Light is one member of a large family of waves called the *electromagnetic spectrum* and shown in Fig. 16.18. While each is produced differently, all result from electrically charged particles (such as electrons, which we shall discuss in Unit 24.1) undergoing an energy change. For example, radio waves are created when electrons oscillate in an aerial. Although they differ greatly in their wavelengths and effects, all electromagnetic waves have the following properties in common:

1. They travel through space at 300 000 km/s (3×10^8 m/s), that is, with the speed of light.

2. They exhibit diffraction and interference as well as reflection and refraction.

3. They obey the equation $c = f\lambda$ where c is the speed of light, f is the frequency of the wave and λ is its wavelength. Since c is constant (for a given medium), it follows that the larger the frequency of a wave, the smaller is its wavelength.

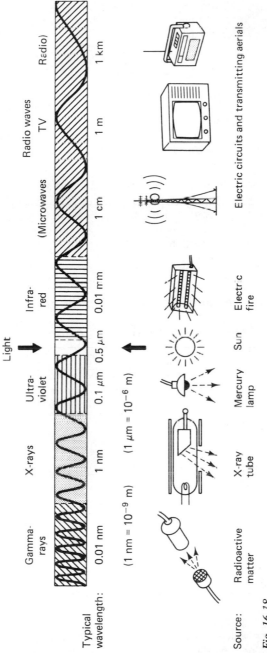

Fig. 16.18

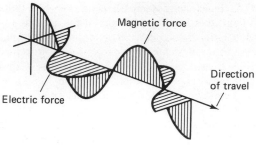

Fig. 16.19

4. Because of their electrical origin and ability to travel in a vacuum (for example, from the sun to the earth), they are regarded as progressive transverse waves consisting of a combination of travelling electric and magnetic forces, which vary in value and are directed at right angles to each other and to the direction of travel. Fig. 16.19 is a representation of an electromagnetic wave.

16.9 Infrared and Ultraviolet Radiation

(i) **Infrared radiation.** Infrared (i.r.) radiation, which cannot be seen, has wavelengths longer than those of visible light. Its presence in the radiation from the sun or from the filament of an electric lamp can be detected by the response of a phototransistor placed just beyond the red end of the spectrum formed (as explained in Unit 14.9(i)) by a prism (Fig. 16.20). Our bodies detect i.r. radiation (also sometimes called 'radiant heat' or 'heat radiation') by its heating effect.

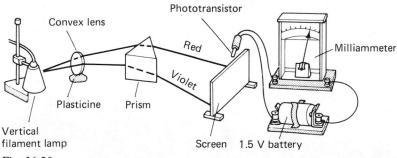

Fig. 16.20

Anything which is hot but not glowing (that is, below 500 °C) emits i.r. radiation alone. At about 500 °C a body becomes red-hot and emits both red light and i.r. radiation; the heating element of an electric fire is an example. At about 1000 °C things such as lamp filaments are white-hot and radiate both i.r. and white light, that is, all the colours of the spectrum.

Infrared radiation is also detected by special photographic films and pictures can be taken in the dark: the hot parts of an object appear white. Infrared lamps are used to dry the paint on cars during manufacture and in the treatment of muscular complaints. A keypad for the remote control of a television set contains a small infrared transmitter.

(ii) **Ultraviolet radiation.** Ultraviolet (u.v.) rays have shorter wavelengths than those of visible light. They can be detected just beyond the violet end of the spectrum of sunlight or the radiation of a filament lamp, using fluorescent paper; this absorbs energy from u.v. radiation and re-radiates it as visible light so that it can be seen to glow brightly.

Ultraviolet radiation also causes teeth, finger nails, fluorescent paints and clothes washed in some detergents to fluoresce. The shells of fresh eggs fluoresce with a reddish colour, while those of 'bad' eggs appear violet in u.v. radiation.

A u.v. lamp used for scientific or medical purposes contains mercury vapour and this emits u.v. radiation when an electric current passes through it. Fluorescent tubes also contain mercury vapour and their inner surfaces are coated with powders which radiate light when struck by u.v. radiation (see Unit 20.5(ii)).

16.10 Radio Waves

These have the longest wavelengths in the electromagnetic spectrum. They are radiated from *aerials* (antennae) and used to 'carry' sound, pictures and other information over long distances.

(i) **Long, medium and short waves** (2 km to 10 m) can bend (diffract) round obstacles and so can be received even if, say, a hill or a tower block is in their way (Fig. 16.21(a)). This allows them to be used for local radio broadcasts. They are also reflected by the layers of electrically charged particles in the upper atmosphere (the *ionosphere*), thus making long-distance reception possible (Fig. 16.21(b)).

(a)   (b)

Fig. 16.21 (a) Diffraction of radio waves, (b) reflection of radio waves

(ii) **VHF (very-high-frequency) and UHF (ultra-high-frequency) waves** have shorter wavelengths and need a clear, straight-line path to the receiver. Local radio and television use them. They pass through the ionosphere.

(iii) **Microwaves** (with wavelengths of a few cm) are used for radar and also for international (as well as national) telephone and television links. The international links are via *geostationary* communication satellites, which go round the equator at the same rate as the earth spins and so appear to be at rest. Signals are beamed by large dish aerials to the satellite where they are amplified and sent back to a dish aerial in another part of the world.

Microwaves are also used for cooking since like all electromagnetic waves they have a heating effect when absorbed.

16.11 X-rays and Gamma-rays

Both of these have wavelengths smaller than those of ultraviolet radiation. X-rays are produced when fast-moving electrons are stopped by matter and lose energy very rapidly. Gamma-rays are emitted by some radioactive materials when large energy changes occur within the nuclei of their atoms.

X-rays can penetrate solid objects and affect photographic film. Very penetrating X-rays are used in hospitals to kill cancer cells. They damage healthy cells as well, so the X-ray tube must be carefully shielded with lead. Less penetrating X-rays have longer wavelengths and penetrate flesh but not bone: they are used in dental X-ray photography. In industry they are used to inspect welded joints and castings for faults.

Gamma-rays are more penetrating and dangerous than X-rays and will be studied in Unit 23.2.

16.12 Revision Questions and Problems

Waves: Wave Equation
1. (*a*) Explain the following terms: progressive transverse wave, wavelength, frequency, amplitude.
   (*b*) State the equation connecting the speed, frequency and wavelength of a wave.

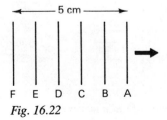

Fig. 16.22

2. The lines in Fig. 16.22 are crests of straight waves.
   (a) What is the wavelength of the waves?
   (b) If crest A occupied 5 seconds ago the position now occupied by F, what is the frequency of the ripples?
   (c) What is the speed of the ripples?

3. A vibrator of frequency 10 Hz produces waves with crests 5 mm apart. If the frequency is reduced to 5 Hz, what is (a) the wave speed, (b) the distance between crests?

Reflection and Refraction
4. A straight ripple ABC is shown in Fig. 16.23 moving towards a wall XY. Draw one diagram to show the position of the ripple when B reaches the wall and another to show its position when C reaches it. On each diagram mark the angles which are 30°.

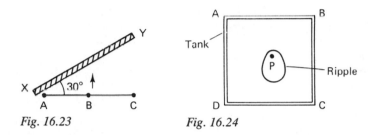

Fig. 16.23   Fig. 16.24

5. One side of a ripple tank ABCD is raised slightly (Fig. 16.24), and a ripple is started at P by a finger. After a second the shape of the ripple is as shown.
   (a) Why is it not circular?
   (b) Which side of the tank has been raised?

6. In Fig. 16.7 the 'fast' waves have a wavelength of 6 cm and a speed of 30 cm/s. The 'slow' waves have a speed of 20 cm/s and the angle r is 30°. Find (a) the wavelength of the 'slow' waves and (b) angle i. (sin 30 = 0.5).

Diffraction and Interference
7. (a) When straight waves in a ripple tank pass through a narrow gap what happens? What is the effect called?
   (b) What happens if the gap is widened?

8. What happens when two sets of identical waves cross if they are (a) in phase, (b) out of phase? What name is given to the effect?

Fig. 16.25   Fig. 16.26

9. Copy Fig. 16.25 and show on it what happens to the waves as they pass through the gap when the water is much shallower on the right-hand side than on the left.

10. The wave pattern in a ripple tank 1 second after the vibrator was started is shown in Fig. 16.26. The dark lines represent crests.

    (*a*) What is represented at A at this instant?

    (*b*) Estimate (i) the wavelength, (ii) the speed of the waves and (iii) the frequency of the vibrator.

    (*c*) Explain how the waves combine at B and C.

Light Waves

11. (*a*) Why is the diffraction of light not easy to detect?

    (*b*) Why is it not possible to produce a steady interference pattern using two light sources?

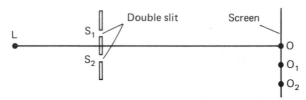

Fig. 16.27

12. In Fig. 16.27, L is a source of light, wavelength λ, S_1S_2 a double slit and O, O_1 and O_2 are points on a screen.

    (*a*) If the central bright band is formed at O, how do the distances S_1O and S_2O compare?

    (*b*) If the first dark band next to the central bright band is formed at O_1, how do S_1O_1 and S_2O_1 compare?

    (*c*) If the first bright band occurs at O_2 next to the first dark band, how do S_1O_2 and S_2O_2 compare?

13. In the double-slit experiment using monochromatic light, how would the fringe pattern be affected if

    (*a*) the separation of the slits was increased?

    (*b*) the screen was moved farther away?

    (*c*) light of longer wavelength was used?

    (*d*) white light was used instead of monochromatic light?

14. Give the approximate wavelengths in micrometres (μm) of (*a*) red light, (*b*) violet light.

Electromagnetic Waves

15. Name four properties common to all electromagnetic waves.

16. List the members of the electromagnetic spectrum in order of increasing wavelength.

17. Name one type of electromagnetic radiation in each case which (*a*) causes sun-tan, (*b*) passes through a thin sheet of lead, (*c*) is used for satellite communication, (*d*) is used for the remote control of a television receiver.

18. Explain why a long- or medium-wave radio signal can be received (a) at the other side of a hill near the transmitting aerial, (b) on the other side of the earth.

19. A VHF radio station transmits on a frequency of 100 MHz (1 MHz = 10^6 Hz). If the speed of radio waves is 3×10^8 m/s, (a) what is the wavelength of the waves? (b) how long does the transmission take to travel 60 km?

Unit Seventeen

Sound

17.1 About Sound

Sources of sound such as a drum, a guitar and the human voice have some part that vibrates. The sound travels through the air to our ears and we hear it. We can show that the air is necessary by pumping out the air from a glass jar containing a ringing electric bell (Fig. 17.1); the sound disappears though the striker can still be seen hitting the gong. Evidently sound cannot travel in a vacuum, as light can.

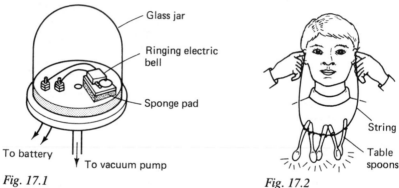

Fig. 17.1

Fig. 17.2

Other materials beside air, including solids and liquids, transmit sound. 'Cathedral chimes' may be heard if you jingle together some spoons tied to a piece of string with its ends in your ears (Fig. 17.2). Not only does string (a solid) transmit sound but it does so better than air does.

Sound also gives interference and diffraction effects, as we will see in this Unit. Because of these and other properties, we believe it is a form of energy (a view confirmed by the damage from supersonic booms) which travels as a progressive wave; unlike electromagnetic waves, however, sound waves are of a type called *longitudinal*.

17.2 Progressive Longitudinal Waves

(i) **Waves on a spring.** In a longitudinal wave the particles of the transmitting medium vibrate *in the same direction* as that in which the wave is travelling, not

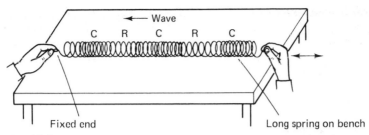

Fig. 17.3

at right angles to it as in a transverse wave. A progressive longitudinal wave can be sent along a spring stretched out on the bench with one end fixed, if the free end is repeatedly pushed and pulled sharply. *Compressions* C (where the coils are closer together) and *rarefactions* R (where the coils are farther apart) travel along the spring (Fig. 17.3); the speed at which they travel increases if the spring is stretched further, because the forces between the coils are then greater.

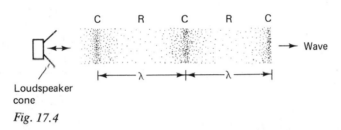

Fig. 17.4

(ii) **Sound waves.** A sound wave, produced for example by a loudspeaker, consists of a train of compressions and rarefactions in the air (Fig. 17.4). The speaker contains a cone, which is made to vibrate in and out by an electric current. When the cone moves out the air in front is compressed; when it moves inwards the air is rarefied (becomes 'thinner'). The wave progresses through the air but the air as a whole does not move, although the air particles vibrate backwards and forwards a little as it passes. When the compressions and rarefactions enter your ear they cause small, rapid pressure changes on the ear drum, and you experience the sensation of sound. A sound wave is a progressive longitudinal pressure wave.

The number of compressions produced per second is the frequency f of the sound wave (and equals the frequency of the vibrating cone); the distance between successive compressions is the wavelength λ. As for progressive transverse waves, the speed $v = f\lambda$.

Human beings hear only sounds that have frequencies from about 20 Hz to 20 000 Hz (20 kHz). These are the *limits of audibility*; the upper limit decreases with age.

(iii) **Graphical representation.** A *displacement–distance* graph can also be drawn to represent a progressive longitudinal wave. It shows the displacement from their undisturbed position, *at a certain time*, of vibrating particles at different distances from the source in the transmitting medium (such as a spring or the air).

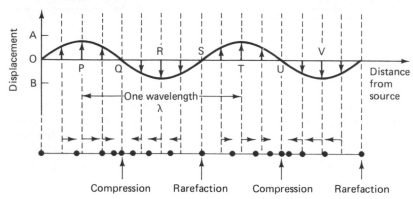

Fig. 17.5

Remember, however, that even though the graph shows displacements at right angles to the distance axis, they are in fact *in the line of travel* of the sound wave—that is, that the graph represents a longitudinal displacement as if it were transverse (Fig. 17.5).

17.3 Reflection and Refraction

(i) **Reflection and echoes.** Sound waves are reflected well from hard, flat surfaces such as walls or cliffs and obey the same laws of reflection as light. The reflected sound forms an *echo*.

If the reflecting surface is nearer than 15 m, the echo joins up with the original sound which then seems to be prolonged. This is called *reverberation*. Some reverberation is desirable in a concert hall to stop it sounding 'dead'; too much causes 'confusion', however. In modern concert halls, walls and seats are covered with sound-absorbing material to reduce reverberation to an acceptable level.

(ii) **Refraction.** At night distant sounds, such as traffic, are often louder than during the day due to the refraction of sound waves. The reason is that after sunset air near the ground cools down more than air above it and since sound travels more slowly in cold air (as we shall see in Unit 17.4), the waves from the source of sound are refracted back towards the ground (Fig. 17.6(*a*)). During the day, on the other hand, the upper air is usually cooler than that near the ground and sounds tend to travel upwards (Fig. 17.6(*b*)).

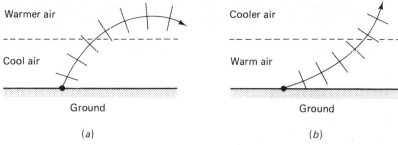

Fig. 17.6 (a) Night, (b) day

17.4 Speed of Sound

The speed of sound depends on the material through which it is passing, being greater in solids than in liquids or gases. Some values are given in the table below:

Material	Air (0 °C)	Water	Concrete	Steel
Speed (m/s)	330	1400	5000	6000

In air, *the speed increases with temperature* and at high altitudes, where the temperature is lower, it is less than at sea level. Changes of atmospheric pressure do not affect it.

An estimate of the speed of sound can be made directly if you stand about 100 m from a high wall and clap your hands. Echoes are produced. If you adjust your clapping rate so that each clap coincides with the echo of the previous one, the sound must then have travelled to the wall and back in the time (interval) between two claps. By timing 30 intervals with a stopwatch, the time t of one interval can be found more accurately. If you know the distance d to the wall, you can obtain a rough value from

$$\text{speed of sound} = \frac{2d}{t}$$

17.5 Diffraction and Interference

(i) **Diffraction.** Audible sounds have wavelengths from about 1.5 cm (frequency 20 kHz) up to 15 m (frequency 20 Hz) and so suffer diffraction by objects of similar size, such as a doorway 1 m wide. This explains why we can hear sound round corners.

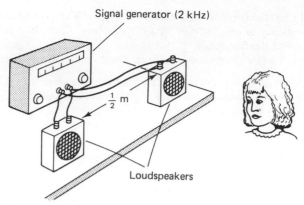

Fig. 17.7

(ii) **Interference.** In Fig. 17.7 sound waves of the same frequency from two loudspeakers (supplied by one signal generator) produce a steady interference pattern. As you walk past the speakers you can hear the resulting variations in the loudness of the sound, due to the waves reinforcing and cancelling one another.

17.6 Ultrasonics

Sound waves with frequencies above 20 kHz are called *ultrasonic* waves. They are emitted by bats, which can judge the distance of an object from the time taken by the reflected wave to return.

In the ship-borne echo-sounding system called *sonar*, ultrasonic waves are used to measure the depth of the sea and to detect shoals of fish. In medicine they are used to study the development of the foetus during pregnancy, and in industry to reveal flaws in welded joints. Another industrial use depends on the fact that a slurry of abrasive particles agitated at ultrasonic frequencies will wear away even a very hard surface, and can be used to cut holes of any shape or size in materials such as glass or steel.

17.7 Musical Notes

Irregular vibrations cause *noise* (discussed in Unit 17.11); regular vibrations such as those of the instruments of an orchestra produce *musical notes*. A note has three properties—pitch, loudness and quality.

(i) **Pitch and frequency.** The pitch of a note depends on the frequency of the sound wave reaching the ear, that is, on the frequency of the source of sound. A high-pitched note has a high frequency and a short wavelength. The frequency of middle C is 256 vibrations per second or 256 Hz and that of upper

C is 512 Hz: the two notes are an octave apart. This is true of any two notes if the frequency of one is twice that of the other. Pitch, like colour in light, depends on the frequency.

Notes of known frequency can be produced in the laboratory in two ways.

1. When a signal generator supplies alternating electric current (a.c.) to a loudspeaker, the cone of the speaker vibrates at the frequency of the a.c.; the frequency, which can be varied, is read off a scale on the generator.

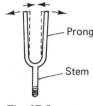

Fig. 17.8

2. Alternatively, a set of tuning forks with frequencies marked on them can be used. A tuning fork (Fig. 17.8) has two steel prongs which vibrate when struck; the prongs move in and out together, generating compressions and rarefactions.

(ii) **Loudness and amplitude.** A note becomes louder if the amount of sound energy entering our ears each second increases, which happens when the source vibrates with a larger amplitude. If a violin string is bowed more strongly, its amplitude of vibration increases; so does that of the resulting sound wave and the note heard becomes louder because more energy is being used to produce it.

(iii) **Quality and overtones.** The same note sounds different when it is played on different instruments—a flute and a piano, for instance. We say the notes differ in *quality* or *timbre*. The difference arises because no instruments (except a tuning fork and a signal generator) emit a 'pure' note, that is, a note of one frequency only. A musical note consists of a main or *fundamental* frequency mixed with others, called *overtones*, which are usually weaker and have frequencies that are exact multiples of the fundamental; for instance, overtones of 256 Hz (middle C) are 512 Hz, 768 Hz and so on. The number and strength of the overtones decides the quality of a note. A note played on a violin has more and stronger higher overtones than the same note played on a piano.

(iv) **Waveforms.** The waveform of a note played near a microphone connected to an oscilloscope (this instrument will be described in Unit 24.2) can be displayed on its screen. Waveforms of the same note on three instruments are shown in Fig. 17.9. Their different shapes show that while they have the same fundamental frequency, their quality differs. The 'pure' note of

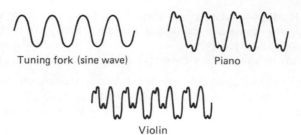

Tuning fork (sine wave)   Piano

Violin

Fig. 17.9

a tuning fork has a sine waveform and is the simplest kind of sound wave. (Notice that although the waveform on the oscilloscope screen is transverse it represents a longitudinal sound wave.)

17.8 Beats

When two notes of almost equal pitch are sounded together, the loudness rises and falls regularly and *beats* are said to be heard. The effect may be demonstrated with two signal generators each connected to a loudspeaker. Alternatively, two tuning forks of the same frequency can be used, one with a little Plasticine on one prong to lower its frequency slightly; they are struck at the same time and the stems pressed on the bench.

It can be shown that if f_1 and f_2 are the frequencies of the two notes, the number of beats per second (the *beat frequency f*) is $f_1 - f_2$; clearly, f decreases as f_1 and f_2 get closer together.

Beats are due to interference, and offer more evidence for the wave nature of sound.

17.9 Resonance

All objects have a natural frequency of vibration, and such a vibration can be first started and then increased by another object vibrating at the same frequency. This effect is called *resonance*. For example, when the heavy pendulum X in Fig. 17.10 is set swinging, it forces all the light ones to swing at the same frequency (that is, it sets up *forced vibrations*) but the pendulum D, which has the same length as X, swings with a much larger amplitude than the others, that is, D resonates with X.

> *Resonance occurs when a system is forced to vibrate*
> *at its natural frequency because it receives vibrations*
> *from another system vibrating at the same frequency.*

If a large structure such as a suspension bridge starts vibrating at its natural frequency the result can be disastrous. The Tacoma Narrows Bridge, USA,

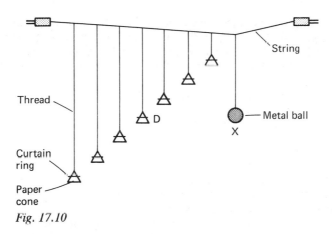

Fig. 17.10

collapsed in 1940 because a cross wind of just the 'right' speed caused resonant vibrations. Models of new bridges are now tested in wind tunnels to check that their natural frequencies are not dangerous.

Resonance is important to designers of musical instruments in which a column of air is made to vibrate in a tube (see Unit 17.10(ii)).

Certain electrical circuits have a natural frequency of vibration for electric currents and are used as *oscillators*. When used as *tuning circuits* in a radio (see Unit 24.15) they select only signals in the receiving aerial of the same frequency as their natural frequency. This is an example of electrical resonance.

17.10 Musical Instruments and Standing Waves

(i) **String instruments.** In a string instrument such as a guitar, the 'string' is a tightly stretched wire or length of gut. When it is plucked it vibrates and the frequency (pitch) of the note produced depends on its

1. *length*—short strings emit high notes and halving the length doubles the frequency,
2. *mass per unit length*—thin strings give high notes, and
3. *tension*—tight wires produce high notes.

(ii) **Wind instruments.** In these, musical notes are produced by vibrating columns of air. In an organ, for example, the vibration is started by a jet of air hitting a sharp edge and making the air columns vibrate over a range of frequencies. Those that equal the natural frequencies of the air column cause resonance and produce a loud note; the shorter the air column, the higher the pitch of the note produced.

(iii) **Standing (stationary) waves.** In both string and wind instruments progressive waves travel outwards in opposite directions from the point where the vibration was started; the waves are transverse in string and longitudinal in wind instruments. When they reach the ends of the string or pipe they are reflected back inwards. Interference occurs between the outwards and inwards waves and a *standing wave* is produced. In this, certain points called *nodes* (N) are always at rest, while midway between each pair of nodes is a point that vibrates continuously with maximum amplitude; these points are called *antinodes* (A).

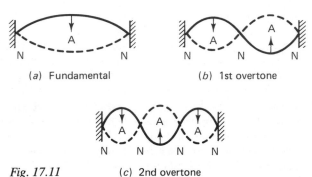

(*a*) Fundamental   (*b*) 1st overtone

Fig. 17.11   (*c*) 2nd overtone

Various standing wave patterns can be produced. For example, if there is a node at each end of a string and just one antinode between them, the standing wave has one loop and the fundamental note is emitted (Fig. 17.11(*a*)). If there is more than one loop, overtones are produced (Fig. 17.11(*b*) and (*c*)). Several notes may be emitted at the same time depending on where the vibration is started and this decides the quality of the note. Standing waves on a vibrating string or rubber cord may be viewed using a stroboscope to 'freeze' the patterns (the apparatus is shown in Fig. 17.12) or, more simply, on a 'Slinky' spring by generating progressive waves at each end simultaneously, so that they travel in opposite directions.

In a string or air column in a musical instrument the standing waves cause

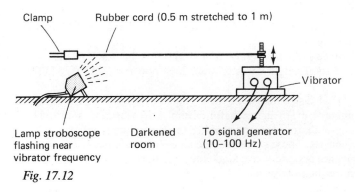

Fig. 17.12

progressive *longitudinal* waves of the same frequency to travel from the instrument into the surrounding air.

17.11 Noise

Unwanted sounds are called *noises*, and often consist of random, constantly changing frequencies caused by irregular vibrations. High-pitched noises are usually more annoying than low-pitched ones and are also more likely to damage the ears. Some of the main noise 'polluters' are aircraft, motor vehicles, greatly amplified music and many types of machinery, including certain domestic appliances. Unwanted noise can sometimes be reduced or eliminated at the design stage; quieter engines and better exhaust systems have been developed; well-balanced rotating shafts in machinery cause less vibration. Car engines are often mounted on metal brackets via rubber blocks which absorb vibrations and do not pass them on to the car body.

In the home, it can also help to use sound insulating materials, such as carpets and curtains, and to double-glaze windows. The farther away the noise originates the weaker it is, so distance is a natural barrier, as are trees planted between houses and a noisy road. Tractor drivers, factory workers, pneumatic drill operators and others exposed regularly to noise have often to wear ear protectors to prevent hearing damage, tiredness and loss of concentration.

Noise levels are measured in *decibels* (dB) by a noise meter. The sound level the average human ear can just detect, called the *threshold of hearing*, is taken as 0 dB. The level of normal conversation is about 60 dB, that of a jet plane overhead is 100 dB, and the threshold of pain (a term which explains itself) is 120 dB. For some sources of noise, including aircraft, maximum limits have been set that can be enforced by law.

17.12 Revision Questions and Problems

Sound Waves

1. How does a transverse wave differ from a longitudinal one? Which type of wave motion is sound?

2. What properties of sound suggest that it is a wave motion? Why can sound be heard round corners?

3. (*a*) Explain the following: (i) echo, (ii) reverberation.
   (*b*) Why does distant traffic often sound louder and nearer at night?

Speed of Sound

4. (*a*) What is the equation connecting the speed v of a sound wave with its frequency f and its wavelength λ?
   (*b*) If the speed of sound is 330 m/s, what is the wavelength of a note of frequency (i) 330 Hz, (ii) 165 Hz?
   (*c*) What happens to the speed of sound in air (i) if the temperature falls, (ii) if the air pressure falls?

5. A rocket is seen to burst in the sky and the bang is heard 10 seconds later. If the speed of sound is 330 m/s, how far away is the exploding rocket?

6. In a 110 m race, the time-keeper stands near the finishing tape and starts his stopwatch on hearing the bang from the starting pistol.
   (*a*) When should he have started his stopwatch? Explain your answer.
   (*b*) Calculate the error in his timing assuming he makes no further errors. (Speed of sound = 330 m/s.)

7. If the speed of sound in sea-water is 1500 m/s, calculate (*a*) the wavelength in sea-water of a sound of frequency 3000 Hz, (*b*) the depth of the sea-bed if a sound pulse produced by an echo sounder in a ship gives an echo after 0.6 s.

8. If 5 seconds elapse between a lightning flash and the clap of thunder, how far away is the storm? (Speed of sound = 330 m/s.)

9. (*a*) A girl stands 160 m away from a high wall and claps her hands at a steady rate so that each clap coincides with the echo of the one before. If she makes 60 claps in 1 minute, what is the speed of sound?
   (*b*) If she moves 40 m closer to the wall she finds the clapping rate has to be 80 per minute. What value do these measurements give for the speed of sound?
   (*c*) If she moves again and finds the clapping rate becomes 30 per minute, how far is she from the wall if the speed of sound is the value you found in (*a*)?

Musical Notes

10. (*a*) On what does (i) the loudness, (ii) the pitch of a sound depend?
    (*b*) Why does middle C on the piano sound different from the same note on the violin?

11. Draw the waveform of (*a*) a loud, low-pitched note and (*b*) a soft, high-pitched note.

12. What happens to the pitch of a note from a guitar string if (*a*) the length is halved, (*b*) the string is tightened?

13. What happens to the pitch of a note from a trombone if the tube length is increased?

14. How is a standing wave produced? How does it differ from a progressive wave?

15. (*a*) State four major sources of noise today.
    (*b*) Name some possible effects of noise on human beings.
    (*c*) List ways in which noise 'pollution' can be controlled or reduced.

Part Five

Electricity and Magnetism

Unit Eighteen

Electric Charge and Current

18.1 About Electric Charges

(i) **Static electricity.** A nylon garment often crackles when it is taken off. We say it has become 'charged with static electricity'; the crackles are caused by tiny electric sparks which can be seen in the dark. Pens and combs made of certain plastics become charged when rubbed on the sleeve and can then attract scraps of paper.

Sparks from static electricity can be dangerous when flammable vapour is present. For example, an aircraft in flight may become charged by 'rubbing' the air. Aircraft tyres are therefore made of conducting rubber, which lets the charge pass harmlessly to earth on landing. Otherwise an explosion could be 'sparked off' when the aircraft refuels.

A flash of lightning is nature's most spectacular static electricity effect.

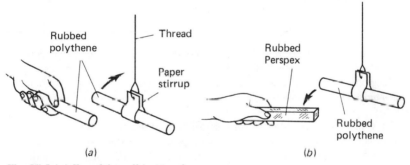

Fig. 18.1 (a) Repulsion, (b) attraction

(ii) **Positive and negative charges.** When a rod of polythene is rubbed with a cloth it becomes charged. If it is hung up and another rubbed polythene rod is brought near, the two rods can be seen to repel each other (Fig. 18.1(a)). But if a rubbed Perspex (or cellulose acetate) strip approaches the polythene rod, the two attract each other instead (Fig. 18.1(b)).

This suggests that there are two kinds of electric charge. That on Perspex (and cellulose acetate) is taken as *positive* (+) and that on polythene as *negative* (−). Experiments like these also show that:

1. *like charges* (positive and positive, or negative and negative) *repel* each other;

2. *unlike charges* (positive and negative) *attract* each other;

3. *the closer the charges are, the greater is the force between them*, that is, the force increases as the distance decreases, and
4. *the larger the charges, the greater the force.*

18.2 Charged Objects

(i) **Model of the atom.** There is evidence (see Unit 23.5) that we can picture an atom as made up of a small central nucleus containing positively charged particles called *protons*, surrounded by an equal number of negatively charged *electrons*. The charges on a proton and an electron are equal in size although opposite in sign, and so an atom as a whole is normally electrically neutral, that is, it has no net charge.

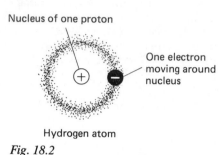

Fig. 18.2

Hydrogen is the simplest atom: it has one proton and one electron (Fig. 18.2). A copper atom has 29 protons in the nucleus and 29 surrounding electrons. Every nucleus, except that of hydrogen, also contains uncharged particles called *neutrons*.

(ii) **Charging by rubbing.** Using this picture of the atom, we can explain the production of charges by rubbing by supposing that electrons are transferred from one material to the other. For example, when Perspex is rubbed with a cloth, electrons go from the Perspex to the cloth, leaving the Perspex short of electrons, that is, positively charged. The cloth now has more electrons than protons and becomes negatively charged (Fig. 18.3(a)). Note that it is electrons that move; the protons remain in the nucleus.

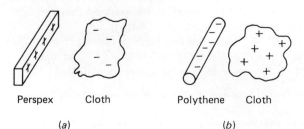

Fig. 18.3   (a)   (b)

Polythene does not lose electrons as easily as Perspex does; when it is rubbed with a cloth, the cloth loses electrons to the polythene. The polythene is then left with a negative charge and the cloth with a positive one (Fig. 18.3(*b*)).

(iii) **Insulators and conductors.** In an *insulator* all electrons are bound firmly to their atoms; you can charge an insulator by rubbing it, because the charge produced cannot move from the area that is rubbed, that is, the electric charge is static. In a conductor, on the other hand, some outer electrons can move from atom to atom, that is, there are 'free' electrons. You can charge a conductor only if you hold it in an insulating handle; otherwise, the charge passes to earth via your body.

Plastics such as polythene, cellulose acetate, Perspex and nylon are good insulators. All metals and carbon are good conductors. In between are materials that are both poor conductors and (because they conduct to some extent) poor insulators: examples are wood, paper, cotton, the human body, the earth. Water is a conductor; if there were no water in materials like wood and on the surface of, for example, glass, these would be good insulators. Dry air insulates well.

(iv) **Quantity of charge.** The same amount of charge is carried by every electron, so the more electrons an object loses or gains (by rubbing, for example) the greater is its positive or negative charge.

Charge is measured in *coulombs* (C), 1 coulomb being the charge on about 6 million million million (6×10^{18}) electrons. For most purposes the coulomb is too large a unit, and the microcoulomb (μC: one-millionth of a coulomb) is used: $1 \ \mu C = 10^{-6} \ C$.

The negative charge on a polythene rod charged by rubbing is extremely small, perhaps of the order of a few ten-thousandths of a microcoulomb, or about $10^{-4} \ \mu C$.

(v) **Some uses of static electricity.** The electrostatic precipitation of flue-ash from coal-fired power stations is a vital factor in the reduction of pollution. The ash particles obtain a charge from charged wires as they rise up the chimney and are then attracted to oppositely charged metal plates. The plates are shaken, causing the ash to fall to the bottom of the chimney.

Office copying machines depend on the attraction of charged powder particles to a metal drum that carries a pattern of charge that is the same as the pattern of the desired image.

Paint droplets become charged by friction when they are sprayed; if the object to be painted, such as a car body, is given a charge of opposite sign the paint is attracted to the object and covers it without wastage.

18.3 Gold-leaf Electroscope

(i) **Description.** A gold-leaf electroscope is useful for investigating charges. It consists of a metal cap on a metal rod, at the foot of which is a metal plate

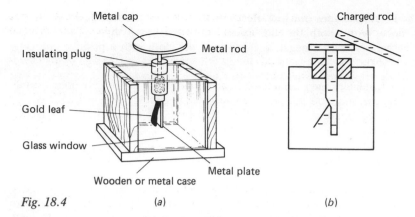

Metal cap

Insulating plug

Metal rod

Charged rod

Gold leaf

Glass window

Metal plate

Wooden or metal case

Fig. 18.4   (a)   (b)

having a leaf of gold foil attached (Fig. 18.4(*a*)). The rod is held by an insulating plastic plug in a case that protects the leaf from draughts.

(ii) **Detecting a charge.** If a charged object, such as a rubbed polythene rod, is drawn across the cap at the top of the electroscope, so as to make good contact with it, some of the charge passes to the leaf and metal plate at the bottom. The leaf rises, due to the charges on the plate and leaf repelling each other (since they have the same sign—negative when a polythene rod is used, Fig. 18.4(*b*)); the leaf stays up when the charged rod is removed. The electroscope is said to have been charged *by contact*.

(iii) **Finding the sign of a charge.** A charged electroscope can be used to find whether the charge on an object is positive or negative. Suppose the electroscope is negatively charged (Fig. 18.5(*a*)), that is, the cap, plate and leaf have more electrons than normal.

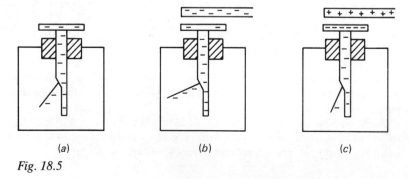

(a)   (b)   (c)

Fig. 18.5

If a negatively charged object is brought near the cap (Fig. 18.5(*b*)), free electrons are repelled from the cap into the plate and leaf. The repulsion between plate and leaf increases, and the leaf rises farther.

If a positively charged object approaches the cap (Fig. 18.5(c)), free electrons in the plate and leaf are attracted up to the cap and the leaf falls.

We can conclude from this that *if the leaf rises more, the sign of the charge being tested is the same as the charge on the electroscope*, but it does not always follow that it is of opposite sign if the leaf falls. An uncharged object has the same effect, as you can show by holding your hand near the cap of a charged electroscope (for a reason to be considered shortly, in Unit 18.4). The sure test is first to give the electroscope a charge of a sign which makes the leaf rise farther when the charged object is brought near the cap. The charged object then has the *same* sign as the electroscope.

(iv) **Insulators and conductors.** When items made of different materials (such as a piece of paper, a copper wire, a plastic pen, your finger, a piece of wood, a glass rod) are held in contact with the cap of a charged electroscope, the behaviour of the leaf enables insulators and conductors to be identified.

If the leaf falls rapidly, the material is a good conductor (free electrons pass easily to or from the electroscope through your body to the earth). A slow fall indicates a poor conductor; no fall means the material is a good insulator.

18.4   Electrostatic Induction

(i) **Charging by induction.** This may be shown by bringing a negatively charged polythene rod near to an insulated metal sphere X which is touching a similar sphere Y (Fig. 18.6(a)). Free electrons in the spheres are repelled to the far side of Y.

If X and Y are now separated, with the charged rod still in position, X is left with a positive charge (deficient of electrons) and Y with a negative charge (excess of electrons) (Fig. 18.6(b)). The signs of the charges can be tested by

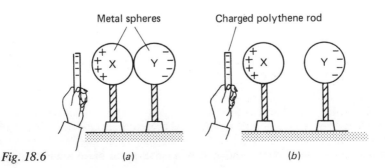

Metal spheres   Charged polythene rod

Fig. 18.6   (a)   (b)

removing the charged rod, and taking X up to the cap of a positively charged electroscope and Y to a negatively charged one. In both cases the leaf should rise farther.

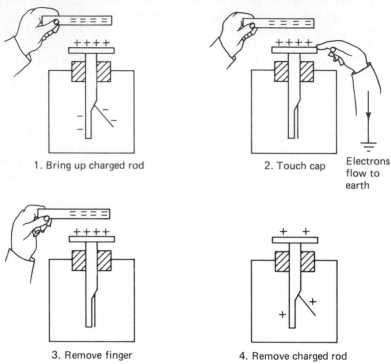

1. Bring up charged rod

2. Touch cap   Electrons flow to earth

3. Remove finger

4. Remove charged rod

Fig. 18.7

(ii) **Charging an electroscope by induction.** An electroscope can be charged more reliably by induction than by contact. The process is shown in Fig. 18.7, using a negatively charged polythene rod (the rod used must carry a charge of opposite sign to that required on the electroscope). When the cap is 'earthed' by touching it with the finger, electrons flow from the electroscope to earth through the body. Removal of the negatively charged rod leaves the electroscope with a positive charge.

To charge the electroscope negatively by induction a positively charged Perspex rod is used; in this case earthing the electroscope causes electrons to flow to the electroscope from earth.

(iii) **Attraction of uncharged objects.** An object with zero net charge (that is, an uncharged object) can be attracted by a charged object near it, as a result of electrostatic induction.

For example, Fig. 18.8(*a*) shows how a small piece of aluminium foil is

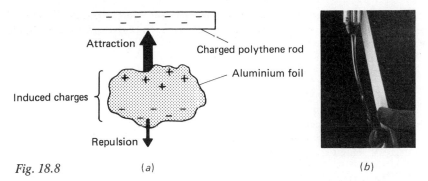

Fig. 18.8   (a)   (b)

attracted to a negatively charged polythene rod held just above it. The rod
pushes free electrons to the bottom of the foil (aluminium is a conductor),
leaving the top of the foil short of electrons (that is, with a net positive charge)
and the bottom negatively charged. Since the top of the foil is nearer to the rod
than the bottom is, the force of attraction between the unlike charges on the
rod and the top of the foil is greater than the force of repulsion between the like
charges on the rod and the bottom of the foil. The foil is therefore pulled to the
rod.

A small scrap of paper, although an insulator, is also attracted by a charged
rod. There are no free electrons in the paper but the charged rod pulls the
electrons of the atoms in the paper towards it slightly (by electrostatic
induction), so distorting the atoms. If a negatively charged polythene rod is
used, the paper behaves as if it had a positively charged top and a negative
charge at the bottom (it is said to be *polarized*).

Fig. 18.8(*b*) shows a slow, uncharged stream of water attracted by a charged
polythene rod.

18.5 van de Graaff Generator

This machine contains a rubber belt driven over a Perspex roller, either by
hand or by an electric motor, with the result that a continuous supply of
negative charge is produced on a large metal dome. Large versions are used in
nuclear research.

An *insulated* conductor can be given either (i) a negative charge by
connecting it to the dome with a wire, or (ii) a positive charge if it is placed
about 0.5 m away from the dome and charged by induction as explained in
Unit 18.4(i).

Some demonstrations are shown in Fig. 18.9. In (*a*) sparks jump between
the dome and the discharging sphere; in (*b*) the 'hair' stands on end (why?); in
(*c*) the 'windmill' revolves (why?); in (*d*) the 'body' on the insulating stool first
charges itself by touching the dome and a neon lamp can then be lit from it.

The dome can be discharged (painlessly) by bringing your elbow close to it.

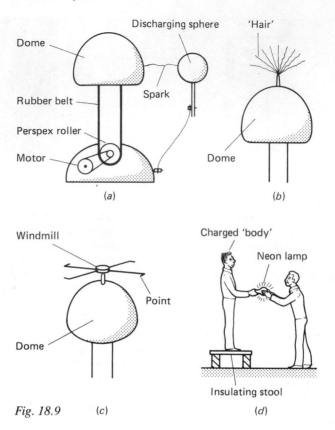

Fig. 18.9   (c)   (d)

18.6 Electric Fields

The space around an electric charge where it exerts a force on another charge is an *electric field*. We represent it by drawing *field lines* or *lines of force*.

The direction of the field at any point is taken as the direction of the force on a positive charge at the point. It is shown by arrows on the lines; we can therefore imagine each line as starting on a positive charge and ending on a negative one.

Electric field patterns can be obtained using semolina powder or grass seed floating in castor oil. The field is created by charging metal plates or wires dipping in the oil using a van de Graaff generator. Fig. 18.10(*a*) shows the pattern given by a pair of parallel plates, one positively and one negatively charged. Fig. 18.10(*b*) was given by the field of two like charges and Fig. 18.10(*c*) by that of two unlike charges.

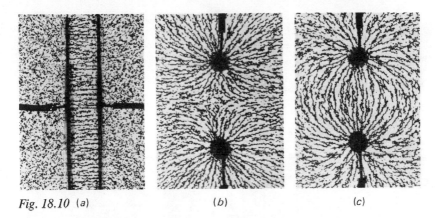

Fig. 18.10 (a)   (b)   (c)

18.7 Capacitors

A *capacitor* stores a small quantity of charge. In its simplest form it consists of two parallel metal plates separated by an insulator called the *dielectric* (Fig. 18.11(a)).

The more charge a capacitor can store, the greater is its *capacitance* (C). This increases

1. as the area of the plates increases,
2. as the separation of the plates decreases,
3. if the dielectric is a solid and not air.

The unit of capacitance is the *farad* (F), but a more convenient unit is the *microfarad* (μF), which equals one-millionth of a farad, that is, $1 \mu F = 10^{-6} F$.

The capacitors used in laboratories and in industry (with capacitances ranging from about 0.01 μF to 100 000 μF or so) often consist of two long strips of metal foil, separated by two long strips of dielectric, rolled up like a 'Swiss roll' (Fig. 18.11(b)). This arrangement allows plates of large area to be close

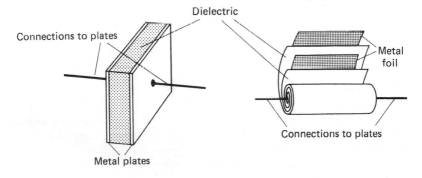

Fig. 18.11   (a)   (b)

together in a small volume. Common dielectric materials are plastics (such as polyesters and polycarbonates) and aluminium oxide. Some different capacitors are shown in Fig. 18.12.

Fig. 18.12

Capacitors are used widely in radio, television, computer and other electric circuits. An electroscope acts as a capacitor, the leaf and the case functioning as the two plates.

18.8 Electric Current

(i) **What is it?** An electric current consists of *electric charges moving in a definite direction*. A metallic conductor contains free electrons which can be made to 'flow' along it when, for example, it is connected to a cell or battery (Fig. 18.13(*a*)). The electrons move quite slowly, often at less than 1 mm per second (because they collide with metal atoms). They all start together as soon as the battery is connected, just as all the links in a bicycle chain begin to move at the instant the pedals are pushed. If the flow is in one direction only, a *direct current* (shortened to d.c.) is produced.

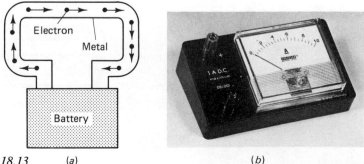

Fig. 18.13   (a)   (b)

(ii) **Effects.** An electric current can be detected in a conductor because of three effects:

1. *heating effect*—the temperature of the conductor rises (see Unit 20.1),
2. *magnetic effect*—a magnetic compass near the conductor is deflected (see Unit 21.6), and
3. *chemical effect*—chemical changes are produced in certain conducting liquids called *electrolytes* (see Unit 20.9).

(iii) **The ampere.** Current is the rate of flow of electric charge and is measured in *amperes* (A) by an *ammeter* (Fig. 18.13(b)). The current in a conductor is 1 ampere if 1 coulomb of charge flows past each point in it every second, that is, if the flow consists of about 6 million million million electrons per second (see Unit 18.2(iv)). Hence

$$1 \text{ ampere} = 1 \text{ coulomb per second}$$

or $$1 \text{ A} = 1 \text{ C/s}$$

The current through a large torch bulb is about 0.5 A and that through a car headlamp bulb 3 to 4 A. Two smaller units of current are the *milliampere* (mA) $= 1/1000 \text{ A} = 10^{-3} \text{ A}$, and the *microampere* (μA) $= 1/1\,000\,000 \text{ A} = 10^{-6} \text{ A}$. The current through a pocket calculator is roughly 5 mA.

If a current flowing through a conductor is 3 A, 3 C would pass each point in the conductor in 1 s. Therefore in 2 s, $2 \times 3 = 6$ C would pass. In general, if a steady current I (amperes) flows for time t (seconds), the charge Q (coulombs) passing any point in that time is given by

$$Q = It$$

Rearranging, we can also say

$$I = \frac{Q}{t}$$

This is a useful expression connecting current and charge.

18.9 Circuits and Diagrams

(i) **Circuits.** Continuous currents require complete conducting paths or *circuits*, in which copper wires are used to connect batteries, lamps, switches and so on. If the wires are covered with insulation, perhaps a plastic such as PVC (poly(vinyl chloride)), the insulation must be removed from the ends before connecting up.

(ii) **Symbols.** Symbols (signs) used in diagrams of circuits are shown in Fig. 18.14.

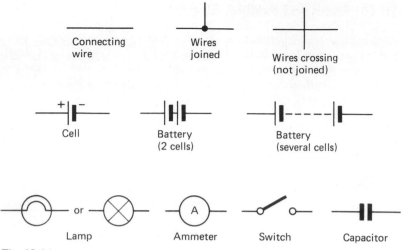

Fig. 18.14

(iii) **Current direction.** Before the electron was discovered, scientists agreed to think of current as positive charges moving round a circuit from the positive (+) terminal of a battery to the negative (−) terminal. We now know that this is not true for metals (though it is partly true for electrolytes and gases when they conduct electricity).

The original agreement is still kept, however, partly because it does not really matter which direction is chosen (since negative charge moving one way is in effect equivalent to positive charge moving the opposite way) and partly because the laws of electricity were first drawn up using wording that implied that positive charges moved.

Arrows on circuit diagrams show the direction of what is called the *conventional current*, that is, the direction in which positive charges would flow.

(iv) **Measuring current.** The ammeter used to measure a current must be connected in a circuit in such a way that all the current goes through it. It must also be designed so as to ensure that it has very little effect on the current to be measured when it is connected (see Unit 21.11(ii)).

Ammeters for use in d.c. circuits (for example, those in which batteries produce currents) must have the terminal marked + (or coloured red) leading to the + terminal of the battery, as in Fig. 18.15(*a*) below; conventional current thus enters the + terminal of the ammeter and leaves by the − terminal. Otherwise the pointer on the ammeter is deflected in the wrong direction and the instrument may be damaged.

18.10 Series and Parallel Circuits

(i) **Series.** In a series circuit the different parts follow one after the other around the circuit. In the circuit of Fig. 18.15(a) the two lamps L_1 and L_2 are in series with the three ammeters A_1, A_2 and A_3. The ammeters measure the current at different points in the circuit and the readings show that

the current is the same at all points in a series circuit.

That is, the current in the circuit is not used up; if this were not so, it would mean either that electrons were leaking away, or that they were gathering at some point in the circuit.

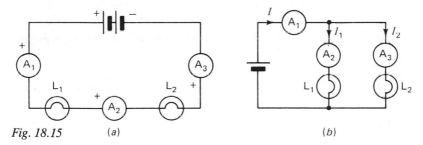

Fig. 18.15   (a)   (b)

(ii) **Parallel.** In a parallel circuit alternative branches are available to the current, which therefore divides. In Fig. 18.15(b) the lamps L_1 and L_2 are in parallel and the readings on the ammeters A_1, A_2 and A_3 show that

the sum of the currents in the branches of a parallel circuit equals the current entering the parallel circuit.

That is, in Fig. 18.15(b), $I = I_1 + I_2$.

18.11 Revision Questions and Problems

Static Electricity
  1. What kind of charge is produced on (a) Perspex, (b) polythene, when it is rubbed with a cloth?

  2. Name the three types of particle from which atoms are built and say what kind of charge each carries.

  3. Explain in terms of electron movement what happens when (a) polythene, (b) Perspex, is charged by rubbing.

  4. What is the unit of charge?

  5. When a charged rod is brought near the cap of a negatively charged electroscope the leaf rises farther. What kind of charge does the rod have? Explain your answer.

  6. (a) Why are metals good conductors?
     (b) Why are plastics good insulators?

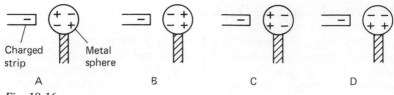

Charged strip   Metal sphere

A   B   C   D

Fig. 18.16

7. A negatively charged strip is held near an uncharged metal ball mounted on an insulated stand.

    (*a*) Which of the diagrams in Fig. 18.16 best shows how the charge is distributed on the sphere when the strip is near?

    (*b*) What would be the effect of earthing the sphere while the charged strip was close?

8. If a balloon is rubbed, it will often 'stick' to the wall where it has been rubbed. Why?

9. Explain the term *electric field*.

10. (*a*) What are the basic components of a capacitor?
    (*b*) State three ways in which the capacitance of a capacitor can be increased.
    (*c*) State the unit of capacitance.
    (*d*) Give three uses of capacitors.

Electric Current

11. (*a*) What is an electric current?
    (*b*) Name the three effects of an electric current.
    (*c*) State the unit of current.

12. (*a*) Express the following in mA: (i) 0.54 A, (ii) 0.085 A, (iii) 0.002 A.
    (*b*) Express the following in A: (i) 1500 mA, (ii) 610 mA, (iii) 35 mA.
    (*c*) Express the following in μA: (i) 1 mA, (ii) 0.47 mA, (iii) 0.015 mA.

13. Write down the equation connecting current and charge.

14. If the current through a lamp is 5 A, what charge passes in (*a*) 1 s, (*b*) 10 s, (*c*) 5 minutes?

15. What is the current in a circuit if the charge passing each point is (*a*) 10 C in 2 s, (*b*) 20 C in 40 s, (*c*) 240 C in 2 minutes?

16. Draw the symbols for (*a*) a cell, (*b*) a battery of two cells, (*c*) a lamp, (*d*) an ammeter, (*e*) a switch, (*f*) two wires joined, (*g*) two wires crossing but not joined.

17. What is meant by the term *conventional current*?

18. Draw circuit diagrams for the two circuits shown in Fig. 18.17(*a*) and (*b*).

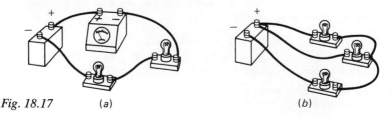

Fig. 18.17   (*a*)   (*b*)

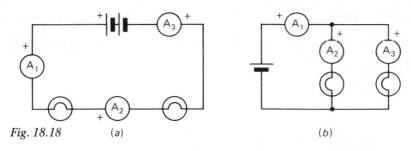

Fig. 18.18   (a)   (b)

19. (a) In Fig. 18.18(a) if ammeter A_1 reads 0.2 A, what are the readings on A_2 and A_3?
    (b) In Fig. 18.18(b) if ammeter A_2 reads 0.3 A and ammeter A_3 reads 0.2 A, what is the reading on A_1?

20. If the lamps are both the same in Fig. 18.19 and if ammeter A_1 reads 0.5 A, what do A_2, A_3, A_4 and A_5 read?

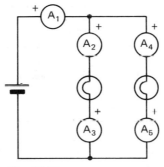

Fig. 18.19

Electromotive Force, Potential Difference and Resistance

19.1 Electromotive Force (e.m.f.)

(i) **Energy changes in a circuit.** In a circuit electrical energy is provided by a source such as a *dry cell* or *battery* (see (iv) below) and is changed into other forms of energy by devices in the circuit. For example, the battery in Fig. 19.1(*a*) supplies the electrical energy and force to drive the electrons round the circuit as a current because of the chemical action inside the battery (we shall discuss this action in Unit 20.8). The electrons give up most of their energy as heat and light in the lamp.

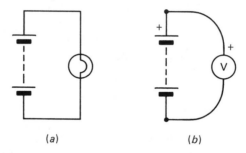

Fig. 19.1   (a)   (b)

(ii) **Definition of e.m.f.** It is useful to imagine that as each coulomb of charge (equivalent to more than 6×10^{18} electrons) leaves the battery, it receives a fixed amount of electrical energy which depends on the battery.

> *The e.m.f. (E) of a battery is the electrical energy it gives to each coulomb of charge passing round a complete circuit.*

The unit of e.m.f. is the *volt* (V). A battery has an e.m.f. or *voltage* of 1 V if it gives 1 joule (J) of electrical energy to each coulomb (C). That is, 1 volt = 1 joule per coulomb (1 V = 1 J/C). A 6 V battery gives 6 J of energy to each coulomb.

(iii) **Measuring e.m.f.** The e.m.f. of a battery can be measured by connecting a *voltmeter* across it (Fig. 19.1(*b*)). This instrument takes current from the battery to make a reading but it is designed so as to ensure that this is negligible—otherwise it would not give a true reading (see Unit 19.11).

As with an ammeter for use in d.c. circuits, the terminal marked + (or coloured red) on a voltmeter should lead to the + terminal of the battery (as in

Fig. 19.1(*b*)), to ensure that conventional current deflects the pointer in the correct direction.

(iv) **Cells in series and parallel.** Greater e.m.f.s are obtained when cells are joined in series, that is, the + terminal of one to the − terminal of the next, to give a battery. A carbon–zinc or dry cell (see Unit 20.8(i)) has an e.m.f. of 1.5 V and two joined in series (Fig. 19.2(*a*)) give an e.m.f. of 3 V. If two 1.5 V cells are connected in parallel (Fig. 19.2(*b*)) they still give an e.m.f. of 1.5 V but they behave like one larger cell with more energy, and last longer.

The two 1.5 V cells in Fig. 19.2(*c*) are in opposition and their combined e.m.f. is zero.

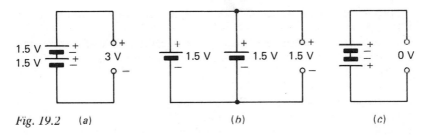

Fig. 19.2   (*a*)   (*b*)   (*c*)

19.2 Potential Difference (p.d.)

(i) **P.d. across a device.** The charge leaving the positive terminal of a cell has p.e. It loses this p.e. in a device (as heat and light in a lamp, for instance) and returns to the negative terminal of the cell with negligible p.e., that is, there is a difference in p.e. per coulomb from one side of the device to the other. This difference is called *potential difference* (p.d.). The definition of the p.d. across a device is, like that of e.m.f., based on the energy changes in a circuit.

The p.d. (V) across a device in a circuit is the electrical energy changed into other forms of energy for each coulomb passing through it.

P.d., like e.m.f., is measured in volts and if the energy change in a device is 1 joule per coulomb, the p.d. or *voltage* across it is 1 volt. If it changes 2 J when 1 C passes through it, the p.d. across it is 2 V. If 6 J are changed when 2 C passes, the p.d. is 6 J/2 C = 3 V. In general, if W joules is changed when Q coulombs pass, the p.d. V in volts across the device is given by

$$V = \frac{W}{Q}$$

If Q is in the form of a steady current I in amperes passing through the device for time t in seconds, then since $Q = It$ (see Unit 18.8(iii)) we can write

$$V = \frac{W}{It} \quad \text{or} \quad W = ItV$$

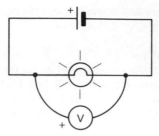

Fig. 19.3

A voltmeter is used to measure p.d., being connected across the device as in Fig. 19.3.

A very small amount of electrical energy is changed to heat in the copper connecting wires of a circuit, the p.d. across them is thus almost zero, and can be ignored.

(ii) **Terminal p.d. of a battery.** When a battery drives current round a circuit some of the electrical energy carried by the charge is needed to get current through the battery itself. This energy is changed to heat in the battery. There is therefore less electrical energy available to drive each coulomb round the rest of the circuit.

The *terminal p.d.* (V) of a battery when it is driving current (that is, on closed circuit) is *less* than the e.m.f. of the battery because some energy and volts are 'lost'. In Fig. 19.4(a), when the switch is open, the voltmeter records the e.m.f. of the battery (provided the current through the voltmeter is negligible). Suppose it is 3.0 V; then

terminal p.d. on open circuit = e.m.f. = 3.0 V

When the switch is closed and the battery drives current round the circuit

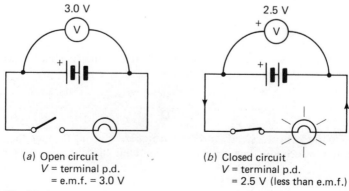

(a) Open circuit
  V = terminal p.d.
    = e.m.f. = 3.0 V

(b) Closed circuit
  V = terminal p.d.
    = 2.5 V (less than e.m.f.)

Fig. 19.4

(Fig. 19.4(*b*)), the terminal p.d. (as measured by the voltmeter) falls and is less than the e.m.f. Suppose it is 2.5 V; then

$$\text{terminal p.d. on closed circuit} < \text{e.m.f.} = 2.5 \text{ V}$$

The 'lost' voltage (v) in this example is 0.5 V. It cannot be measured *directly* by a voltmeter but is found by subtracting the terminal p.d. on closed circuit from that on open circuit, that is, from the e.m.f.

To sum up: a voltmeter connected across a battery always measures its terminal p.d., which equals the e.m.f. only when the battery is on open circuit. On closed circuit the terminal p.d. is less than the e.m.f. and equals the p.d. across the devices in the external circuit (in Fig. 19.4(*b*), one lamp), if we neglect the very small p.d.s across the switch and the connecting wires.

19.3 The E.m.f.–P.d. Equation for a Circuit

If we consider the energy changes that occur in an electric circuit (and assume that the principle of conservation of energy holds), we can say

energy supplied per coulomb by battery
  =energy changed per coulomb in devices in external circuit
                    +energy 'lost' per coulomb inside battery

From the definitions of e.m.f. and terminal p.d. it follows that

$$\text{e.m.f.} = \text{terminal p.d.} + \text{'lost' voltage}$$

In symbols,

$$E = V + v \qquad\qquad \textbf{1}$$

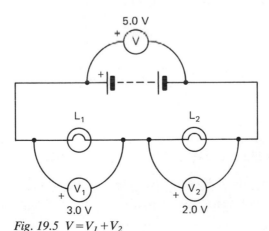

Fig. 19.5 $V = V_1 + V_2$

This is an important equation which is true for all circuits. For example, if the external circuit contains two lamps L_1 and L_2 connected in series (Fig. 19.5), then

terminal p.d. = p.d. across L_1 + p.d. across L_2

In symbols,

$$V = V_1 + V_2 \qquad\qquad 2$$

For example, if $V = 5.0$ V then we might find $V_1 = 3.0$ V and $V_2 = 2.0$ V. In general,

The terminal p.d. of a battery equals the sum of the p.d.s across the devices in the external circuit from one battery terminal to the other.

If the e.m.f. E of the battery in this example is 6.0 V, then the 'lost' voltage v is 1.0 V and from equation 1 we have

$$E = V + v = (V_1 + V_2) + v$$

That is, the sum of all the p.d.s round a circuit, including the 'lost' voltage, must *add up* to equal the e.m.f. of the battery.

19.4 Resistance

(i) **Definition and unit.** Electrons move more easily through some conductors than others when a p.d. is applied. The opposition of a conductor to current is called its *resistance*. A good conductor has a low resistance and a poor conductor has a high resistance. A long thin wire has more resistance than a short thick one of the same material—that is, a given p.d. causes a smaller current in it.

If the current through a conductor is I when the p.d. across it is V, its resistance R is defined by the equation

$$R = \frac{V}{I} \qquad\qquad 3$$

This is a reasonable way to measure resistance since the smaller I is for a given V, the greater is R. If V is in volts and I in amperes, R is in *ohms* (shortened to Ω, pronounced omega). For example, if $I = 2$ A when $V = 12$ V then $R = 12$ V/3 A $= 4\,\Omega$. But if $I = 1$ A when $V = 12$ V, $R = 12$ V/1 A $= 12\,\Omega$. The unit of resistance, the ohm, is the resistance of a conductor in which the current is 1 A when a p.d. of 1 V is applied across its ends. Larger units are the *kilohm* (kΩ) and the *megohm* (MΩ): 1 kΩ = 1000 Ω and 1 MΩ = 1 000 000 Ω.

(ii) ***V, I, R* equations.** Equation 3 can be rearranged so that

1. V can be calculated when R and I are known; the equation is

$$V = IR$$

2. I can be calculated when R and V are known, using the equation

$$I = \frac{V}{R}$$

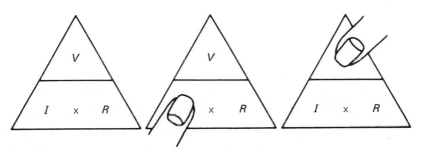

Fig. 19.6

The triangle in Fig. 19.6 is an aid to remembering the three equations. Cover with your finger the quantity you want—I, for instance; it equals what you still see (V/R). To find V, cover V and you get $V = I \times R$. To find R, cover R and $R = V/I$.

(iii) **Worked examples.** Here are some simple examples.

1. What is the resistance of a lamp when a p.d. of 12 V across it causes a current of 2 A?

$$V = 12\,\text{V}, \quad I = 2\,\text{A}, \quad R = ?$$

$$R = \frac{V}{I} = \frac{12}{2} = 6\,\Omega$$

2. Find the p.d. across a wire of resistance 10 Ω carrying a current of 0.5 A.

$$R = 10\,\Omega, \quad I = 0.5\,\text{A}, \quad V = ?$$

$$V = IR = 0.5 \times 10 = 5\,\text{V}$$

3. Calculate the current through a wire of resistance 3 Ω when the p.d. across it is 9 V.

$$R = 3\,\Omega, \quad V = 9\,\text{V}, \quad I = ?$$

$$I = \frac{V}{R} = \frac{9}{3} = 3\,\text{A}$$

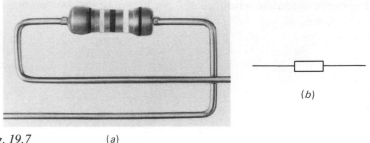

Fig. 19.7   (*a*)

(*b*)

19.5 Resistors

Resistors are devices which provide resistance so that when connected in a circuit they reduce the current to a desired value. They are made either from wire coils of special alloys or from carbon. Those used in radio and television sets have resistances ranging from a few ohms to several megohms. One is shown in Fig. 19.7(*a*) (about twice actual size); Fig. 19.7(*b*) shows the symbol for a resistor.

Variable resistors are used in electronics (and are then called *potentiometers*) as volume and other controls; one is shown in Fig. 19.8(*a*). Versions for use with larger currents are employed in laboratory experiments;

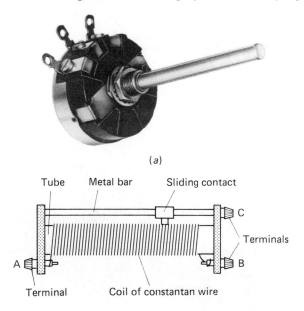

(*a*)

(*b*)

Fig. 19.8

these consist of a coil of constantan wire (an alloy of 60 per cent copper and 40 per cent nickel, also called eureka) wound on a tube, with a sliding contact on a metal bar above the tube (Fig. 19.8(b)).

There are two ways of using a variable resistor. It may be used as a *rheostat* for changing the current in a circuit; only one end-connection (either A or B) and the sliding contact C are then required. In Fig. 19.9(a), moving the sliding contact to the left reduces the resistance (by reducing the length of constantan wire through which the current has to pass between C and A or B) and increases the current. It can also act as a *potential divider* for changing the p.d. applied to a device, all three connections being used (we will explain this in Unit 19.10(ii)). The symbols used for a variable resistor are shown in Fig. 19.9(b).

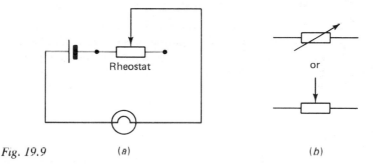

Fig. 19.9   (a)   (b)

19.6 More About Resistance

(i) **Measuring resistance.** The resistance R of a conductor can be found by measuring the current I through it when a p.d. V is applied across it and then using the relationship $R = V/I$. This is called the *ammeter–voltmeter* method.

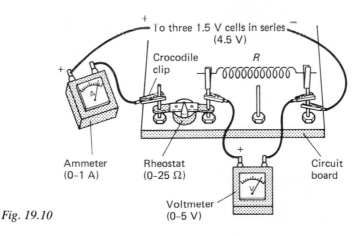

Fig. 19.10

In the circuit of Fig. 19.10 the unknown resistance R is 1 metre of constantan wire (SWG 34). Altering the rheostat changes both the p.d. V and the current I. The values of V for current values I of, say, 0.10, 0.15, 0.20, 0.25 and 0.30 A are recorded in a three-column table. The value of R for each pair of readings is worked out and entered in the third column of the table.

The experiment can be repeated, the constantan wire being replaced by

1. a semiconductor diode (such as 1N4001) connected first one way and then the other way round,
2. a torch bulb (2.5 V 0.3 A, for example), and
3. a thermistor (TH 7 is suitable).

(ii) *I–V* **graphs: Ohm's law.** The results of the previous experiments can be used to plot graphs showing the relationship between I and V for different conductors.

1. *Metallic conductors.* For metals and some alloys (such as constantan) at constant temperature, a graph of I against V is a *straight line through the origin* (Fig. 19.11(*a*)). I is therefore directly proportional to V, that is, $I \propto V$: doubling V doubles I, and so on. Such conductors obey *Ohm's law*, which is stated as follows:

The current through a metallic conductor is directly proportional to the p.d. across its ends if the temperature and other physical conditions are constant.

Conductors like these are called *ohmic* or *linear* conductors and, since $I \propto V$, it follows that $V/I =$ a constant (given by the reciprocal of the slope AB/OB of the *I–V* graph in Fig. 19.11(*a*), that is, by OB/AB). This means that the resistance of an ohmic conductor does not change when the p.d. across it changes, provided the temperature is constant.

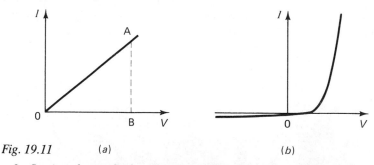

Fig. 19.11   (*a*)   (*b*)

2. *Semiconductor diodes.* Fig. 19.11(*b*) illustrates a typical *I–V* graph for a semiconductor diode; it shows that current passes when the p.d. is applied in one direction but is almost zero when it is applied in the opposite direction. A diode thus has a small resistance if the p.d. is applied one way round but a very large resistance when the p.d. is reversed. It conducts in one direction only and is a *non-ohmic* (or *non-linear*) conductor. This one-way property makes it useful as a *rectifier* for changing a.c. to d.c. (see Unit 24.6).

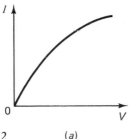 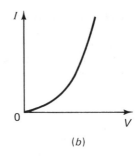

Fig. 19.12   (a)   (b)

19.7 Resistance and Temperature

(i) **Metals and alloys.** In general, *the resistance of metals increases when their temperature increases.* This is shown by the *I–V* graph of a torch bulb (Fig. 19.12(*a*)), which bends over as *V* and *I* increase, indicating that a given change of *V* causes a smaller change in *I* at larger values of *V*. That is, the resistance (*V/I*) of the tungsten wire filament increases as the current raises its temperature and makes it white-hot.

Certain alloys such as constantan show very small changes of resistance with temperature and are used to make standard resistors.

(ii) **Semiconductors and carbon.** The resistance of semiconductors and carbon decreases as their temperature increases. (Semiconductors are substances which are less good conductors than metals are, but which are not very good insulators either—see Unit 24.5(i).)

Thermistors are made from semiconductors (usually oxides of metals) and the resistance of most decreases sharply as their temperature rises, giving an *I–V* graph like that in Fig. 19.12(*b*). Sometimes they are connected into circuits to compensate for resistance increases caused by metal conductors heating up.

19.8 Resistor Networks

(i) **Series.** Fig. 19.13(*a*) shows two resistors, having resistances R_1 and R_2, in series. We know that (*a*) the same current *I* passes through each one, and (*b*) the total p.d. *V* across both equals the sum of the separate p.d.s V_1 and V_2 across each resistor. That is,

$$V = V_1 + V_2$$

But $V_1 = I_1 R_1$ and $V_2 = I_2 R_2$. Also, if R_s is the combined resistance of R_1 and R_2, $V = IR_s$ and so

$$IR_s = IR_1 + IR_2 = I(R_1 + R_2)$$

Dividing both sides by *I* gives

$$R_s = R_1 + R_2$$

Connecting resistors in series gives a resistance higher than that of any one of the resistors. For example, resistors of 3 Ω and 6 Ω in series have a combined resistance of 9 Ω.

In general, the combined resistance of several resistors in series equals the sum of their separate resistances, and they could be replaced by a single equivalent resistor.

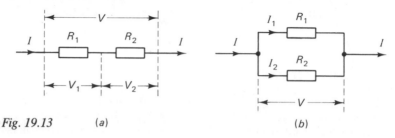

Fig. 19.13   (a)   (b)

(ii) **Parallel.** In Fig. 19.13(*b*), the resistors of resistances R_1 and R_2 are connected in parallel. Therefore (*a*) the same p.d. *V* acts across each one, and (*b*) the total current *I* equals the sum of the separate currents through each resistor, that is,

$$I = I_1 + I_2$$

Since $I_1 = V/R_1$ and $I_2 = V/R_2$, we have

$$I = \frac{V}{R_1} + \frac{V}{R_2} = V\left(\frac{1}{R_1} + \frac{1}{R_2}\right)$$

If R_p is the combined resistance, then $I = V/R_p$ and

$$\frac{V}{R_p} = V\left(\frac{1}{R_1} + \frac{1}{R_2}\right)$$

Dividing both sides by *V* gives

$$\frac{1}{R_p} = \frac{1}{R_1} + \frac{1}{R_2}$$

This can be written

$$\frac{1}{R_p} = \frac{R_2}{R_1 \times R_2} + \frac{R_1}{R_2 \times R_1} = \frac{R_2 + R_1}{R_1 \times R_2}$$

$$\therefore R_p = \frac{R_1 \times R_2}{R_1 + R_2} = \frac{\text{resistances multiplied}}{\text{resistances added}}$$

For example, if $R_1 = 3\,\Omega$ and $R_2 = 6\,\Omega$, then

$$R_p = \frac{3 \times 6}{3 + 6} = \frac{18}{9} = 2\,\Omega$$

Connecting resistors in parallel gives a combined resistance R_p which is *lower* than either resistance: putting resistors in parallel provides alternative paths for the current and lowers the resistance.

If more than two resistors are in parallel their combined resistance R_p is given by

$$\frac{1}{R_p} = \frac{1}{R_1} + \frac{1}{R_2} + \frac{1}{R_3} + \ldots$$

and so on.

19.9 Worked Examples

1. The terminal p.d. of the battery applied to the circuit in Fig. 19.14(*a*) is 24 V

(*a*) What is the combined resistance of the 6 Ω and 12 Ω resistors in parallel?

(*b*) What is the current in the 8 Ω resistor?

(*c*) What is the p.d. across the parallel network?

(*d*) What is the current in the 6 Ω resistor?

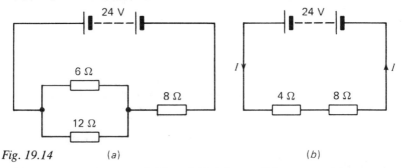

Fig. 19.14   (a)   (b)

(*a*) Let R_p = resistance of 6 Ω and 12 Ω in parallel.

$$\therefore R_p = \frac{R_1 \times R_2}{R_1 + R_2} = \frac{6 \times 12}{6 + 12} = \frac{72}{18} = \underline{4\,\Omega}$$

(*b*) Let R = total resistance of circuit $-4 + 8 - 12\,\Omega$.

The equivalent circuit is shown in Fig. 19.14(*b*). If I is the current in it then (since $V = 24$ V)

$$I = \frac{V}{R} = \frac{24\text{ V}}{12\,\Omega} = 2\text{ A}$$

$\therefore$ Current in 8 Ω resistor = main current = $\underline{2\text{ A}}$

(*c*) Let V_1 = p.d. across parallel network.

$$\therefore V_1 = I \times R_p = 2\text{ A} \times 4\,\Omega = \underline{8\text{ V}}$$

since the parallel network is equivalent to a single 4 Ω resistor with a current of 2 A through it.

(d) Let I_1 =current in 6 Ω resistor. Then, since V_1 =p.d. across parallel network =p.d. across both the 6 Ω and 12 Ω resistors =8 V,

$$I_1 = \frac{V_1}{6} = \frac{8}{6} = \underline{\underline{\frac{4}{3}}} A$$

2. If the terminal p.d. of the battery in Fig. 19.15(a) is 9 V, what is the current through the 3 Ω resistor when the switch S is closed?

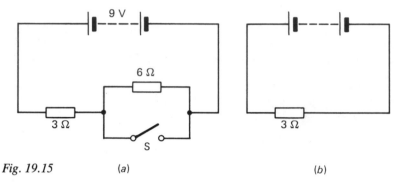

Fig. 19.15   (a)   (b)

The 6 Ω resistor is 'short-circuited' when S is closed and the total resistance of S and the 6 Ω resistor in parallel is zero. The equivalent circuit is then as in Fig. 19.15(b). The current I through the 3 Ω resistor is therefore given by

$$I = \frac{V}{R} = \frac{9\,V}{3\,\Omega} = \underline{\underline{3\,A}}$$

19.10 Potential Divider

A potential divider divides a p.d. into a number of equal parts. It consists of either several (often two) fixed resistors in series or a variable resistor.

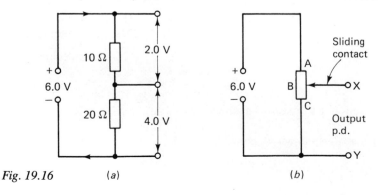

Fig. 19.16   (a)   (b)

(i) **Using two fixed resistors.** In the circuit of Fig. 19.16(a) the 10 Ω and 20 Ω resistors are connected in series across a 6.0 V supply, and divide it into three (1 +2) equal parts. One part (2.0 V) is the p.d. across the 10 Ω resistor and two parts (4.0 V) exist as the p.d. across the 20 Ω resistor. The division of the 6.0 V supply is in the ratio of the two resistances, that is, $10/20 = 1/2$ since the same current passes through each.

In general, if two resistors of resistances R_1 and R_2 are connected in series across a p.d. V and a current I passes, the p.d.s V_1 and V_2 across each are related by

$$\frac{V_1}{V_2} = \frac{IR_1}{IR_2} = \frac{R_1}{R_2}$$

For example, suppose that $R_1 = 5.0 \, \Omega$, $R_2 = 25 \, \Omega$ and $V = 6.0$ V. We then know that $V_1/V_2 = 1/5$. Hence $V_1 = 1.0$ V and $V_2 = 5.0$ V, making $V_1 + V_2 = 6.0$ V $= V$.

(ii) **Using a variable resistor.** A variable resistor connected as in Fig. 19.16(b) provides an easier way of changing the ratio R_1/R_2. The resistance between connections A and B represents R_1 and that between B and C represents R_2. A continuously variable output p.d. from 0 to 6.0 V is available between X and Y, depending on the position of the sliding contact: it will be 3.0 V when $R_1 = R_2$.

19.11 Internal Resistance of a Supply

Cells, batteries and other power supplies have some resistance themselves, called *internal* or *source resistance*. It causes the energy loss which occurs inside a battery (that is, the 'lost' voltage we encountered in Unit 19.2(ii)) when a current is driven round an external circuit: the greater the current, the greater is the loss and the smaller is the terminal p.d. of the battery.

In the circuit of Fig. 19.17(a) the voltmeter measures the e.m.f. E of the cell since it is on open circuit (if the resistance of the voltmeter is sufficiently high not to draw much current from the cell). In Fig. 19.17(b) the voltmeter records the terminal p.d. V of the cell which drives current I through R (where $V - IR$).

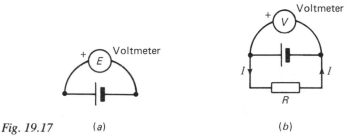

Fig. 19.17   (a)   (b)

If r is the internal resistance of the cell, then since I is also the current through it, the 'lost' voltage v is given by

$$v = Ir$$

From the e.m.f.–p.d. equation (see Unit 19.3) we get

$$v = E - V$$
$$\therefore Ir = E - V$$

That is,

$$r = \frac{E - V}{I}$$

For example, if $E = 1.5$ V and $V = 1.2$ V when $I = 0.3$ A, then

$$r = \frac{1.5 - 1.2}{0.3} = \frac{0.3}{0.3} = \underline{\underline{1.0\,\Omega}}$$

Note that r cannot be measured directly but is obtained from E, V and I. The internal resistance of a battery increases with age and so reduces the current it can drive. A knowledge of it is important when considering how a source of electrical energy can deliver maximum power to an appliance connected to it. It can be shown that this occurs when the internal resistance of the source equals the resistance of the appliance—a statement known as the *maximum power theorem*.

19.12 Resistivity

(i) **Definition.** Experiments show that the resistance R of a wire
  (a) is directly proportional to its length l, that is, $R \propto l$,
  (b) is inversely proportional to its cross-section area A, that is, $R \propto 1/A$ (so that doubling A halves R), and
  (c) depends on the material of the wire.

Combining (a) and (b) we get

$$R \propto l \times \frac{1}{A}$$

This can be written as an equation if we insert a constant:

$$R = \rho \frac{l}{A}$$

where ρ (the Greek letter *rho*) is a constant, called the *resistivity* of the material. If we put $l = 1$ m and $A = 1$ m^2 in the equation, then $\rho = R$.

The resistivity of a material is numerically equal to the resistance
of a 1 m length of it of cross-section area 1 m^2.

The unit of resistivity is the *ohm metre* (Ω m), as can be seen by rearranging the equation in the form $\rho = RA/l$. Knowing ρ for a material, the resistance of any sample of it may be calculated.

(ii) **Measuring resistivity.** The resistivity of a metal such as constantan can be found if the resistance R of a known length l (say 1 m) of wire is measured by the ammeter–voltmeter method of Unit 19.6(i) (for example, using a 0–1 A ammeter and a 0–5 V voltmeter).

The cross-section area A is obtained by finding the average diameter d of the wire using a micrometer screw gauge, taking several readings at different points along it and in different directions across it in case it is not circular. Then $A = \frac{1}{4}\pi d^2$ (in m^2 if d is in m): standard wire gauge 30 (SWG 30) has a diameter of about 0.3 mm and is suitable.

The resistivity ρ is calculated from

$$\rho = \frac{RA}{l}$$

For copper it is $1.7 \times 10^{-8} \, \Omega$ m and for constantan $49 \times 10^{-8} \, \Omega$ m.

(iii) **Strain gauge.** This instrument is used by engineers to obtain information about the size and distribution of strains in structures such as bridges and aircraft. One type consists of a length of parallel-folded, very fine wire, attached with strong adhesive to the part under test. If, for example, an increase of length strain occurs, the gauge wire gets longer and thinner and both of these changes increase its resistance, which is measured (the gauge having first been calibrated for a range of strains, so that the strain corresponding to a given resistance change can be read off).

19.13 Revision Questions

1. State and define the unit of (a) e.m.f., (b) p.d.

2. (a) How can the e.m.f. of a battery be measured roughly?
   (b) What is the advantage of connecting cells (i) in series, (ii) in parallel?

3. (a) What does it mean to say that the p.d. across a device is 6 V?
   (b) Write an expression for the electrical energy changed when a current I passes for time t through a conductor with a p.d. V across it.

4. (a) Explain the terms *open circuit* and *closed circuit* as applied to a battery.
   (b) When is the terminal p.d. of a battery equal to its e.m.f.?
   (c) Write down the 'e.m.f.–p.d. equation' for a circuit.

5. (a) Write down the equation which defines resistance. Rewrite it in two other ways.
   (b) State and define the unit of resistance.
   (c) State how the resistance of a wire would change (i) if its length increased, (ii) if its diameter decreased.

6. Draw a circuit diagram for the ammeter–voltmeter method of measuring resistance.

7. Draw the *I–V* graphs for (*a*) a metallic conductor, (*b*) a semiconductor diode, (*c*) a torch bulb, and (*d*) a thermistor.

8. (*a*) What is an ohmic conductor?
 (*b*) State Ohm's law.

9. What would be the effect of increasing the temperature on the resistance of (*a*) a metal, (*b*) carbon, (*c*) a semiconductor?

10. Write an equation for the combined resistance of two resistors of resistances R_1 and R_2 if they are (*a*) in series, (*b*) in parallel.

11. What does a potential divider do?

12. (*a*) Explain the term *internal resistance*.
 (*b*) How is the terminal p.d. of a battery affected (i) if its internal resistance increases, (ii) if it supplies a larger current?

19.14 Problems

E.m.f. and P.d.

1. If a battery has an e.m.f. of 12 V, how much electrical energy does it supply when a charge passes through it of (*a*) 1 C, (*b*) 5 C?

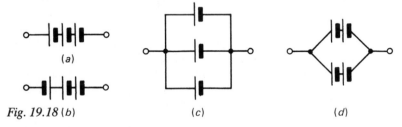

Fig. 19.18 (*a*) (*b*)   (*c*)   (*d*)

2. What are the e.m.f.s of the batteries of 1.5 V cells connected as in Fig. 19.18(*a*), (*b*), (*c*) and (*d*)?

3. What is the p.d. across a lamp in which 48 J of electrical energy are changed to heat and light every second by a steady current of 2 A?

4. In the circuits of Fig. 19.19 the voltmeter V requires almost zero current to make a reading. Calculate (*a*) the e.m.f. of the battery, (*b*) its terminal p.d. when driving current through the lamp L and (*c*) the 'lost' voltage.

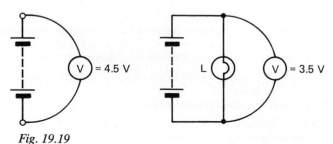

Fig. 19.19

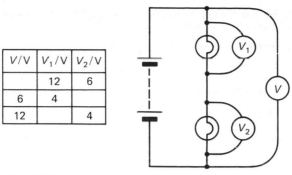

V/V	V_1/V	V_2/V
	12	6
6	4	
12		4

Fig. 19.20

5. Three voltmeters are connected as in Fig. 19.20. Copy and complete the table of voltmeter readings (which were obtained with three different batteries).

6. (a) In the circuit of Fig. 19.21 if the ammeter A reads 0.5 A and voltmeters V and V_2 read 18 V and 12 V respectively, how much electrical energy is changed to heat and light in L_1 in 1 minute?
   (b) Copy Fig. 19.21 and mark with + signs the positive terminals of the ammeter and voltmeters for correct connection.

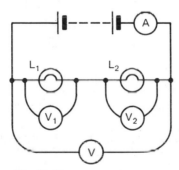

Fig. 19.21

Resistance

7. (a) What is the resistance of a lamp if a p.d. of 12 V across it causes a current of 4 A?
   (b) Calculate the p.d. across a wire of resistance 10 Ω carrying a current of 2 A.
   (c) The p.d. across a wire of resistance 2 Ω is 4 V. What is the current through it?
   (d) What is the p.d. across a 10 kΩ resistor carrying a current of 0.4 mA?

8. In the circuits of Fig. 19.22(a) and (b), what do the meters L, M and N read?

9. Calculate the combined resistance between A and B in each of Figs. 19.23(a), (b), (c), (d), (e) and (f).

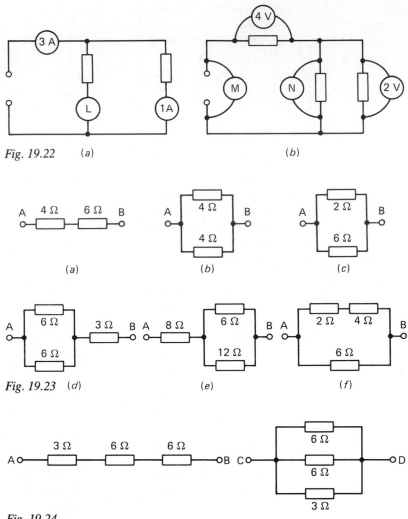

Fig. 19.22   (a)   (b)

(a)   (b)   (c)

Fig. 19.23   (d)   (e)   (f)

Fig. 19.24

10. In Fig. 19.24, what is the effective resistance (a) between A and B, (b) between C and D?

11. For the circuit in Fig. 19.25, calculate (a) the total resistance of the circuit, (b) the current in the 1 Ω resistor, (c) the current in one of the 6 Ω resistors, (d) the p.d. across the 1 Ω resistor, and (e) the p.d. across one of the 6 Ω resistors.

12. In the network of Fig. 19.26, calculate I, I_1 and I_2.

13. In Fig. 19.27(a) and (b), the circled letters are either ammeters or voltmeters. State which each is and calculate the reading on it.

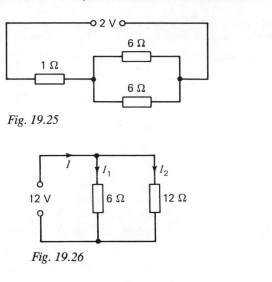

Fig. 19.25

Fig. 19.26

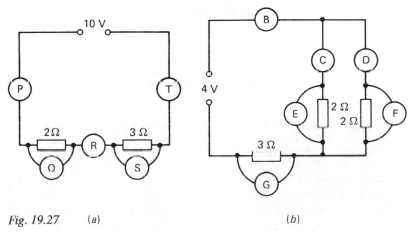

Fig. 19.27   (a)   (b)

14. In Fig. 19.28, what will ammeter A read when S is (a) open, (b) closed?

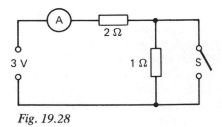

Fig. 19.28

Potential Divider: Internal Resistance

15. What are the p.d.s across R_2 in Figs. 19.29(a), (b) and (c)?

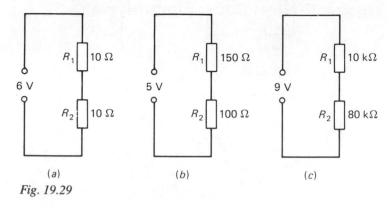

(a)   (b)   (c)

Fig. 19.29

16. In Fig. 19.30, what is the p.d. across (a) R_1, (b) R_2, (c) R_3?

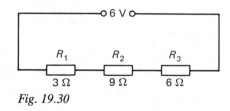

Fig. 19.30

17. A high-resistance voltmeter reads 3.0 V when connected across the terminals of a battery on open circuit, and 2.6 V when the battery drives a current of 0.2 A through a lamp.

Calculate (a) the e.m.f. of the battery, (b) the terminal p.d. of the battery when the current is 0.2 A, (c) the 'lost' voltage, (d) the internal resistance of the battery and (e) the resistance of the lamp.

18. What is the terminal p.d. of a cell of e.m.f. 2.0 V and internal resistance 0.01 Ω when it is maintaining a current of 10 A? Calculate the maximum current the cell can supply.

Electric Power: Cells: Electrolysis

20.1 Power in Electric Circuits

(i) **Equation for power.** In many circuits it is important to know the *rate* at which electrical energy is being changed into other forms of energy. Earlier (in Unit 6.5) we said that energy changes were measured by the work done, and power was defined by the equation

$$\text{power} = \frac{\text{work done}}{\text{time taken}} = \frac{\text{energy change}}{\text{time taken}}$$

or, in symbols;

$$P = \frac{W}{t} \qquad\qquad 1$$

where P is in watts (W) if W is in joules (J) and t in seconds (s).

We have seen (in Unit 19.2(i)) that if W is the electrical energy changed when a steady current I (in amperes) passes for time t (in seconds) through a device (such as a lamp) with a p.d. V (in volts) across it, then

$$W = ItV \qquad\qquad 2$$

Substituting for W in equation 1 gives

$$P = \frac{W}{t} = \frac{ItV}{t} = IV$$

Therefore to calculate the power P of an electrical appliance we multiply the current I through it by the p.d. V across it. For example, if a lamp on a 240 V supply has a current of 0.25 A through it, the power is $240 \times 0.25 = 60$ W. The lamp is changing 60 J of electrical energy into heat and light each second. In units,

$$\text{watts} = \text{amperes} \times \text{volts}$$

(ii) **Power of a resistor.** The rate at which a resistor changes electrical energy to heat can be calculated using $P = IV$, but two other forms of the equation are sometimes more useful. If the resistor has resistance R then, since $V = IR$, we can write

$$P = IV = I(IR) = I^2R$$

Hence if the current is doubled, four times as much heat is produced per second. We can also substitute for I in $P=IV$, putting $I=V/R$ to give

$$P=IV=\frac{V}{R}V=\frac{V^2}{R}$$

All three equations give the same answer but sometimes it is more convenient to use one than another.

20.2 Worked Examples

1. A small laboratory immersion heater is rated at 12 V 36 W. Calculate (*a*) the current through it, and (*b*) the resistance of the heater element.

    (*a*) P.d. across heater $=V=12$ V

      Power of heater $=P=36$ W

  Current through heater $=I=?$

$$P=IV$$

$$\therefore I=\frac{P}{V}=\frac{36}{12}=3\text{ A}$$

  (*b*) $V=12$ V, $I=3$ A, $R=$ resistance of heater $=?$

$$R=\frac{V}{I}=\frac{12}{3}=4\,\Omega$$

2. A $3\,\Omega$ resistor has a p.d. of 6 V connected across its ends. Calculate the power dissipated in the resistor (that is, the heat produced per second).

    Resistance of resistor $=R=3\,\Omega$

    P.d. across resistor $=V=6$ V

    Power dissipated $=P=?$

$$P=\frac{V^2}{R}=\frac{6^2}{3}=\frac{36}{3}=12\text{ W}$$

3. Calculate the maximum safe current which can be passed through a $100\,\Omega$ 4 W resistor.

    Power of resistor $=P=4$ W

    Resistance of resistor $=R=100\,\Omega$

    Maximum current $=I=?$

$$P=I^2R$$

$$\therefore I^2=\frac{P}{R}\text{ and }I=\sqrt{\frac{P}{R}}$$

$$\therefore I=\sqrt{\frac{4}{100}}=\frac{2}{10}=0.2\text{ A}$$

20.3 Measuring Electric Power

(i) **Lamp.** If the circuit of Fig. 20.1 is connected and the current I and p.d. V noted from the ammeter and voltmeter respectively, the electric power P supplied to the lamp can be found using $P = IV$.

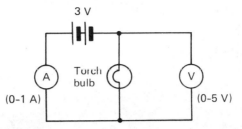

Fig. 20.1

(ii) **Motor.** The lamp in Fig. 20.1 is replaced by a small electric motor. A known mass m (in kg) is attached to the axle of the motor with a length of thin string. The time t (in s) to raise the mass through a known height h (in m) at a steady speed is found. Then the power output P_o (in W) of the motor is given by

$$P_o = \frac{\text{work done in raising mass}}{\text{time taken}}$$

$$= \frac{mgh}{t}$$

If the ammeter and voltmeter readings I and V are also noted *while the mass is being raised*, the power input P_i (in W) can be found from

$$P_i = IV$$

The efficiency (symbol η—the Greek letter *eta*) of the motor is given by

$$\eta = \frac{P_o}{P_i} \times 100\%$$

20.4 Electric Heating

(i) **Heating elements.** In domestic appliances such as electric fires, cookers, kettles and irons the 'elements' are made from *Nichrome* wire (Fig. 20.2). Nichrome is an alloy of nickel and chromium which does not oxidize (and thus become brittle) when the current makes it red-hot.

The elements in *radiant* electric fires are at red heat (about 900 °C) and the radiation they emit is directed into the room by polished reflectors. In *convector* types the element is below red heat (about 450 °C) and is designed to

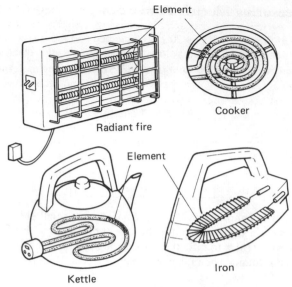

Fig. 20.2

warm air which is drawn through the heater by natural or forced convection (see Unit 11.5). In *storage* heaters the elements heat fire-clay bricks during the night using low-priced 'off-peak' electricity. During the following day these cool down, giving off the stored heat to warm the room.

(ii) **Three-heat switch.** This is sometimes used to control heating appliances. It has three settings and uses two identical elements. When the switch is set on

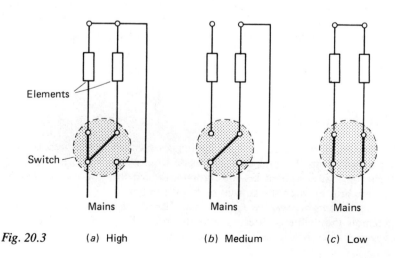

Fig. 20.3   (a) High   (b) Medium   (c) Low

'high', the elements are in parallel across the supply voltage (Fig. 20.3(a)); on 'medium', current passes through only one (Fig. 20.3(b)); on 'low', they are in series (Fig. 20.3(c)).

(iii) **Fuses.** A fuse is a short length of wire made of some material with a low melting-point (often tinned copper), which melts and breaks the circuit when the current through it exceeds a certain value. Two possible reasons for excessive currents are 'short-circuits', due to worn insulation on connecting wires, and overloaded circuits; in the absence of a fuse these would cause the wiring to become hot, with the consequent risk of fire.

Two types of fuse are shown in Fig. 20.4. *Always switch off before replacing a fuse.*

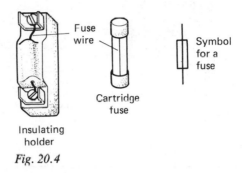

Fuse wire

Symbol for a fuse

Cartridge fuse

Insulating holder

Fig. 20.4

20.5 Electric Lighting

(i) **Filament lamps** (Fig. 20.5(a)). The filament is a small coiled coil of tungsten wire (Fig. 20.5(b)) which becomes white-hot when current flows through it. The higher the temperature of the filament the greater is the

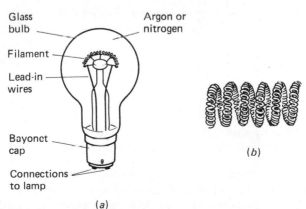

Glass bulb

Argon or nitrogen

Filament

Lead-in wires

Bayonet cap

Connections to lamp

(b)

Fig. 20.5   (a)

proportion of electric energy changed to light and this is why it is made of tungsten, a metal with a high melting-point (3400 °C).

Most lamps are gas-filled and contain nitrogen or argon, not air. The gas reduces evaporation of the tungsten which would otherwise condense on the bulb and blacken it. The compactness of the coiled coil reduces cooling by convection currents in the gas.

(ii) **Fluorescent lamps.** A filament lamp changes only 10 per cent of the electrical energy supplied into light; the other 90 per cent becomes heat. Fluorescent lamps are three times as efficient as filament lamps are, and may last 3000 hours compared with the 1000-hour life of filament lamps. They cost more to install but running costs are less and, being extended sources, they cause fewer problems with shadows.

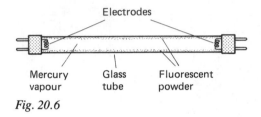

Electrodes

Mercury   Glass   Fluorescent
vapour   tube   powder

Fig. 20.6

A simplified diagram of a fluorescent lamp is shown in Fig. 20.6. When the lamp is switched on, the mercury vapour emits ultraviolet radiation (invisible—see Unit 16.9(ii)) which makes the powder on the inside of the tube fluoresce (glow), that is, light (visible) is emitted. Different powders give different colours; a filament lamp always gives a 'reddish' white light, however.

20.6 House Circuits

Electricity usually comes to our homes by an underground cable containing two wires, the *live* (L) and the *neutral* (N). The neutral is earthed at the local substation and although current passes through it you would not get a shock if you touched it accidentally because the p.d. between it and earth is zero. The supply is a.c. (we shall discuss this in Unit 22.8) and the live wire is alternately positive and negative.

Study the modern house circuit shown in Fig. 20.7.

(i) **Circuits in parallel.** Every circuit in the system is connected in parallel with the supply, that is, across the live and neutral, and receives the full mains p.d. of 240 V.

(ii) **Switches and fuses.** These are always in the live wire. If they were in the neutral, lamp and power sockets would be 'live' when switches were 'off' or

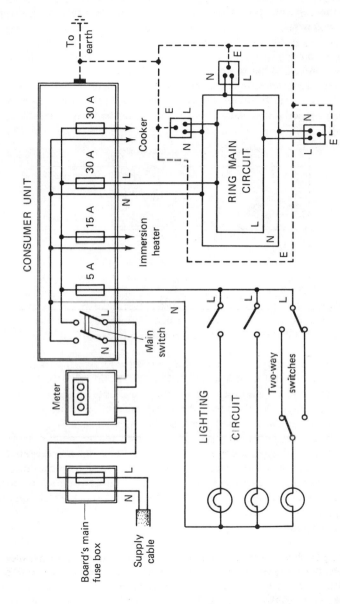

Fig. 20.7 House circuit

fuses 'blown'. A dangerous shock could then be obtained by, for example, touching the element of an electric fire when it was switched off.

(iii) **Staircase circuit.** The lamp is controlled from two places by the two two-way switches.

(iv) **Ring main circuit.** Both the live and neutral wires run in a complete ring round the house, and the power sockets, each rated at 13 A, are tapped off from them. Thinner wires can be used since the current to each socket flows by two paths, that is, in the whole ring. The ring has a 30A fuse; thus as many sockets as required can be used at once, so long as the total current does not exceed 30 A.

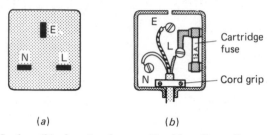

(a)   *(b)*

Fig. 20.8 (a) Socket, (b) plug; L = brown, N = blue, E = yellow-green

(v) **Fused plug.** Only one type of plug is used in a ring main circuit. It is wired as in Fig. 20.8 and has its own cartridge fuse, 3 A (blue) for appliances with powers up to 720 W and 13 A (brown) for those between 720 W and 3 kW.

(vi) **Earthing and safety.** A ring main has a third wire, which goes to the top connections on all power sockets (E in Fig. 20.7) and is earthed by being connected either to a metal water pipe in the house or to an earth connection on the supply cable. This third wire is a safety precaution to prevent electric shock should an appliance develop a fault.

The earth pin on a three-pin plug is connected to the metal case of the appliance which is thus joined to earth by a path of almost zero resistance. If, for example, the element of an electric fire breaks or sags and touches the case, a large current flows to earth and 'blows' the fuse. Otherwise the case would become 'live' and anyone touching it would receive a shock which might be fatal, especially if they were 'earthed' by, say, standing on a concrete floor or holding a water tap.

(vii) **Circuit breakers.** These are now used in consumer units instead of fuses. They contain an electromagnet (see Unit 21.7) which, when the current exceeds the rated value of the circuit breaker, becomes strong enough to separate a pair of contacts and breaks the circuit. Their advantage is that the circuit is broken much more quickly than by a fuse. Also they are closed again (reset) by simply pressing a button.

(viii) **Double insulation.** Appliances such as vacuum cleaners, hair dryers and food mixers are usually double-insulated, shown by the sign ▣ on the specification plate.

Connection to the supply is by a two-core insulated cable, with no earth wire, and the appliance is enclosed in an insulating plastic case. Any metal attachments that the user might touch are fitted into this case so that they do not make a direct connection with the internal electrical parts, such as a motor. There is then no risk of a shock should a fault develop.

20.7 Paying for Electricity

(i) **The kilowatt-hour.** Electricity boards charge for the electrical energy they supply. A joule is a very small amount of energy and a larger unit, the *kilowatt-hour* (kW h) is used.

A kilowatt-hour is the electrical energy used by a 1 kW appliance in 1 hour.

A 3 kW electric fire working for two hours uses 6 kW h of electrical energy—usually called 6 'units'. Energy in 'units' is calculated from

energy = power (kW) × time (hours)

Electricity meters are marked in kW h; at present (1985) a 'unit' costs about 5p.

Typical powers of some appliances are:

Lamps	60, 100 W	Fire	1, 2, 3 kW
Fridge	150 W	Kettle	2–3 kW
TV set	200 W	Immersion heater	3 kW
Iron	750 W	Cooker	8 kW

(ii) **Worked example.** If electrical energy costs 5p per unit, calculate the cost of (a) leaving on five 100 W light bulbs for 6 hours, (b) leaving on a 2 kW electric fire for 8 hours, and (c) heating a tank containing 100 kg of water from 20 °C to 50 °C by a 3 kW immersion heater. Assume there are no heat losses and take the specific heat capacity of water as 4200 J/(kg K).

$\qquad$ (a) Power of five 100 W light bulbs $= P = 500$ W $= 0.5$ kW
$\qquad\qquad$ Time bulbs on $= t = 6$ hours
$\qquad$ Electrical energy supplied $=$ power in kW × time in hours
$\qquad\qquad\qquad\qquad = 0.5$ kW × 6 h $= 3$ kW h
$\qquad$ ∴ Cost at 5p per unit $= 5 \times 3 = 15$p

$\qquad\qquad$ (b) Electrical energy supplied $= 2$ kW × 8 h
$\qquad\qquad\qquad\qquad\qquad = 16$ kW h
$\qquad\qquad$ ∴ Cost at 5p per unit $= 5 \times 16 = 80$p

(c)   Electrical energy supplied by immersion heater (J)
                              = heat gained by tank of water (J)

In symbols,

$$Pt = mc\Delta\theta \qquad\qquad \text{(see Unit 10.1(iii))}$$

where P =power of heater =3 kW =3000 W (J/s)
    t =time in *seconds* to raise temperature of water
       from 20 °C to 50 °C =?
    m =mass of water =100 kg
    c =specific heat capacity of water =4200 J/(kg K)
    $\Delta\theta$ =rise in temperature of water =(50 −20) =30 °C

$$\therefore\ 3000 \times t = 100 \times 4200 \times 30$$

$$\therefore\ t = \frac{100 \times 4200 \times 30}{3000} = 4200 \text{ s}$$

$$= \frac{4200}{3600} = \frac{7}{6} \text{hrs}$$

But energy in units is given by

$$\text{energy} = \text{power (kW)} \times \text{time (hours)}$$

$$= 3 \text{ kW} \times \frac{7}{6} \text{ hrs} = 3.5 \text{ units}$$

$$\therefore\ \text{Cost at 5p per unit} = 3.5 \times 5 = \underline{\underline{17.5 \text{ p}}}$$

20.8 Electric Cells

In an electric cell a conducting liquid called an electrolyte (see Unit 20.9(i))
reacts chemically with two electrodes, making one positive and the other
negative, to produce electrical energy—that is, chemical energy becomes
electrical energy.

(i) **Primary cells.** A primary cell is one which is discarded when the chemicals
are used up.

   1. *Simple cell* (Fig. 20.9). It has an e.m.f. of about 1.0 V but stops working
after a short time due to *polarization*, that is, the collection of hydrogen
bubbles on the copper plate. The cell is depolarized by adding potassium
dichromate which oxidizes the hydrogen to water. A second defect is *local
action*. This is due to impurities in the zinc and results in the zinc being used up
even when current is not supplied. The simple cell is no longer used for
practical purposes.
   2. *Zinc–carbon cell* (Fig. 20.10). This cell—also called the *Leclanché cell* or

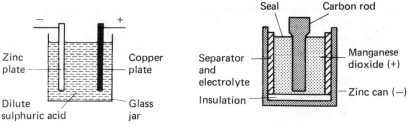

Fig. 20.9   Fig. 20.10

dry cell—has a zinc negative electrode and a manganese dioxide positive electrode, and the electrolyte is a solution of ammonium chloride. The carbon rod is in contact with the positive electrode (but takes no part in the chemical reaction) and is called the *current collector*. The e.m.f. is 1.5 V and the internal resistance about 0.5 Ω. This is the most popular cell where low current (about 0.3 A) is required, or for occasional use, as in torches. The high-power (HP) version uses specially prepared manganese dioxide rather than the natural ore.

3. *Alkaline–manganese cell*. The same electrode materials are used as in the zinc–carbon cell. The electrolyte is a strong solution of the alkali potassium hydroxide which has more ions (to carry current) than an ammonium chloride solution of the same strength. This allows the cell to give larger continuous currents than the zinc–carbon type; it is also leak-proof since the steel case has no part in the reaction, the zinc being in powder form. The e.m.f. is 1.5 V. It is a longer-lasting (but dearer) replacement for the HP zinc–carbon cell in, for example, electric shavers and tape recorders.

(ii) **Secondary cells.** Secondary cells, or *accumulators*, can be recharged by passing a current through them in the opposite direction to that in which they supply one.

In the *lead–acid* cell (Fig. 20.11(*a*)), the positive electrode is lead dioxide (brown) and the negative one is lead (grey), the materials being held in lead-alloy plates. The electrolyte is dilute sulphuric acid. During discharge, both electrodes change to lead sulphate (white) and the acid becomes more dilute.

The e.m.f. is steady at 2 V and the low internal resistance of 0.01 Ω allows

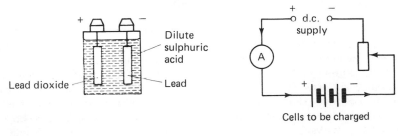

Fig. 20.11   (a)   (b)

quite large continuous currents to be maintained. The 'lost' voltage is negligible for currents of several amperes.

The state of a cell can be found by measuring the relative density of the acid with a hydrometer (see Unit 7.12). When the cell is fully charged the relative density is 1.25; it falls to 1.18 at full discharge (the e.m.f. stays fairly constant at 2 V). A 'flat' cell should not be left, otherwise the lead sulphate hardens and cannot be changed back to lead dioxide and lead.

Recharging once a month is advisable, using a circuit like that in Fig. 20.11(b). The supply must be d.c. of greater e.m.f. than that of the cells to be charged; the + of the charging supply goes to the + of the cells, and the current is adjusted by the rheostat to the value recommended on the cells.

Overcharging splits water in the acid solution into hydrogen and oxygen gases which bubble up round the electrodes. The gas mixture can cause an explosion if charging is done near a naked light. Any water lost must be replaced by topping up with distilled water to keep the electrodes covered. Maintenance-free sealed types of accumulator are now available.

A 12 V car battery consists of six lead–acid cells in series (Fig. 7.24(b)).

The *capacity* of an accumulator is stated in *ampere-hours* (A h) for a 10-hour discharge time. A 30 A h accumulator would supply 3 A for 10 hours; however, while 1 A would be supplied for more than 30 hours, 6 A could not be obtained for 5 hours.

20.9　Electrolysis

(i) **Terms.** The production of chemical action in a liquid by an electric current is called *electrolysis*. The liquid is an *electrolyte*. Solutions in water of acids, bases and salts are electrolytes. Mercury conducts electricity but without any chemical change occurring, and so mercury is not an electrolyte.

The two conductors (wires or plates) where current enters and leaves the liquid are *electrodes*. The electrode joined to the positive terminal of the battery at which the current (conventional) enters is the *anode*; the other electrode is the *cathode*. The vessel in which the electrolysis takes place is called a *voltameter* (*not* voltmeter).

In electrolysis electrical energy is changed to chemical energy and the process is the reverse of that in an electric cell.

(ii) **Electrolysis of copper sulphate with copper electrodes.** Electrolysis can be demonstrated using the apparatus and circuit of Fig. 20.12, with a strong copper sulphate solution (10 g to 100 cm^3 of water) in the beaker. No bubbles appear at the electrodes; if they are removed after a few minutes, however; the cathode will be seen to be covered with a fresh layer of copper while the anode is dull. Weighing shows that the mass of copper lost by the anode (if it is pure) equals that gained by the cathode. Also, the concentration of the copper sulphate solution is unchanged. It seems that copper is transferred from the anode to the cathode.

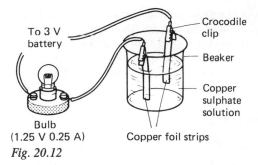

Fig. 20.12

(iii) **Ionic theory.** Current is considered to be carried in an electrolyte by *ions*. An ion is an atom or group of atoms which has either a positive charge due to losing one or more electrons or a negative charge due to gaining one or more electrons (Fig. 20.13(*a*)).

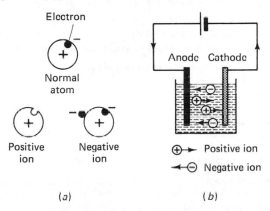

Fig. 20.13   (*a*)   (*b*)

During electrolysis, according to the ionic theory, positive ions are attracted to the negative cathode and negative ions to the positive anode (Fig. 20.13(*b*)). In an electrolyte the charge carriers are therefore both positive and negative.

Copper sulphate solution contains copper ions and sulphate ions and since copper is deposited on the cathode during electrolysis, the copper ions must be positively charged. The negative sulphate ions go to the anode, where they form copper sulphate.

In general, metals and hydrogen form positive ions, while non-metals form negative ions.

(iv) **Uses of electrolysis.** In electroplating, articles of one metal are electrically plated with another, either to improve their appearance or (if they are made of iron or steel) to prevent rusting. Cutlery is often made of nickel, plated with silver. Steel car bumpers are chromium-plated. The object to be plated is made the cathode in a voltameter with a salt of the plating metal as electrolyte—a silver salt for silver-plating, for example.

In the refining of copper the cathode is a thin sheet of copper, the electrolyte is copper sulphate solution and the anode is the impure copper to be refined. During electrolysis, pure copper is deposited on the cathode from the anode which slowly disappears. Impurities fall to the bottom of the voltameter.

Electrolysis is also used to make records and in the extraction of aluminium from its ores.

20.10 Revision Questions

1. What is meant by the statement that an electric kettle has a power of 2 kW?

2. What is the power P of an appliance through which a current I passes when it is connected to a supply of terminal p.d. V?

3. If the current in a resistor of resistance R is I when a p.d. V is applied across its ends, write down two expressions for the power it dissipates.

4. What material is used to make heating elements? Why is it used?

5. (a) What is a fuse?
   (b) Give two reasons why fuses 'blow'.
   (c) What safety precaution should be taken before replacing a fuse?

6. Why is tungsten used as the filament in a lamp?

7. State four advantages of fluorescent lamps and one disadvantage.

8. (a) Why does connecting the neutral wire to earth in an electricity supply system reduce the risk of shock?
   (b) Why are fuses and switches in the live rather than the neutral wire of a mains circuit?
   (c) Why is the metal body of an electric fire earthed?

9. When connecting an appliance to a three-pin mains plug using three-core cable, state the colour of insulation on the wire that should be connected to (a) the live (L) pin, (b) the neutral (N) pin and (c) the earth (E) pin.

10. (a) What is the e.m.f. of (i) a simple cell, (ii) a zinc–carbon cell, (iii) a lead–acid cell?
    (b) What materials are used for the positive and negative electrodes and the electrolyte in each of the cells in (a)?

11. (a) State the difference between a primary and a secondary cell.
    (b) What advantages does a lead–acid cell have over a carbon–zinc (dry) cell?
    (c) How is the state of charge of a lead–acid cell checked? Why must it not be left discharged ('flat') for any length of time?
    (d) A battery has a capacity of 40 A h. What does this mean?

12. State two different industrial applications of electrolysis.

20.11 Problems

Power in Electric Circuits
1. How much electrical energy (in J) does a 100 W lamp change in (a) 1 s, (b) 5 s, (c) 1 minute?

2. (*a*) What is the power of a lamp rated at 12 V 2 A?
   (*b*) How much electrical energy is changed per second by a 6 V 0.5 A lamp?

3. A lamp is marked 12 V 48 W. Calculate (*a*) the resistance of the filament, (*b*) the current through it.

4. What is the maximum power in kilowatts of the appliance(s) that can be connected safely to a 13 A 240 V mains socket?

5. (*a*) Calculate the power dissipated in a 10 Ω resistor when the current through it is (i) 1 A, (ii) 2 A.
   (*b*) What is the total power used when two 4 Ω resistors, connected to a 4 V battery, are joined (i) in series, (ii) in parallel?

Electric Heating
Specific heat capacity of water = 4200 J/(kg K). Neglect heat losses.

6. A small immersion heater, connected to a 12 V supply from which it takes a current of 3.5 A, is immersed in 0.6 kg of cold water for 5 minutes (300 s). Calculate the increase in temperature of the water.

7. How long will a 2.1 kW electric kettle take to raise the temperature of 1.2 kg of water from 10 °C to its boiling-point at 100 °C?

House Circuits
8. Copy Fig. 20.14 (but make it larger) and complete it so that the two 13 A switch sockets are connected in a ring main circuit from the consumer unit.

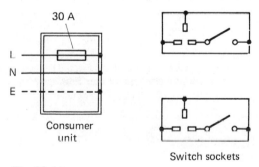

Fig. 20.14

9. Copy Fig. 20.15 and complete it so that the two lamps are connected to the mains supply but are controlled separately.

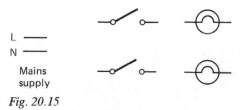

Fig. 20.15

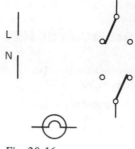

Fig. 20.16

10. Copy Fig. 20.16 and complete it so that the lamp can be controlled by either of the two-way switches.

11. State the current rating of the fuse (3 A or 13 A) which should be fitted in a plug for (*a*) a 150 W refrigerator, (*b*) a 360 W electric drill, (*c*) a 750 W electric iron and (*d*) a 2.4 kW electric kettle.

Paying for Electricity
12. If electrical energy costs 5p per unit, find the cost of (*a*) using seven 100 W lamps and two 150 W lamps for 5 hours, and (*b*) using a 200 W television receiver for 10 hours.

13. What is the cost of using a 3 kW night storage heater for 8 hours if the 'off-peak' cost of electrical energy is 2p per unit?

14. An electric cooker operating from the 240 V mains supply has an oven rated at 3 kW, a grill rated at 1 kW and four rings each rated at 500 W.
    (*a*) If all parts were on, would a 30 A fuse be suitable for the cooker circuit? Justify your answer.
    (*b*) If electrical energy costs 5p per unit what would be the total cost of operating the oven for 2 hours, and the grill and all four rings for 30 minutes?

Magnets, Motors and Meters

21.1 Permanent Magnets

(i) **Properties of magnets.** Simple experiments with magnets show that they have four main properties.

1. *Magnetic materials.* Magnets attract strongly certain materials such as iron, steel, nickel and cobalt, which are called *ferromagnetic materials*.

2. *Magnetic poles.* These are the places in a magnet to which magnetic materials, such as iron filings, are attracted. They occur in pairs of equal strength; in a bar magnet they are to be found near the ends.

3. *North and south poles.* If a magnet is supported so that it can swing in a horizontal plane it always comes to rest with one pole, the north-seeking or N pole, pointing roughly towards the earth's north pole. A magnet can therefore be used as a compass.

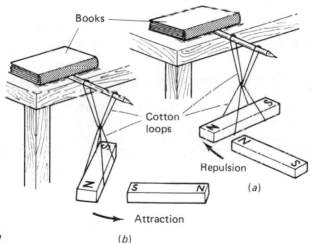

Fig. 21.1

4. *Law of magnetic poles.* If the N pole of a magnet is brought near the N pole of a suspended magnet, the two poles can be seen to repel each other (Fig. 21.1(*a*)). Two S poles also repel each other. By contrast, N and S poles always attract each other (Fig. 21.1(*b*)). The law of magnetic poles summarizes these facts and states:

Like poles repel, unlike poles attract.

The force, whether of attraction or repulsion, acts through space and increases as the distance between the poles decreases. Also the stronger the poles, the greater is the force.

Permanent magnets do not readily lose their magnetism.

(ii) **Testing for a magnet.** You can test whether an object is a magnet by bringing it near to a suspended magnet; one of the poles of a permanent magnet will cause repulsion. An unmagnetized magnetic material would attract *both* poles of the suspended magnet.

Repulsion is the only sure test for a magnet.

(iii) **Composition of magnets.** The first permanent magnets were made of steel (an alloy of iron); modern magnets are much stronger and are of two types.

1. *Alloy magnets* contain metals such as iron, nickel, copper, cobalt and aluminium. They have trade names such as Alnico and Alcomax.

2. *Ceramic magnets* are made from powders called *ferrites* which are compounds of iron oxide with other metal oxides. They are brittle. One has the trade name Magnadur.

(iv) **Uses of magnets.** Magnets are used in door catches, cycle dynamos, electric motors, loudspeakers and telephones. Ferrite powder can be bonded with plastic and rubber to give either a flexible magnet or one of any shape. Very fine powder, each particle of which can be magnetized, is used to coat tapes for tape recorders and microcomputer data storage.

21.2 Methods of Magnetizing and Demagnetizing

(i) **Making a magnet by stroking.** Steel knitting needles, hair grips and pieces of clockspring can be magnetized; the methods of single and double touch are shown in Fig. 21.2(a) and (b). In single touch, the steel is stroked from end to end about twenty times in the same direction by the same pole of a permanent magnet. In the better method of double touch, stroking is done from the centre

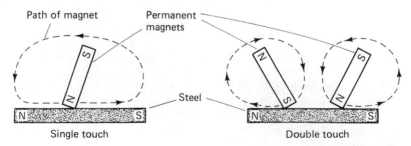

Single touch   Double touch

Fig. 21.2   (a)   (b)

outwards with unlike poles of two magnets at the same time. The magnets must be lifted high above the steel at the end of each stroke in both methods.

The pole produced at the end of the steel where the stroke ends is of the opposite kind to that of the stroking pole and is due, as we will see in Unit 21.3, to an effect called *magnetic induction* (compare with electrostatic induction— see Unit 18.4).

(ii) **Making a magnet electrically.** The material to be magnetized is placed inside a cylindrical coil called a *solenoid*, having several hundred turns of insulated copper wire; this becomes a magnet when it is connected to a direct current (d.c.) supply (Fig. 21.3(*a*)). If the current is switched on for a second and then off, the material is found to be a magnet when removed from the solenoid.

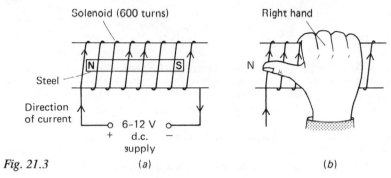

Fig. 21.3 (*a*) (*b*)

The polarity of the magnet depends on the direction of the current and is given by the *Right-hand grip rule* (Fig. 21.3(*b*)):

If the fingers of the right hand grip the solenoid in the direction of the current (that is, from the positive of the supply), the thumb points to the N pole.

In practice magnets are made electrically using a very large current for a fraction of a second.

(iii) **Demagnetizing a magnet.** The magnet is placed inside a solenoid through which *alternating current* (a.c.) is flowing (Fig. 21.4). With the current still passing, the magnet is slowly removed to a distance from the solenoid.

Heating a magnet strongly or hammering it also causes demagnetization.

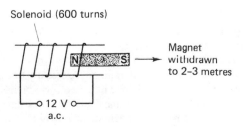

Fig. 21.4

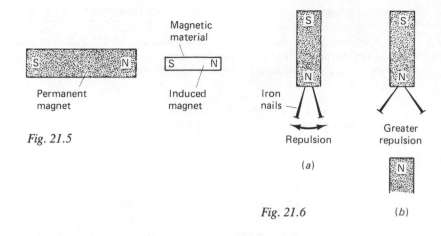

Fig. 21.5

Fig. 21.6

21.3 Magnetic Induction: Iron and Steel

(i) **Inducing magnetism.** When a piece of unmagnetized magnetic material touches or is brought near to the pole of a permanent magnet, it becomes a magnet itself. The material is said to have magnetism *induced* in it. Fig. 21.5 shows that a N pole induces a N pole in the far end.

This can be checked by hanging two iron nails from the N pole of a magnet. Their lower ends repel each other (Fig. 21.6(*a*)) and both are repelled by the N pole of another magnet (Fig. 21.6(*b*)).

(ii) **Iron and steel.** Chains of small iron paper clips and steel pen nibs can be hung from a magnet (Fig. 21.7). Each clip or nib magnetizes the one below it by induction and the unlike poles so formed attract each other.

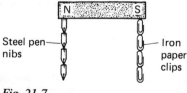

Fig. 21.7

If the iron chain is removed by pulling the top clip away from the magnet, the chain collapses, showing that *magnetism induced in iron is temporary*. When the same is done with the steel chain, it does not collapse; *magnetism induced in steel is permanent*.

Magnetic materials like iron, which magnetize easily but do not keep their magnetism, are said to be 'soft'. Those like steel, which are more difficult to magnetize but stay magnetized, are 'hard'. Both types have their uses; very 'hard' materials are used to make permanent magnets.

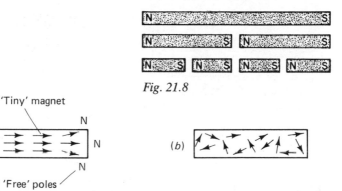

Fig. 21.8

(a)

'Tiny' magnet

S   N

S   N

S   N

'Free' poles

(b)

Fig. 21.9 (a) Magnetized bar, (b) unmagnetized bar

21.4 Theory of Magnetism

If a magnetized piece of steel clockspring or thin rod is cut into smaller and then even smaller pieces, every piece is a magnet with a N and a S pole (Fig. 21.8). It is therefore reasonable to suppose that a magnet is made up of lots of 'tiny' magnets all lined up with their N poles pointing in the same direction (Fig. 21.9(a)). At the ends, the 'free' poles of the 'tiny' magnets repel each other and fan out so that the poles of the magnet are *round* the ends.

In an unmagnetized bar we can imagine the 'tiny' magnets pointing in all directions, the N pole of one being neutralized by the S pole of another. Their magnetic effects cancel out and there are no 'free' poles near the ends (Fig. 21.9(b)).

There is evidence to show that each of the 'tiny' magnets is a group of millions of atoms, called a *domain*. In a ferromagnetic material each atom is a magnet and the magnetic effect of every atom in a particular domain acts in the same direction.

As well as explaining the effect of breaking up a magnet, this theory accounts for the following.

1. *Magnetic saturation.* There is a limit to the strength of a magnet, which reaches a maximum when all the 'tiny' magnets are lined up.

2. *Demagnetization by heating or hammering* (see Unit 21.2(iii)). Both processes cause the atoms of the magnet to vibrate more vigorously and disturb the alignment of the 'tiny' magnets.

3. *Storage of magnets using keepers.* A magnet tends to become weaker with time due to the 'free' poles near the ends repelling each other and upsetting the alignment of the domains. This can be prevented by storing bar magnets in pairs with unlike poles opposite and pieces of soft iron, called keepers, across the ends (Fig. 21.10). The keepers become induced magnets and their poles neutralize the poles of the bar magnets. The domains in both magnets and keepers form closed chains with no 'free' poles.

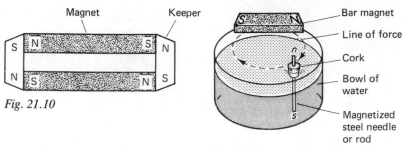

Fig. 21.10

Fig. 21.11

21.5 Magnetic Fields

(i) **Direction of field.** The space surrounding a magnet in which it produces a magnetic force is called a *magnetic field*. The force around a bar magnet can be detected and shown to vary in direction using the apparatus in Fig. 21.11. If the floating magnet is released near the N pole of the bar magnet, it is repelled to the S pole and moves along a curved path known as a *line of force*, a *line of magnetic flux* or a *field line*. It moves in the opposite direction if its south pole is uppermost.

It is useful to regard a magnetic field as having a direction and to represent the field by lines of force. It has been decided that *the direction of the field at any point should be the direction of the force on a N pole*. To show the direction on a diagram, arrows are drawn on the lines of force pointing away from a N pole towards a S pole.

(ii) **Plotting lines of force.** One method, suitable for both weak and strong fields, uses a *plotting compass* which consists of a small pivoted magnet in a glass case with brass walls (Fig. 21.12(*a*)).

A bar magnet NS is laid on a sheet of paper (Fig. 21.12(*b*)) and the plotting compass placed at a point near one pole of the magnet. The positions taken up by the poles n and s of the compass are marked by dots A and B. The compass is moved so that pole s is exactly over B, and the new position of n marked by dot C.

The process is continued until the S pole of the bar magnet is reached. Joining the dots gives one line of force. Other lines can be plotted by starting at

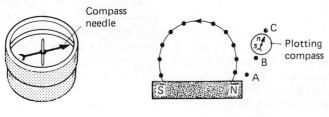

Fig. 21.12   (a)   (b)

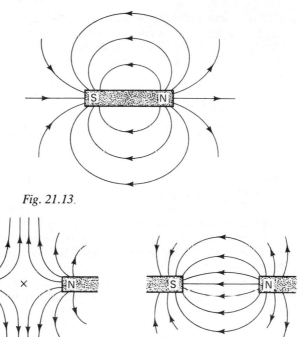

Fig. 21.13.

Fig. 21.14   (*a*)   (*b*)

different points round the magnet. A typical field pattern is shown in Fig. 21.13.

The combined field due to two neighbouring magnets can also be plotted in the same way to give patterns like those in Fig. 21.14(*a*) and (*b*). In Fig. 21.14(*a*) the point X is called a *neutral point* because the field due to one magnet cancels out that due to the other and there are no lines of force there.

In the *iron filings* method a sheet of paper is placed on top of a bar magnet and iron filings sprinkled thinly and evenly on to the paper from a pepper pot. If the paper is tapped gently with a pen, the filings form patterns of the lines of

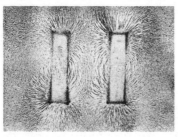
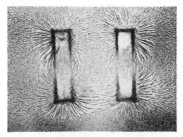

Fig. 21.15   (*a*)   (*b*)

force. This is because each filing is magnetized by induction and turns in the direction of the field when the paper is tapped.

The method is quick but of no use for weak fields. Fig. 21.15(a) and (b) show typical patterns produced using two magnets. Why are they different?

21.6 Magnetic Effect of a Current

Magnetic fields are also produced around current-carrying conductors, different field patterns being given by differently shaped conductors.

(i) **Field due to a straight wire.** If a straight vertical wire passes through the centre of a piece of card held horizontally and a current of several amperes is passed through the wire, iron filings sprinkled on the card set in concentric circles when the card is tapped (Fig. 21.16(a)).

Plotting compasses placed on the card set along the field lines and show the direction of the field at different points. When the current direction is reversed the compasses point in the opposite direction, showing that the direction of the field reverses when the current reverses. Current going down into the paper is shown by the tail of an arrow, ⊕ (Fig. 21.16(b)), and current coming up out of the paper by the point of an arrow, ⊙ (Fig. 21.16(c)).

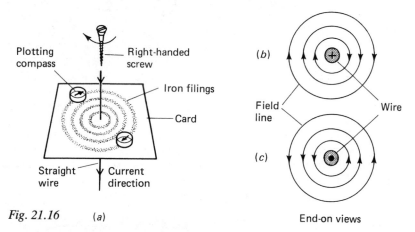

Fig. 21.16   (a)   End-on views

If the current direction is known, the direction of the field can be predicted by the *Right-hand screw rule*:

>*If a right-handed screw moves forward in the direction of the current (conventional), the direction of rotation of the screw gives the direction of the field.*

(ii) **Field due to a circular coil.** The field pattern is shown in Fig. 21.17. At the centre of the coil the field lines are straight and at right angles to the plane of the coil. The Right-hand screw rule again gives the direction of the field at any point. The field is like that produced by a very short bar magnet, one face of the coil behaving like a N pole and the other like a S pole.

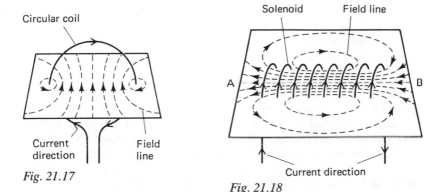

Fig. 21.17

Fig. 21.18

(iii) **Field due to a solenoid.** A solenoid (a long cylindrical coil) produces a field similar to that of a bar magnet; in Fig. 21.18 end A behaves like a N pole and end B like a S pole. The polarity is found as before by applying the Right-hand screw rule to a short length of one turn of the solenoid. Alternatively the *Right-hand grip rule* can be used (see Unit 21.2(ii)).

The field inside a solenoid can be made very strong if it has a large number of turns and a large current flows. Previously we used it to magnetize materials (see Unit 21.2(ii)).

21.7 Electromagnets and Their Uses

(i) **Electromagnets.** An electromagnet consists of a coil or solenoid of many turns of insulated copper wire wound on a core of *soft*, ferromagnetic material

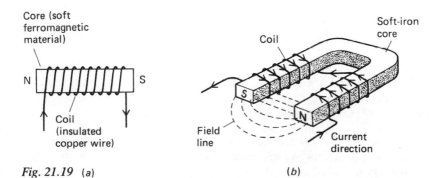

Fig. 21.19 (a)

(b)

such as iron or the alloy mumetal (Fig. 21.19(a)). When current passes through the coil, the core is magnetized and produces a magnetic field about one thousand times stronger than that due to the coil alone. The core, being magnetically soft, loses its magnetism when the current is switched off. An electromagnet is therefore a *temporary* magnet; its strength increases if

1. the current in the coil increases,
2. the number of turns on the coil increases, or
3. the poles are closer together.

In C-core (or horseshoe) electromagnets condition 3 is achieved (Fig. 21.19(b)), and a strong magnetic field is created in the gap between the poles. Note that the coil is wound in *opposite* directions on the limbs of the core.

Large, powerful electromagnets are used as cranes to lift objects made of iron and steel—in a scrapyard, for instance. Electromagnets are also an essential part of many electrical devices.

(ii) **Electric bell.** Fig. 21.20 shows the circuit. When the bell push is depressed, the circuit is completed and current flows in the coils of the electromagnet; this becomes magnetized and attracts the soft-iron bar (the *armature*). The hammer hits the gong but the circuit is now broken at the point of the contact screw (C).

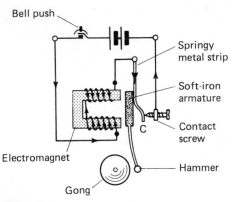

Fig. 21.20

The electromagnet loses its magnetism and no longer attracts the armature. The springy metal strip is then able to pull the armature back, remaking contact at C and so completing the circuit again. This cycle is repeated so long as the bell push is depressed, and the bell rings continuously.

(iii) **Relay.** This is a switch worked by an electromagnet. It is useful if we want one circuit to control another, especially if the current is large in the second circuit. Fig. 21.21(a) shows a typical relay. When current flows in the coil from

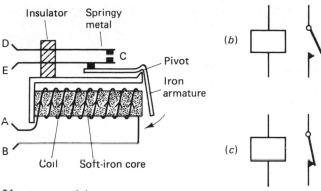

Fig. 21.21 (a)

the circuit connected to AB, the soft-iron core is magnetized and attracts the L-shaped iron armature. This rocks on its pivot and closes the contacts at C in the circuit connected to DE. The relay is then 'energized' or 'on'. The symbol for a relay with normally open contacts is shown in Fig. 21.21(b) and for one with normally closed contacts in Fig. 21.21(c).

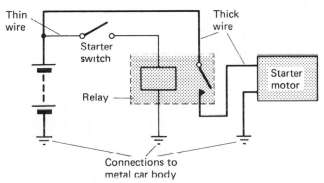

Fig. 21.22

In a *vehicle starter-motor circuit* (Fig. 21.22) the starter motor requires a very large current (up to 100 A or more). By using a relay this large current in the motor circuit (which has thick, short leads) is switched on by a small current in the starter switch circuit (which has thin leads).

(iv) **Reed switch.** A reed switch is shown in Fig. 21.23(a), with its symbol. When current flows in the coil, the magnetic field produced magnetizes the strips (called 'reeds') of magnetic material. The ends become opposite poles and one reed is attracted to the other, so completing the circuit connected to AB. The reeds separate when the current in the coil is switched off.

Reed switches can also be operated by permanent magnets. Fig. 21.23(b) shows the use of a normally open reed switch as a burglar alarm.

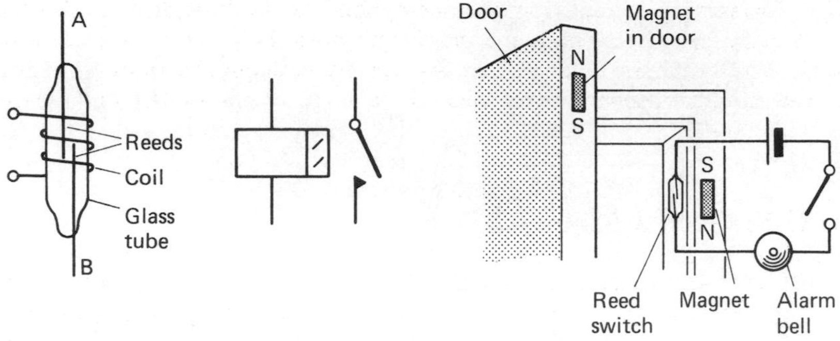

Fig. 21.23   (a)   (b)

21.8 Telephone

A telephone handset consists of a receiver containing an electromagnet and a microphone.

(i) **Carbon microphone** (Fig. 21.24). When someone speaks into the handset, sound waves cause the diaphragm to move backwards and forwards. This varies the pressure on the carbon granules between the front carbon block (which is attached to the diaphragm) and the back one (which is fixed). When the pressure increases, the granules are squeezed closer together and their electrical resistance decreases. A decrease of pressure has the opposite effect. If a current is passing through the microphone (from a battery), this too varies in a similar way to the sound wave variations. The microphone thus changes sound energy into electrical energy, which travels along the telephone cables.

(ii) **Receiver.** The electrical energy from the microphone is changed back into sound by the receiver (Fig. 21.25).

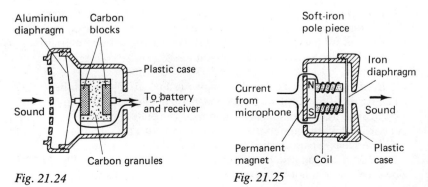

Fig. 21.24   Fig. 21.25

The varying current from the microphone passes through the coils of an electromagnet. This pulls the diaphragm towards it, by a distance which depends on the size of the current. As a result, the diaphragm moves in and out and produces sound waves that are a copy of those that entered the microphone.

21.9 Electric Motors

Electric motors form the heart of a whole host of electrical devices, ranging from domestic appliances such as vacuum cleaners and washing machines to electric locomotives and lifts. In a car the windscreen wipers are usually driven by one and the engine is started by another. One of their newest uses is in robots where 'stepper' motors, driven by a series of electrical pulses, turn the robot arm by a small fixed amount for each pulse.

(i) Force on a current-carrying conductor in a magnetic field. A wire carrying a current in a magnetic field experiences a force. If the wire can move it does. In Fig. 21.26 the flexible wire is loosely supported in the strong magnetic field of a C-shaped magnet (either a permanent magnet or an electromagnet). When the switch is pressed, current flows in the wire which jumps upwards as shown. If either the direction of the current or the direction of the field is reversed, the wire moves downwards. What happens if both are reversed?

In this experiment the wire is at right angles to the magnetic field and further experiments show that the force on it increases with

1. the strength of the magnetic field,
2. the size of the current, and
3. the length of the wire in the field.

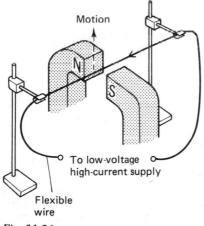

Fig. 21.26

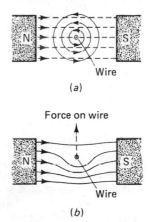

Fig. 21.27

If the wire is not at right angles to the field, the force is smaller; it is zero if the wire is parallel to the field.

The effect can be explained in terms of the field lines. Fig. 21.27(*a*) is a side view of the magnetic field lines due to the wire and the magnet. Those due to the wire are circles and we will suppose their directions are as shown. The dotted lines represent the field lines of the magnet and their direction is to the right.

The resultant field obtained by combining both fields is shown in Fig. 21.27(*b*). There are more lines below the wire than above it, since both fields act in the same direction below but are in opposition above. If we suppose the lines are like stretched elastic, we can think of those below as trying to straighten out and in so doing exerting an upwards force on the wire.

(ii) **Fleming's left-hand rule.** The direction of the force or thrust on the wire can be predicted by this rule, which is also called the 'Motor rule' (Fig. 21.28):

Hold the thumb and first two fingers of the left hand at right angles to each other with the First finger pointing in the direction of the Field and the seCond finger in the direction of the Current; then the Thumb points in the direction of the Thrust.

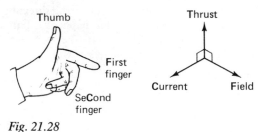

Fig. 21.28

Remember that

1. the field direction is from the N pole to the S pole,

2. the current direction is for conventional current, that is, from the + terminal of the supply to the − terminal, and

3. the rule holds only where the field and current directions are at right angles.

(iii) **Simple d.c. electric motor.** A simple motor to work from direct current (d.c.) consists of a rectangular coil of wire mounted on an axle which can rotate between the poles of a C-shaped magnet (Fig. 21.29). Each end of the coil is connected to half of a split ring of copper, called the *commutator*, which rotates with the coil. Two carbon blocks, the *brushes*, are pressed lightly against the commutator by springs. The brushes are connected to an electrical supply.

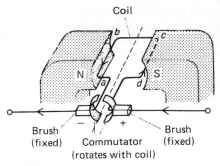

Fig. 21.29

If Fleming's left-hand rule is applied to the coil in the position shown, we find that side *ab* experiences an upward force and side *cd* a downward force. (No forces act on *ad* and *bc* since they are parallel to the field.) These two forces form a couple (see Unit 3.7(ii)) which rotates the coil in a clockwise direction until it is vertical.

The brushes are then in line with the gaps in the commutator and the current stops. Because of its inertia, however, the coil overshoots the vertical and the commutator halves change contact from one brush to the other. This reverses the current through the coil and so also the directions of the forces on its sides. Side *ab* is on the right now, acted on by a downward force, while *cd* is on the left subject to an upward force. The coil thus carries on rotating clockwise.

(iv) **Practical motors.** These have

1. *a coil of many turns wound on a soft-iron cylinder or core* that rotates with the coil, which makes it more powerful; the coil and core together are called the *armature*;

2. *several coils each in a slot in the core* and each having a pair of commutator segments, giving increased power and smoother running;

3. *an electromagnet* (usually) to produce the field in which the armature rotates.

Most electric motors used in industry are *induction motors*, which work off a.c. using a different principle from that of the d.c. motor.

21.10 Moving Coil Loudspeaker

Most loudspeakers are of the moving coil type which uses the fact that a current-carrying conductor experiences a force when in a magnetic field (see Unit 21.9(i)). A loudspeaker consists of

1. a *permanent magnet* with a central cylindrical pole and a surrounding ring

pole which creates a strong radial field in the gap between the poles (that is, the field lines are directed towards or away from the centre of the cylindrical pole) (Fig. 21.30(a));

2. a *short cylindrical coil* which can move backwards and forwards through a short distance in the magnetic field and whose turns are at right angles to the field; and

3. a *paper cone* attached to the coil (Fig. 21.30(b)).

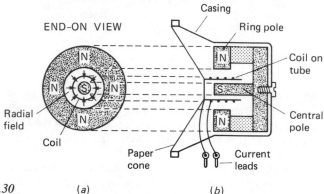

Fig. 21.30   (a)   (b)

When alternating current from, say, a radio or a record-player passes through the coil it is forced to move in or out, depending on the current direction—according to Fleming's left-hand rule. The paper cone moves with the coil and thus sets up sound waves in the surrounding air of the same frequency as that of the alternating current.

21.11 Electric Meters

(i) **Moving coil galvanometer.** A galvanometer detects small currents or small p.d.s, often of the order of milliamperes (mA) or millivolts (mV) or, with some instruments, even less.

In the moving coil *pointer-type* meter, a coil is pivoted on jewelled bearings between the poles of a permanent magnet (Fig. 21.31(a)). Current enters and leaves the coil by hair springs above and below it. When current flows, a couple acts on the coil (as in an electric motor), causing it to rotate until it is stopped by the springs: the greater the current the greater the deflection, which is shown by a pointer attached to the coil.

The soft-iron cylinder at the centre of the coil is fixed and along with the concave poles of the magnet it produces a radial field (Fig. 21.31(b)). The scale on the meter is then even or *linear*, that is, all the divisions on the scale are the same size.

The *sensitivity* of a galvanometer—the deflection of the pointer caused by a given current, say 1 mA—is increased by having

1. more turns on the coil,
2. a stronger magnet,
3. weaker hair springs or a wire suspension,
4. as a pointer, a long beam of light reflected from a mirror on the coil.

The last two are used in highly sensitive *light-beam* meters (see Unit 13.11(i)) which have a full-scale deflection (f.s.d.) of a few microamperes (μA). (1μA $=10^{-6}$ A.)

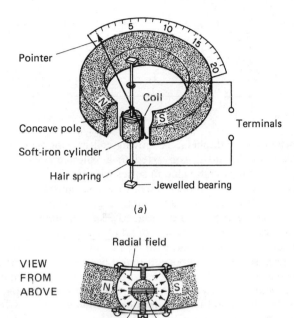

Pointer

Coil

Concave pole

Soft-iron cylinder

Hair spring

Jewelled bearing

Terminals

(a)

Radial field

VIEW
FROM
ABOVE

Soft-iron cylinder   Coil

Fig. 21.31   (b)

A moving coil galvanometer measures d.c., not a.c. (unless it is used with a rectifier—see Unit 24.6).

A galvanometer can be modified for use either as an ammeter (to measure higher currents) or as a voltmeter (to measure higher p.d.s).

(ii) **Ammeters and shunts.** Suppose a moving coil meter has resistance 5 Ω (due largely to the coil) and gives a f.s.d. when 1 mA (0.001 A) passes through it.

To convert it to an ammeter to read 0–1 A, a resistor of low value is connected in parallel with it as a by-pass. The resistor is called a *shunt*; when the current to be measured is 1 A, it must allow only 0.001 A to go through the meter and the rest (0.999 A) must flow through the shunt (Fig. 21.32). Shunts consist of short lengths of thick manganin wire or strip (manganin is an alloy whose resistance does not change when it is warmed by the current).

An ammeter is placed *in series* in a circuit and must have a *low resistance* compared with the rest of the circuit—otherwise it changes the current to be measured.

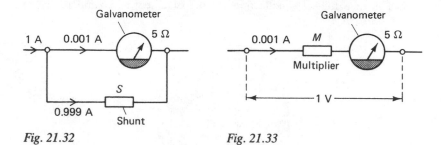

Fig. 21.32   Fig. 21.33

(iii) **Voltmeters and multipliers.** A moving coil galvanometer of resistance $5\,\Omega$ and f.s.d. $1\,\text{mA}$ can be converted to a voltmeter to read 0–$1\,\text{V}$ by connecting a resistor of high value in series with it.

The resistor is called a *multiplier* and its resistance must be such that when a p.d. of $1\,\text{V}$ is applied across it and the meter together, the current is $0.001\,\text{A}$, that is, the meter records a f.s.d. (Fig. 21.33). Multipliers consist of long lengths of insulated manganin wire wound on a bobbin.

A voltmeter is placed *in parallel* with the part of the circuit across which the p.d. is to be measured. It is important that it has a *high resistance* compared with the resistance across which it is connected—otherwise the total resistance of the whole circuit is reduced, so changing the current and the p.d. required. The ideal voltmeter would have an infinite resistance.

21.12 Revision Questions and Problems

Permanent Magnets

1. (*a*) Name two types of permanent magnet.
   (*b*) State four properties of a permanent magnet.

2. If a piece of metal was thought to be a magnet, which one of the following observations would offer conclusive evidence?
   A It attracts a steel screwdriver
   B It attracts a known magnet
   C It repels a known magnet

3. The metal bar AB in Fig. 21.34 is stroked by the N pole of a magnet in the direction shown.
   (*a*) Name a metal that would be permanently magnetized by this process.
   (*b*) Which end of AB would become a N pole in such a metal?

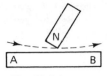

Fig. 21.34

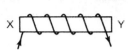

Fig. 21.35

4. In Fig. 21.35 the steel rod XY is being magnetized electrically by a current passing through the coil in the direction shown. What kind of pole would be produced at X?

5. State two ways in which a magnet can be demagnetized.

6. Explain why needles hung from either end of a bar magnet held horizontally incline towards one another as shown in Fig. 21.36.

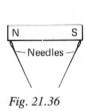

Fig. 21.36

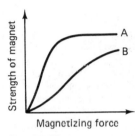

Fig. 21.37

7. What is the difference between a 'soft' and a 'hard' ferromagnetic material? Name one example of each. Which would be used to make a permanent magnet?

8. The graphs in Fig. 21.37 are for two magnetic materials.
   (a) Does material A or B become the stronger magnet?
   (b) Which material is easier to magnetize?

9. Explain in terms of the theory of magnetism (a) the difference between a magnetized and an unmagnetized bar, (b) why there is a limit to the strength of a magnet, (c) why heating or dropping a magnet reduces its strength, and (d) why keepers are used to store magnets.

Magnetic Fields
10. Copy Fig. 21.38, mark the N pole of the magnet and draw the field line on which the plotting compass lies.

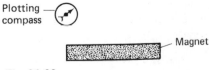

Fig. 21.38

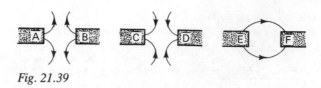

Fig. 21.39

11. The lines of force between the poles of three pairs of magnets are shown in Fig. 21.39. What kind of poles are A, B, C, D, E, F?

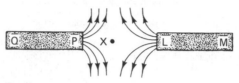

Fig. 21.40

12. A neutral point X is shown in Fig. 21.40 in the magnetic field between two bar magnets.
    (a) What is meant by a neutral point?
    (b) If Q is a S pole, what is (i) P, (ii) L, (iii) M?
    (c) Which is the stronger pole, P or L? Explain your answer.

Magnetic Effect of a Current: Electromagnets
13. The vertical wire in Fig. 21.41 is at right angles to the card. In what direction will a plotting compass at A point (a) when there is no current in the wire, (b) when current flows upwards?

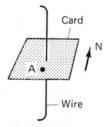

Fig. 21.41

14. Draw the magnetic field patterns due to (a) a single-turn circular coil, (b) a solenoid.

15. (a) Why is the core of an electromagnet made of a soft magnetic material?
    (b) State two ways in which an electromagnet can be made stronger.

16. Why does the hammer of an electric bell (a) strike the gong, (b) spring back after striking it?

17. (a) State one advantage of the relay as a switch.

(*b*) Give one use for a relay.

(*c*) Draw the symbol for a relay with normally open contacts.

18. Explain how the reed switch works in the burglar alarm circuit of Fig. 21.15(*b*).

19. In a telephone handset explain the part played (*a*) by the electromagnet in the receiver and (*b*) by the carbon granules in the microphone.

Electric Motors and Meters

20. A wire, carrying a current out of the page, is shown at right angles to a magnetic field in Fig. 21.42. Copy the diagram and put an arrow on the wire to show the direction of the force acting on it. Name the rule you have used.

State two ways in which the force could be increased.

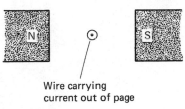

Wire carrying
current out of page

Fig. 21.42

21. The end view of a coil carrying a current in a magnetic field is shown in Fig. 21.43(*a*).

(*a*) Copy the diagram and show by arrows on the sides of the coil the forces acting on them.

(*b*) What do the forces form?

(*c*) In Fig. 21.43(*a*), is the turning effect a maximum or zero?

(*d*) In Fig. 21.43(*b*), is the turning effect a maximum or zero?

(*e*) For the position of the coil in Fig. 21.43(*a*), how could the turning effect be increased?

⊙ = current out of page

⊕ = current into page

Fig. 21.43   (*a*)   (*b*)

22. (*a*) In a d.c. electric motor what is the role of (i) the brushes, (ii) the commutator?

(*b*) Name three ways in which the performance of practical d.c. motors is improved.

23. How does a moving coil loudspeaker produce sound when an alternating current passes through it?

24. (*a*) What does a galvanometer measure?
(*b*) What is the principle of the moving coil galvanometer?
(*c*) State three ways in which the construction of a moving coil galvanometer ensures that it is sensitive.

25. Draw diagrams showing how a galvanometer can be modified to measure (*a*) currents of a few amperes, (*b*) p.d.s of several volts.

26. (*a*) Why should the resistance of an ammeter be very small?
(*b*) Why should the resistance of a voltmeter be very large?

Generators, Transformers and Alternating Current

22.1 Electromagnetic Induction

(i) **Inducing e.m.f.s.** An electric current creates a magnetic field. The reverse effect—that of producing electricity from magnetism—was discovered in 1831 by Faraday and is called *electromagnetic induction*. The discovery led to the construction of generators for producing electrical energy in power stations. The effect can be investigated in two ways.

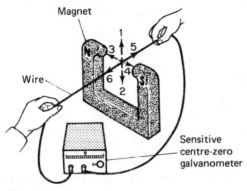

Fig. 22.1

1. *Straight wire and U-shaped magnet* (Fig. 22.1). First the wire is held at rest between the poles of the magnet and the galvanometer observed. It is then moved in each of the six directions shown. Only *when it is moving* upwards (direction 1) or downwards (direction 2) is there a deflection on the galvanometer, indicating an induced current in the wire. The deflections for upward and downward movements are in opposite directions, and last only while the wire is in motion.

2. *Bar magnet and coil* (Fig. 22.2). The magnet is pushed into the coil, one pole first, then held still inside it. It is next withdrawn. The galvanometer shows that current is induced in the coil in one direction *as the magnet moves in* and in the opposite direction *as it is removed*. There is no deflection when the magnet is at rest. The results are the same if the coil is moved instead of the magnet, that is, only *relative motion* is needed.

(ii) **Faraday's law.** To 'explain' electromagnetic induction Faraday suggested that an e.m.f. is induced in a conductor whenever it 'cuts' or moves across

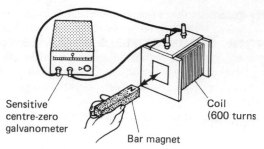

Fig. 22.2

magnetic field lines, but not when it moves along them or is at rest. If the conductor forms part of a complete circuit, an induced current is also produced.

Faraday found (and it can be shown with apparatus like that in Fig. 22.2) that the induced e.m.f. increases with increases of

1. the speed of motion of the magnet or coil,
2. the number of turns on the coil, and
3. the strength of the magnet.

These facts led him to state a law:

The size of the induced e.m.f. is directly proportional to the rate at which the conductor cuts magnetic field lines.

(iii) **Lenz's law.** The direction of the induced current can be predicted by a law due to the Russian scientist, Lenz:

The direction of the induced current is such as to oppose the change causing it.

In Fig. 22.3(*a*) the magnet approaches the coil, N pole first. According to Lenz's law the induced current should flow in a direction which makes the coil behave like a magnet with its top a N pole. The downward motion of the magnet will then be opposed.

When the magnet is withdrawn, the top of the coil should become a S pole

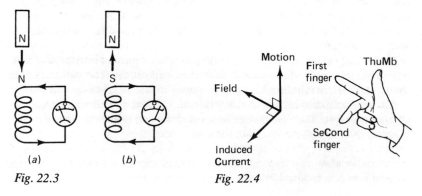

Fig. 22.3

Fig. 22.4

(Fig. 22.3(*b*)) and attract the N pole of the magnet, so hindering its removal. The induced current is thus in the opposite direction to that in (*a*).

Lenz's law is an example of the principle of conservation of energy. If the reverse were true—if the induced current flowed in the direction of the change causing it—electrical energy would be created from nothing. As it is, mechanical energy is provided by whoever moves the magnet, to overcome the forces that arise.

For a straight wire moving at right angles to a magnetic field a more useful form of Lenz's law is *Fleming's right-hand rule* (the 'Dynamo rule') (Fig. 22.4):

Hold the thumb and first two fingers of the right hand at right angles to each other with the First finger pointing in the direction of the Field and the thuMb in the direction of Motion of the wire, then the seCond finger points in the direction of the induced Current.

22.2 Simple Generators

(i) **A.c. generator (alternator).** The simplest alternating current (a.c.) generator consists of a rectangular coil between the poles of a C-shaped magnet (Fig. 22.5(*a*)). The ends of the coil are joined to two slip rings which are carried on the axle and against which carbon brushes press. When the coil is rotated it cuts the field lines and an e.m.f. is induced in it.

Fig. 22.5(*b*) shows how the e.m.f. varies over one complete rotation.

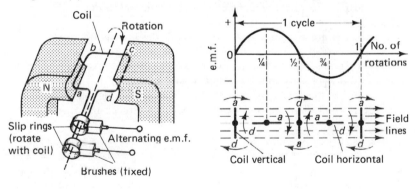

Fig. 22.5   (*a*)   (*b*)

As the coil moves through the vertical position with *ab* uppermost, *ab* and *dc* are moving along the lines (*bc* and *da* do so always) and no cutting occurs. The induced e.m.f. is zero.

During the first quarter-rotation the e.m.f. increases to a maximum when the coil is horizontal. Sides *ab* and *dc* are then cutting lines at the greatest rate.

In the second quarter-rotation the e.m.f. decreases again and is zero when the coil is vertical with *dc* uppermost. After this, the direction of the e.m.f. reverses because, during the next half-rotation, the motion of *ab* is directed upwards and that of *dc* downwards.

An alternating e.m.f. is generated which acts first in one direction and then the other; it would cause a.c. to flow in a circuit connected to the brushes. The *frequency* of an a.c. is the number of complete cycles it makes each second (c/s) and is measured in *hertz* (Hz: 1 c/s =1 Hz), so that if the coil rotates twice per second, the a.c. has frequency 2 Hz. Larger units are the *kilohertz* (kHz: 1 kilohertz =1000 Hz) and the *megahertz* (MHz: 1 megahertz =1 000 000 Hz).

The mains supply in the United Kingdom is a.c. of frequency 50 Hz.

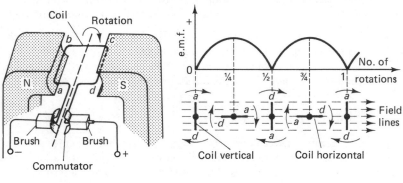

Fig. 22.6   (a)   (b)

(ii) **D.c. generator (dynamo).** An a.c. generator becomes a direct current (d.c.) one if the slip rings are replaced by a commutator like that in a d.c. motor (Fig. 22.6(a)).

The brushes are arranged so that as the coil goes through the vertical, each brush changes over contact from one half of the split ring of the commutator to the other. In this position the e.m.f. induced in the coil reverses and so one brush is always positive and the other negative.

The e.m.f. at the brushes is shown in Fig. 22.6(b); although varying in value, it never changes direction and would produce a direct current (d.c.) in an external circuit.

In construction the simple d.c. dynamo is the same as the simple d.c. motor and one can be used as the other. When an electric motor is working it acts as a dynamo and creates an e.m.f., called a *back e.m.f.*, opposing and nearly equal to the applied p.d. The current in the coil is therefore much less once the motor is running.

(iii) **Practical generators.** In the generators used in practice, several coils are wound in evenly spaced slots in a soft-iron cylinder (the *armature*), and electromagnets (with *field* windings) usually replace permanent magnets.

1. *Cars.* Most cars are now fitted with alternators, because at low engine speeds they give a greater output current than that from a dynamo. The a.c. is rectified (changed to d.c.), part is used to energize the field coils (there is always enough residual magnetism in their iron cores to start the process) and the rest is fed out via slip rings to charge the battery.

2. *Power stations.* In power station alternators, the field coils and their core, composing the electromagnets, rotate (the *rotor*) while the armature coils and their iron core are at rest (the *stator*). The large p.d.s and currents (25 kV at several hundred amperes, for instance) induced in the stator are then led away through stationary cables, as otherwise they would quickly destroy the slip rings by sparking. Instead, the relatively small d.c. required by the rotor is fed via the slip rings from a small dynamo (the *exciter*), which is driven by the same turbine (usually steam-driven) as the rotor (Fig. 22.7).

3. *Bicycles.* In a bicycle dynamo too a.c. is induced in a stationary coil, but here the rotor is a permanent magnet (Fig. 22.8).

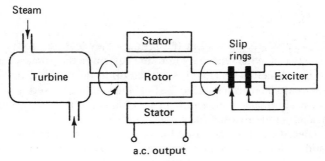

Fig. 22.7

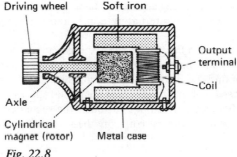

Fig. 22.8

22.3 Mutual Induction

(i) **Using d.c.** When the current in a coil is switched on or off or changed, an e.m.f. and current are induced in a neighbouring coil. The effect, called *mutual induction*, is an example of electromagnetic induction that does not use a permanent magnet and can be demonstrated with the arrangement of Fig. 22.9. Coil A is the *primary* and coil B the *secondary*.

Switching on the current in the primary sets up a magnetic field and as its

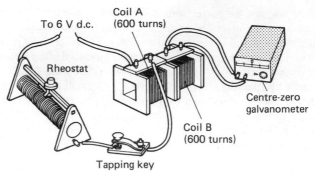

To 6 V d.c.   Coil A
(600 turns)

Rheostat

Centre-zero
galvanometer

Coil B
(600 turns)

Tapping key

Fig. 22.9

field lines 'grow' outwards from the primary they 'cut' the secondary. An e.m.f. is induced in the secondary until the current in the primary reaches its steady value. When the current is switched off in the primary, the magnetic field dies away and we can imagine the field lines cutting the secondary as they collapse, again inducing an e.m.f. in it. Changing the primary current by *quickly* altering the rheostat has the same effect.

The induced e.m.f. is increased by having a soft-iron rod in the coils or, better still, by using coils wound on a complete iron ring. More field lines then cut the secondary due to the magnetization of the iron.

(ii) Using a.c. An alternating current is changing all the time and if it passes through a primary coil, an alternating e.m.f. and current are induced in a secondary coil.

In the circuit shown in Fig. 22.10, the 1 V high-current power unit supplies a.c. to the primary and the lamp detects the secondary current. It gets brighter if the number of turns on the secondary is increased but dims if the secondary turns are decreased or if the iron C-cores are pulled apart slightly (so reducing the number of field lines which pass through the secondary).

The primary and secondary coils on their complete iron core form a *transformer*.

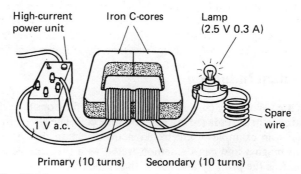

High-current   Iron C-cores   Lamp
power unit   (2.5 V 0.3 A)

1 V a.c.

Spare
wire

Primary (10 turns)   Secondary (10 turns)

Fig. 22.10

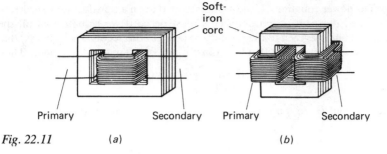

Fig. 22.11   (*a*)   (*b*)

22.4 Transformers

A transformer transforms (changes) an *alternating* p.d. (voltage) to another of greater or smaller value. Its primary and secondary coils are wound either one on top of the other (Fig. 22.11(*a*)), or on separate limbs of the iron core (Fig. 22.11(*b*)).

(i) **The p.d. equation.** An alternating voltage applied to the primary induces an alternating voltage in the secondary whose value can be shown to be given by

$$\frac{\text{secondary voltage}}{\text{primary voltage}} = \frac{\text{secondary turns}}{\text{primary turns}}$$

In symbols,

$$\frac{V_s}{V_p} = \frac{N_s}{N_p}$$

This equation is strictly true only for an ideal transformer, that is, one in which there are no energy losses (see (iii) below) but it is good enough for most purposes.

A *step-up* transformer has more turns on the secondary than on the primary, and V_s is greater than V_p: for example, if the secondary has twice as many turns as the primary, V_s is about twice V_p. In a *step-down* transformer there are fewer turns on the secondary than on the primary, and V_s is less than V_p. The symbols for step-up and step-down transformers are shown in Fig. 22.12(*a*) and (*b*).

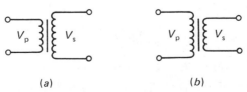

(*a*)   (*b*)

Fig. 22.12 (a) Step-up: $V_s > V_p$, (b) Step-down: $V_s < V_p$

(ii) **The power equation.** If the p.d. is stepped up in a transformer the current is stepped down in proportion. This must be so if we assume that all the electrical energy given to the primary appears in the secondary—that is, that energy is conserved and that the transformer is 100 per cent efficient. Then

$$\text{power in primary} = \text{power in secondary}$$
$$V_p \times I_p = V_s \times I_s$$

where I_p and I_s are the primary and secondary currents respectively.

$$\therefore \quad \frac{I_s}{I_p} = \frac{V_p}{V_s}$$

So, in theory, if the p.d. is doubled the current is halved. In practice, it is more than halved, because there are small energy losses in the transformer. On the other hand, if the p.d. is halved the current is almost doubled.

(iii) **Energy losses.** These have three causes.

1. *Resistance of windings.* The windings of copper wire have some resistance and heat is produced by the current in them.

2. *Eddy currents.* The iron core is in the changing magnetic field of the primary and currents, called eddy currents, are induced in it which cause heating. These can be reduced by using a *laminated* core made of sheets, insulated from each other so as to have a high resistance.

3. *Leakage of field lines.* All the lines produced by the primary may not 'cut' the secondary, especially if the core has an air-gap or is badly designed.

22.5 Worked Example

A transformer steps down the mains supply from 240 V to 12 V which is supplied to a 12 V lamp.

(*a*) What is the turns ratio (N_s/N_p) of the windings?

(*b*) How many turns are on the primary if the secondary has 100 turns?

(*c*) What is the current in the primary if the transformer is 100 per cent efficient and the current in the lamp is 2 A?

$$(a) \qquad \text{Primary p.d.} = V_p = 240 \text{ V}$$
$$\text{Secondary p.d.} = V_s = 12 \text{ V}$$
$$\text{Primary turns} = N_p = ?$$
$$\text{Secondary turns} = N_s = ?$$
$$\text{Turns ratio} = N_s/N_p = V_s/V_p$$
$$= 12 \text{ V}/240 \text{ V} = 1/20$$
$$\therefore N_s/N_p = 1/20$$

$$(b) \qquad N_s = 100 \text{ turns, and from } (a)$$

$$N_p = 20\, N_s = 20 \times 100 = 2000 \text{ turns}$$

(c) Efficiency = 100%

∴. power in primary = power in secondary

$$V_p \times I_p = V_s \times I_s \text{ where } I_s = 2 \text{ A}$$

$$\therefore I_p = \frac{V_s \times I_s}{V_p} = \frac{12 \times 2}{240} = \frac{1}{10} = 0.1 \text{ A}$$

The current is stepped up by the same factor by which the p.d. is stepped down.

22.6 Transmission of Electrical Power

(i) **Grid system.** This is a network of cables, most of which are supported on pylons, connecting about 200 power stations throughout the United Kingdom to consumers. In the largest modern stations, electricity is generated at 25 000 V (25 kilovolts = 25 kV) and stepped up at once in a transformer to 275 or 400 kV to be sent over long distances on the Supergrid. Later, the p.d. is reduced by substation transformers for distribution to local users (Fig. 22.13).

At Area Control Centres engineers direct the flow and re-route it when there is a breakdown. This makes the supply more reliable, and also cuts costs by enabling smaller, less efficient stations to be shut down at off-peak periods.

(ii) **Use of high alternating p.d.s.** 400 000 W of electrical power can be sent through cables as 400 000 V at 1 A or as 400 V at 1000 A (since watts = amperes × volts). But the amount of electrical energy changed to unwanted heat (due to the resistance of the cables) is proportional to the *square of the current* and so the power loss (I^2R) is less if transmission is made at high voltage (high tension) and low current. On the other hand, high p.d.s need good insulation. The high efficiency with which transformers step alternating p.d.s up and down accounts for the use of a.c. rather than d.c.

The advantages of 'high' alternating p.d. power transmission may be demonstrated using the model in Fig. 22.14, connecting it first without the transformers at each end and then including them in the circuit as shown. The constantan resistance wires represent long transmission cables. Without the transformers, the lamp at the 'village end' glows dimly due to the power loss in the wires. When the transformers are connected the 12 V a.c. supply voltage is stepped up to about 240 V (since $N_p/N_s = 1/20$) at the 'power station' end, then stepped down at the 'village end' to 12 V (since $N_s/N_p = 20/1$). The current in the 'power line' is now much less than before; so too therefore is the power loss during transmission, and the lamp at the 'village end' is fully lit.

22.7 Moving Coil Microphone: Car Ignition Coil

These two devices depend on electromagnetic induction.

(i) **Moving coil microphone** (Fig. 22.15). Its construction is similar to that of a moving coil loudspeaker (see Unit 21.10) but the action is reversed. A small

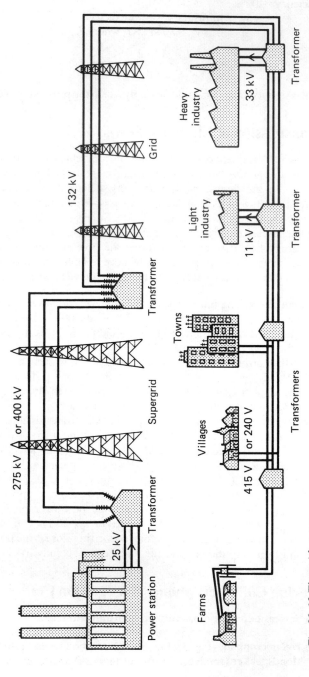

Fig. 22.13 The grid system

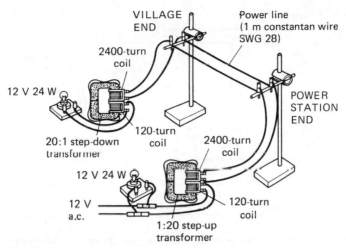

Fig. 22.14

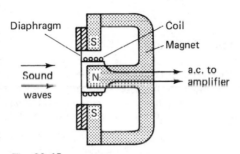

Fig. 22.15

coil of many turns of very thin wire wound on a tube is attached to a light disc (the *diaphragm*). When sound waves strike the diaphragm, it vibrates and makes the coil and tube move backwards and forwards in the circular gap containing the magnetic field of the magnet. Electromagnetic induction produces a small alternating e.m.f. in the coil which has the same frequency as that of the sound.

(ii) **Car ignition coil** (Fig. 22.16). A transformer does not work off d.c. but the *induction coil*, which uses the same principle, does. It is used in a car to produce the high voltage that causes the sparking plug to spark and ignite the mixture of petrol vapour and air.

The primary circuit is broken when the rotating cam separates the 'points'. A high p.d. is induced in the secondary which is applied at the right time to each plug in turn by the rotor arm of the distributor. When the 'points' open, the capacitor acts as a reservoir and stops the sparking, so preventing 'pitting'

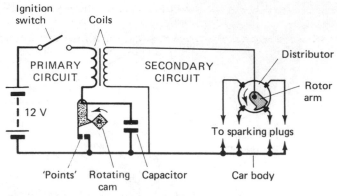

Fig. 22.16

of their surfaces and also ensuring that the primary current falls rapidly, thus giving a larger induced e.m.f. in the secondary.

22.8 Alternating Current

(i) Direct and alternating currents. In a *direct current* (d.c.) flowing in a metal, the electrons move in one direction only. Batteries produce d.c. The *waveform* of a current is a graph whose shape shows what happens to the value of the current over a period of time. Those in Fig. 22.17 are for steady and varying d.c.

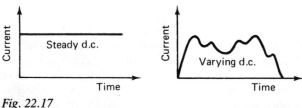

Fig. 22.17

An *alternating current* (a.c.) is one that reverses direction continually. Alternators produce a.c. The simplest a.c. waveform is shown in Fig. 22.18, drawn for an a.c. of frequency (see Unit 22.2) 2 Hz; it has a sine wave shape. The current rises from zero to a maximum value in one direction, falls to zero again before becoming a maximum in the opposite direction, then rises to zero once more, and so on. The circuit symbol for an a.c. supply is $\sim$.

Electric heaters and lamps work off either a.c. or d.c. but radio and television sets need d.c.; so too do processes such as battery charging and electroplating. A.c. can be *rectified* to give d.c. (see Unit 24.6). The pointer of

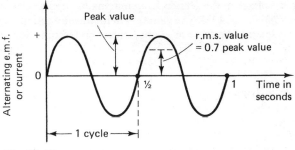

Fig. 22.18

a moving coil meter is deflected one way by d.c.; a.c. makes it move to and fro about the scale zero if the direction changes are slow enough to allow it to respond, but otherwise no deflection occurs.

(ii) **Root mean square values.** Since the value of an alternating quantity changes, the problem arises of what value to take to measure it. The average value of a sine wave over a complete cycle is zero. The *peak* value (that is, the maximum positive or negative value) might be used; however, the *root mean square* (r.m.s.) value is chosen because many calculations can then be done in the same way as for d.c.

The r.m.s. (or effective) value of an alternating current (or p.d.) is the value of the steady direct current (or p.d.) which would give the same heating effect.

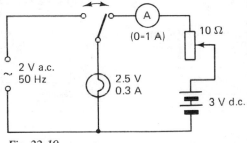

Fig. 22.19

For example, if the lamp in the circuit of Fig. 22.19 is lit first by a.c. (by moving the two-way switch to the left) and its brightness noted, then if 0.3 A d.c. produces the same brightness (when the switch is moved to the right and the rheostat adjusted), the r.m.s. value of the a.c. is 0.3 A. A lamp designed to be fully lit by a current of 0.3 A d.c. will also be fully lit by a.c. of r.m.s. value 0.3 A.

It can be shown that for a sine wave a.c.

$$\text{r.m.s. value} = 0.7 \times \text{peak value}$$

The r.m.s. voltage of the United Kingdom mains supply is 240 V; the peak value is thus 240/0.7 = 340 V. The value given for an alternating current or p.d. is always assumed to be the r.m.s. one, unless stated otherwise.

22.9 Capacitors

Capacitors were introduced in Unit 18.7 as devices that store electric charge. They have other properties as well.

(i) **In d.c. circuits.** In the circuit of Fig. 22.20(a), the supply is d.c. and the lamp does not light, that is, *a capacitor blocks d.c.* When the circuit is closed there is initially a brief flow of charge (a momentary current), which charges the capacitor until the p.d. across it is equal but opposite to that of the supply (here 2 V). Charge flow then stops. If a charge Q (in coulombs) is stored when a p.d. V (in volts) is applied across a capacitor, its *capacitance C* (in farads) is defined by

$$C = \frac{Q}{V} \text{ or } Q = VC$$

In Fig. 22.20(a), we have $V = 2$ V, $C = 1000 \, \mu$F, therefore $Q = VC = 2 \times 1000 = 2000 \, \mu$C.

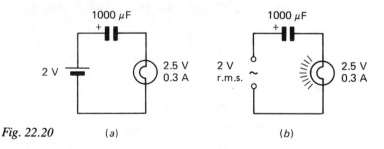

Fig. 22.20   (a)   (b)

(ii) **In a.c. circuits.** In the circuit of Fig. 22.20(b), the supply is a.c. and the lamp does light, that is, a capacitor *seems* to let a.c. pass. The a.c. supply causes the capacitor to be charged, discharged, charged in the opposite direction and discharged again, 50 times a second.

No current actually passes through the capacitor (its plates are separated by an insulator) but electrons flow to and fro so rapidly in the wires joining the plates (as the polarity of the a.c. supply reverses) that it seems to do so. The greater C is, the greater the number of electrons involved and the more easily a.c. appears to flow 'through' it. Also the higher the frequency of the a.c., the faster electrons flow on and off the plates and the greater is the current, that is, the less is the opposition of the capacitor.

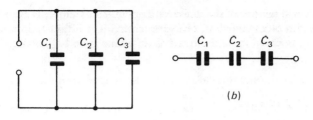

Fig. 22.21   (a)

(iii) **Capacitor networks.** Capacitors connected in parallel behave like one capacitor with larger plates. In Fig. 22.21(a) the combined capacitance C can be shown to be given by

$$C = C_1 + C_2 + C_3$$

In Fig. 22.21(b) the combined capacitance C of the capacitors in series is less than that of the smallest capacitor and is found from

$$\frac{1}{C} = \frac{1}{C_1} + \frac{1}{C_2} + \frac{1}{C_3}$$

(iv) **Capacitor charging and discharging through a resistor.** These processes do not happen instantly but take a time which depends on the values of the

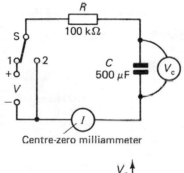

Fig. 22.22   Centre-zero milliammeter

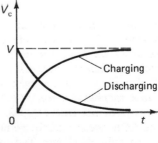

Fig. 22.23   (a)   (b)

capacitor and resistor. Using the circuit of Fig. 22.22, current (I) and p.d. (V_c) readings can be obtained for charging (with S in position 1) and discharging (with S in position 2), and plotted against time as in Fig. 22.23(a) and (b).

During charging:

1. I has its maximum value at the start and decreases more and more slowly towards zero as C charges up, and

2. V_c rises rapidly from zero and slowly approaches the charging voltage V which it equals when C is fully charged.

During discharging:

1. I has its maximum value at the start but is in the opposite direction to the charging current, and

2. V_c falls to zero as C discharges.

The larger the values of C and R, the more slowly both processes occur. Graphs like these are called *exponential* curves.

22.10 Inductors

An *inductor* or *choke* is a coil of wire with an air or ferromagnetic core. It opposes or 'chokes' a changing current and has an *inductance* (L). Inductors are used in electronic circuits.

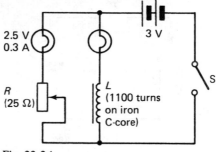

Fig. 22.24

(i) **In d.c. circuits.** In Fig. 22.24, R is adjusted to have the same resistance as the iron-cored inductor L; when S is switched on, the lamp in series with L lights up a second or two *after* that in series with R. L delays the rise of the d.c. to its steady value.

(ii) **In a.c. circuits.** If the 3 V d.c. supply is replaced by a 3 V a.c. supply, the lamp in series with L never lights. This is because the current is changing all the time and the resulting opposition of L reduces the current to one that is too small to light the lamp. The opposition of an inductor increases as the frequency of the a.c. increases. (Compare this with the behaviour of a capacitor.)

22.11 Revision Questions and Problems

Electromagnetic Induction: Generators

1. In Fig. 22.25, the wire AB has an e.m.f. induced in it when it is moved sideways but not in any other direction or when it is at rest.

    (*a*) Explain why this is so.

    (*b*) What will be the direction of the e.m.f. (from A to B or from B to A) when the wire is moved from right to left?

    (*c*) State two ways of making the e.m.f. greater.

    (*d*) Is a direct or an alternating e.m.f. created as the wire is moved to and fro continuously?

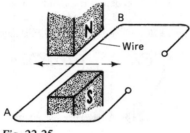

Fig. 22.25

2. What would you observe if you pushed a bar magnet into a coil connected to a centre-zero galvanometer (*a*) N pole first, (*b*) S pole first, (*c*) faster than before?

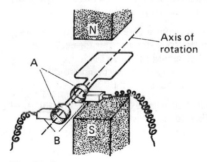

Fig. 22.26

3. A simple generator is shown in Fig. 22.26.

    (*a*) Does it produce d.c. or a.c.?

    (*b*) What are A and B called? What is their purpose?

    (*c*) What changes can be made to increase the e.m.f. generated?

4. Sketch a graph showing the variation with time of the e.m.f. generated between the ends of the coil of a simple alternator.

    On the same axes draw another two graphs to show the effects of (*a*) doubling the number of turns on the coil and keeping the rotation speed and the magnetic field constant, and (b) doubling the speed of rotation and keeping the number of turns and the magnetic field constant.

5. (a) How does the design of a simple dynamo differ from that of a simple alternator?
   (b) How do many practical alternators differ from the simple one in Fig. 22.5(a)?

Transformers: a.c.

6. Two coils of wire, A and B, are placed near one another (Fig. 22.27). Coil A is connected to a switch and battery. Coil B is connected to a centre-reading moving coil galvanometer.

   (a) If the switch connected to coil A were closed for a few seconds and then opened, the galvanometer connected to coil B would be affected. Explain and describe, step by step, what would actually happen.

   (b) What changes would you expect if a bundle of soft-iron wires were placed through the centre of the coils? Give a reason for your answer.

   (c) What would happen if more turns of wire were wound on the coil B?

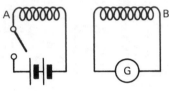

Fig. 22.27

7. (a) Write down the 'p.d. equation' for a perfect transformer.
   (b) What is the 'power equation' for a perfect transformer?
   (c) In a step-down transformer, how does (i) the p.d., (ii) the current, in the secondary compare with its primary value?

8. A step-up transformer has a core made of 'laminations'.
   (a) What is meant by a step-up transformer?
   (b) What does 'laminations' mean?
   (c) What material is used for the laminations?
   (d) Why is the core built like this?

9. (a) If a step-up transformer has a turns ratio of 1 to 4, what is the secondary p.d. when 6 V is applied to the primary?
   (b) If a step-down transformer has a turns ratio of 20 to 1, what p.d. must be applied to the primary to give a secondary p.d. of 12 V?

10. (a) How many turns are required on the secondary of a 240 V mains transformer which has 4800 turns on the primary and is to operate a 6 V lamp?
    (b) If the lamp has a power of 6 W, what is (i) the secondary current, (ii) the primary current?

11. (a) Why is it an advantage to transmit electric power at very high voltage?
    (b) Why is a.c. transmitted rather than d.c.?

12. (a) How does a.c. differ from d.c.?
    (b) Name a source of (i) d.c., (ii) a.c.
    (c) Name a device which (i) works only on a.c., (ii) works equally well on a.c. or d.c.

13. An alternating p.d. has a peak value of 10 V and a frequency of 50 Hz.

   (a) What is the time for one cycle?

   (b) Sketch a graph of p.d. against time. Label your axes and mark the time scale correctly.

   (c) Draw a horizontal line on the graph at the approximate value of the r.m.s. voltage.

14. An a.c. supply lights a lamp with the same brightness as does a 12 V battery. What is (a) the r.m.s. voltage, (b) the peak voltage, of the a.c. supply?

15. A circuit containing a capacitor and an inductor is shown in Fig. 22.28.

   (a) What happens when the supply is (i) a.c., (ii) d.c.?

   (b) What happens if the frequency of the a.c. supply is increased?

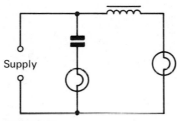

Fig. 22.28

Part Six
Atoms and Electrons

Unit Twenty-three

Radioactivity and Atomic Structure

23.1 About Radioactivity

(i) **Discovery.** The discovery of radioactivity in 1896 by the French scientist Becquerel was accidental. He found that uranium compounds emitted radiation which affected a photographic plate even when they were wrapped in black paper; they also ionized a gas. Soon afterwards Marie Curie discovered an even more strongly radioactive substance, namely radium. Today, radioactivity is used widely in industry, medicine and research.

We are all exposed to background radiation due partly to radioactive materials in rocks, in the air and in our bodies, and partly to cosmic rays from outer space.

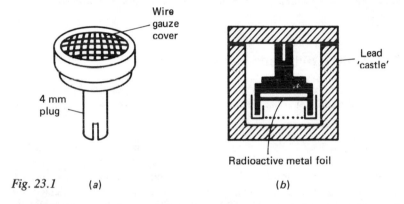

Fig. 23.1   (a)   (b)

(ii) **Radioactive sources.** Those used in school and college laboratories are usually supplied mounted in a holder with a 4 mm plug. A tiny amount of radioactive material is sealed in a metal foil which is protected by a wire gauze cover (Fig. 23.1(a)). When not in use it is stored in a small lead container (a lead 'castle') in a box (Fig. 23.1(b)). For safety reasons it is

1. *always lifted with forceps,*
2. *held so that the open window is directed away from the body,* and
3. *never brought close to the eyes for inspection.*

(iii) **Ionizing effect.** A charged electroscope is discharged when a radium source is brought near the cap (Fig. 23.2). Radiation from the source ionizes the air around the cap, that is, knocks electrons out of air molecules.

If the cap is negatively charged the resulting positive air ions are attracted to

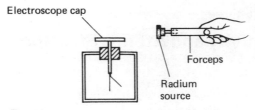

Fig. 23.2

it; if it is positively charged the electrons are attracted. The charge on the electroscope is therefore neutralized, that is, the charge is lost and the leaf falls. It is just as if the ionized air becomes a conductor and allows charge to leak away from the electroscope.

(iv) **Nature of the radiation.** Experiments to study the penetrating power and ionizing ability of the radiation emitted by radioactive materials and its behaviour in magnetic and electric fields show that, depending on the material in question, it may consist of one or more of three types of ray. These are called *alpha-*, *beta-* and *gamma*-rays (from the Greek letters α, β and γ).

23.2 ⁺ Alpha-, Beta- and Gamma-rays

Alpha- and beta-'rays' are made up of tiny, electrically charged *particles* that are emitted at high speeds. Gamma-*rays* behave like very short wavelength X-rays.

(i) **Alpha-particles.** These are stopped by a thick sheet of paper; in air they have a range of a few centimetres, being eventually brought to rest by collisions with air molecules. They cause intense ionization in a gas (by attracting electrons out of their molecules) and are deflected by electric and *very strong* magnetic fields (Fig. 23.3(*a*)); the direction and amount of the deflection suggests they are helium atoms minus two electrons, that is, *helium ions with a double positive charge.* (Each is the nucleus of a helium atom, consisting of two protons and two neutrons—see Unit 23.6.) All alpha-particles emitted by a particular radioactive substance have the same speed, about one-twentieth of the speed of light.

Americium (^{241}Am) is a pure alpha-source (that is, it emits alpha-particles only).

(ii) **Beta-particles.** They are stopped by a few millimetres of aluminium and the most energetic have a range in air of several metres. Their ionizing power is much less than that of alpha-particles, as is their mass. As well as being deflected by electric fields, they are deflected by magnetic fields—more easily than alpha-particles are, but in the opposite direction (Fig. 23.3(*b*)).

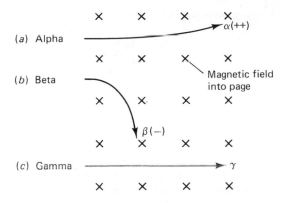

(a) Alpha

(b) Beta

(c) Gamma

Notes. 1. Deflections not to scale
2. Deflections found from
   Fleming's left-hand rule
   (taking negative charge to
   the right as conventional
   current to the left)

Fig. 23.3

Measurements show that they are streams of *electrons* (each carrying a negative charge as all electrons do) emitted with a range of speeds up to that of light.

Strontium (^{90}Sr) emits beta-particles only.

(iii) **Gamma-rays.** These are the most penetrating and are stopped only by many centimetres of lead. They ionize a gas even less than beta-particles do, and are not deflected by electric or magnetic fields (Fig. 23.3(*c*)). They give interference effects and travel at the speed of light; their behaviour resembles that of very short wavelength X-rays, from which they differ only in their origin. Whereas X-rays are due to energy changes *outside* atomic nuclei, as are all forms of electromagnetic radiation (see Unit 23.7(ii)), gamma-rays, like alpha- and beta-particles, come from *inside* atomic nuclei (see Unit 23.5). For this reason, alpha-, beta- and gamma-rays are called *nuclear radiation*.

Gamma-rays are often emitted along with alpha- or beta-particles. Cobalt (^{60}Co) is a pure gamma-source. Radium (^{226}Ra) emits alpha-, beta- and gamma-rays.

23.3 Nuclear Radiation Detectors

The ionizing effect of nuclear radiation is used to detect it.

(i) **Geiger–Müller (G–M) tube** (Fig. 23.4). When radiation enters the tube, either through a thin end-window made of mica or (if it is very penetrating)

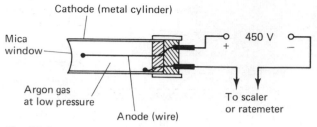

Cathode (metal cylinder)

Mica window

Argon gas at low pressure

Anode (wire)

450 V

To scaler or ratemeter

Fig. 23.4

through the wall, it creates argon ions and electrons. These are accelerated towards the electrodes and cause more ionization by colliding with other argon atoms.

On reaching the electrodes, the ions produce a current pulse which is amplified and fed to either a *scaler* or a *ratemeter*. A scaler counts the pulses and shows the total received in a certain time. A ratemeter has a meter marked in 'counts per second' (or 'per minute') from which the average pulse-rate can be read. It usually has a loudspeaker which gives a 'click' for each pulse. A G–M tube detects alpha-, beta- and gamma-rays.

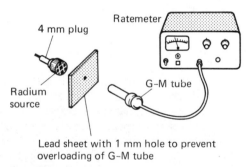

4 mm plug

Ratemeter

G–M tube

Radium source

Lead sheet with 1 mm hole to prevent overloading of G–M tube

Fig. 23.5

The penetrating power of the nuclear radiation from a source such as radium can be investigated using a G–M tube and ratemeter as shown in Fig. 23.5. Sheets of (*a*) thick paper (the radium source, lead sheet and tube must be close together for this), (*b*) aluminium 2 mm thick and (*c*) lead 2 cm thick, are placed in turn between the lead sheet and the tube, and their effect on the count-rate is observed. Other sources may be tried.

(ii) **Diffusion cloud chamber.** When air containing alcohol (ethanol) or other vapour is cooled enough, it becomes saturated. If ionizing radiation passes through the air, further cooling causes the saturated vapour to condense on the air ions created. The resulting white line of tiny liquid drops shows up as a track when illuminated.

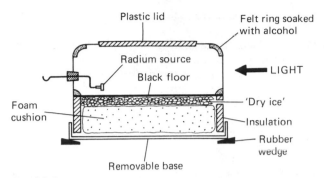

Fig. 23.6

In a diffusion cloud chamber (Fig. 23.6), the felt ring round the top of the chamber is soaked with alcohol. Its vapour diffuses downwards and is cooled by the 'dry ice' (solid carbon dioxide at $-78\,°C$) in the lower section; it condenses near the floor on air ions formed by radiation from the source in the chamber. Tracks are produced continuously, which are sharp if an electric field is created and maintained by frequently rubbing the plastic lid of the chamber with a cloth.

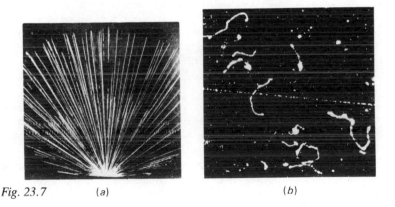

Fig. 23.7   (a)   (b)

Alpha-particles give straight, thick tracks (Fig. 23.7(a)). Very fast beta-particles produce thin, straight tracks; slower ones give short, twisted, thicker tracks (Fig. 23.7(b)). Gamma-rays eject electrons from air molecules: the electrons behave like beta-particles and produce their own tracks spreading out from the gamma-rays.

The *bubble chamber*, in which the radiation leaves a trail of bubbles in liquid hydrogen, is now used in nuclear research.

23.4 Dangers, Safety Precautions, Uses

(i) **Dangers.** The danger from alpha-particles is small unless the source enters the body. Beta-particles and gamma-rays can cause radiation burns (redness and sores on the skin) as well as delayed effects such as cancer, eye cataracts and cell changes that may be transmitted to future generations. Very high dose rates (that is, large amounts received in a short time) can kill by damaging or destroying living cells.

Radioactive waste from nuclear power stations creates problems because it often contains substances which, if they get into water or food supplies, can be taken into people's bodies. Radioactive strontium is an example, the body being unable to distinguish between strontium and calcium (used to make bones). Similar problems arise with the fall-out from nuclear explosions.

(ii) **Safety.** The very weak sources used for laboratory experiments in schools and colleges do not present a problem but *the precautions listed in Unit 23.1(ii) should always be observed*. In industry sources are manipulated by long tongs and transported in thick lead containers. Workers are protected by lead and concrete walls.

In general, keeping *as far from a source as possible* is one of the best safety measures against the effects of nuclear radiation, since its intensity decreases rapidly with distance.

(iii) **Uses.** On the credit side, radioactive substances or *radioisotopes*, now made in nuclear reactors (see Unit 23.10(iii)), have many uses.

1. *Thickness gauge*. If a radioisotope is placed on one side of a moving sheet of material and a G–M tube on the other, the count-rate decreases if the thickness of the sheet increases. This technique is used to control automatically the thickness of paper, plastic and metal sheets during manufacture.

2. *Tracers*. The progress of a small amount of a weak radioisotope injected into a system can be 'traced' by a G–M tube or other detector. The method is used in medicine to detect brain tumours, in agriculture to study the uptake of fertilizers by plants and in industry to measure fluid flow in pipes.

3. *Radiotherapy*. Gamma-rays from strong cobalt radioisotopes are replacing X-rays in the treatment of cancer, often using a computer-controlled radiation beam.

4. *Archaeology*. A radioisotope of carbon, present in the air, is taken in by plants and trees during their life, and archaeological remains of substances like wood and linen can be dated by measuring how much of the radioisotope they contain.

23.5 Rutherford's Model of the Atom

The discovery of radioactivity seemed to indicate that atoms contained negatively and positively charged particles and were not indivisible as was previously thought. The questions then were 'how are the particles arranged inside an atom?' and 'how many are there in the atom of each element?'.

An early theory, called the 'plum-pudding model', regarded the atom as a positively charged sphere in which the negative electrons were distributed through it like currants in a pudding, in sufficient numbers to make the atom electrically neutral. Doubts were soon to arise about this model.

(i) **The scattering experiment.** While investigating radioactivity Rutherford found that alpha-particles could pass straight through very thin metal foil as if it wasn't there; however, some were deflected from their initial direction. With his assistants Geiger (of tube fame) and Marsden, Rutherford investigated this in detail at Manchester University using the arrangement in Fig. 23.8. The fate of the alpha-particles after striking the gold foil was detected by the scintillations (flashes of light) they produced on a glass screen coated with zinc sulphide and fixed to a rotatable microscope.

They found that most of the alpha-particles were undeflected, some were scattered by appreciable angles and a few (about 1 in 8000) surprisingly 'bounced' back.

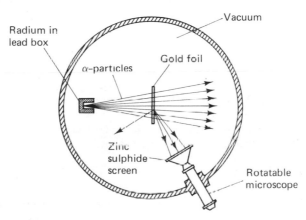

Fig. 23.8

(ii) **The nuclear model.** To explain these results Rutherford proposed in 1911 a nuclear model of the atom in which *all the positive charge and most of the mass of an atom* formed a dense core or *nucleus*, of very small size compared with the whole atom. The electrons surrounded the nucleus some distance away.

He derived a formula for the number of alpha-particles deflected at various angles, assuming that the electrostatic force of repulsion between the positive charge on an alpha-particle and the positive charge on the nucleus of a gold atom obeyed an inverse square law (so that, for instance, the force increases four times if the separation is halved). Geiger and Marsden's results completely confirmed Rutherford's formula and supported the view that an atom is mostly empty space. In fact the nucleus and electrons occupy about one million millionth of the volume of an atom. Putting it another way, the nucleus is like a sugar lump in a very large hall and the electrons a swarm of flies in the hall.

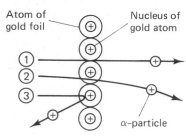

Fig. 23.9

The paths of three alpha-particles are shown in Fig. 23.9. Particle 1 is clear of all nuclei and passes straight through the gold atoms. Particle 2 suffers some deflection. Particle 3 approaches a gold nucleus so closely as to be violently repelled by it and 'rebounds', appearing to have had a head-on collision.

23.6 Protons, Neutrons and Isotopes

As a result of other experiments, we now believe that atoms contain three basic particles—*protons*, *neutrons* and *electrons*.

(i) **Nucleons.** Protons and neutrons are in the nucleus and are together called *nucleons*. The proton has a positive charge which is equal in size (but opposite in sign) to that of an electron, but its mass is about 1800 times greater. It was discovered in 1919 by Rutherford, who found that protons were knocked out of nitrogen nuclei when nitrogen gas was bombarded with high-speed alpha-particles.

The neutron is uncharged, and has almost the same mass as a proton. It was discovered in 1932 by Chadwick when he bombarded beryllium with alpha-particles.

Protons and neutrons together account for the mass of the nucleus (and most of that of the atom). Protons are also responsible for the positive charge of the nucleus and they are held in the nucleus, along with the neutrons, by a force called the *strong nuclear force* which is great enough to overcome the very large repulsion between protons. Table 1 lists the relative masses (in terms of the mass of the electron), charges (in terms of the electronic charge *e*) and locations of the three basic atomic particles.

Table 1

Particle	Relative mass	Charge	Location
Proton	1836	$+e$	In nucleus
Neutron	1839	0	In nucleus
Electron	1	$-e$	Outside nucleus

In a neutral atom the number of protons equals the number of electrons. Table 2 shows the particles in some atoms, starting with the simplest, hydrogen.

Table 2

Particles	Hydrogen	Helium	Lithium	Oxygen	Copper
Protons	1	2	3	8	29
Neutrons	0	2	4	8	34
Electrons	1	2	3	8	29

(ii) **Proton (atomic) and nucleon (mass) numbers.** These terms are useful when considering the numbers of particles in atoms.

The proton or atomic number Z of an atom is the number of protons in the nucleus.

Z is also the number of electrons in the atom (outside the nucleus) and since the outermost electrons form the bonds that join atoms together, it is Z that determines the chemical properties of an atom. If the elements are arranged in proton number order, as they are in the Periodic Table, so that each has one more proton in its nucleus than the element before it, they fall into chemical 'families'.

The nucleon or mass number A of an atom is the number of nucleons in the nucleus.

In general, we can write

$$A - Z + N$$

where N is the *neutron number*. Atomic nuclei are represented by symbols. Hydrogen is written ^1_1H, helium ^4_2He, lithium ^7_3Li and for a nucleus X, we write ^A_ZX where A is its nucleon number and Z its proton number. The difference between the superscript and subscript $(A - Z)$ gives the number of neutrons.

(iii) **Isotopes.** *Isotopes of an element are atoms which have the same number of protons but different numbers of neutrons.* That is, their proton numbers are the same but their nucleon numbers are different.

Isotopes have identical chemical properties since they have the same number of electrons and occupy the same place in the Periodic Table. (In Greek, *isos* means same and *topos* means place.)

Few elements consist of identical atoms; most are mixtures of isotopes. Chlorine has two isotopes; one has 17 protons and 18 neutrons ($Z=17$, $A=35$) and is written $^{35}_{17}Cl$, the other has 17 protons and 20 neutrons ($Z=17$, $A=37$) and is written $^{37}_{17}Cl$. They are present in ordinary chlorine in the approximate ratio of three atoms of $^{35}_{17}Cl$ to one atom of $^{37}_{17}Cl$.

Hydrogen has three isotopes: ^1_1H with one proton, deuterium ^2_1D with one proton and one neutron, and tritium ^3_1T with one proton and two neutrons. Ordinary hydrogen contains 99.99 per cent of ^1_1H atoms. Water made from deuterium is called *heavy water* (D_2O); it has a density of 1.108 g/cm^3, freezes at 3.8 °C and boils at 101.4 °C.

Each form of an element is called a *nuclide*. Nuclides with the same Z but different A are isotopes.

23.7 Bohr's Model of the Atom

(i) **Electron shells.** Shortly after Rutherford proposed his nuclear model of the atom, Bohr, a Danish physicist, developed it to explain how an atom emits electromagnetic radiation. He suggested that the electrons circled the nucleus at high speed in certain orbits which were in groups called *shells*. Atoms were pictured as miniature solar systems with each shell being able to accommodate only a limited number of electron orbits. This number was given by $2n^2$ where $n=1, 2, 3 \ldots$ and so forth, starting with $n=1$ for the shell nearest the nucleus. The first shell ($n=1$) was full when it had $2(1^2)=2$ electrons, the second ($n=2$) when it had $2(2^2)=2\times4=8$ electrons, the third ($n=3$) when it had $2(2^3)=2\times9=18$ electrons and so on. The numbers of electron orbits in the first three shells are 2, 8, 18 respectively.

The arrangement of electrons in shells for six atoms is shown in Fig. 23.10. Hydrogen ($Z=1$), the lightest element, has 1 electron in the first shell. Helium ($Z=2$) fills the first shell with 2 electrons. Both these elements are in Period 1 of the Periodic Table. Period 2 starts with lithium ($Z=3$) which has 2 electrons in the first shell and 1 in the second. Beryllium ($Z=4$), the next element, has 2 electrons in the first shell and 2 in the second. The last element in Period 2 is neon ($Z=10$) with 2 electrons in the first shell and the maximum number of 8 in the second shell. Period 3 starts with sodium ($Z=11$), which has 2 electrons in the first shell, 8 in the second and 1 in the third. The building-up process continues in this way, so that successive elements in the Periodic Table each have one more electron (and one more proton) in their atoms than the last. With a few exceptions, a new shell is started when the previous one is full.

(ii) **Electromagnetic radiation and electrons.** Normally the electrons remain in their orbits but if the atom is given energy (by being heated, for example) electrons may jump to an outer orbit. The atom is then said to be *excited*. Very

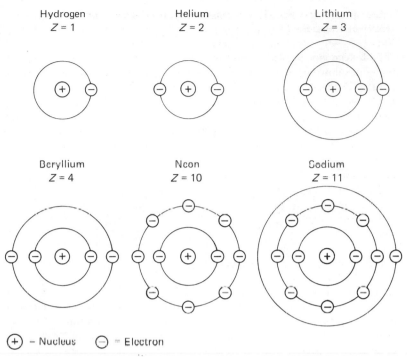

Hydrogen
Z = 1

Helium
Z = 2

Lithium
Z = 3

Beryllium
Z = 4

Neon
Z = 10

Sodium
Z = 11

⊕ – Nucleus   ⊖ = Electron

Fig. 23.10

soon afterwards the electrons return to an inner orbit; as they do, they emit energy in the form of bursts of electromagnetic radiation (called *photons*) such as light, infrared or ultraviolet radiation or X-rays (Fig. 23.11). The wavelength of the radiation emitted depends on the two orbits between which the electrons jump.

If an atom gains enough energy for an electron to escape altogether, the atom becomes an ion and the energy needed to achieve this is called the *ionization energy* of the atom. It can be found from experiments in which gas or

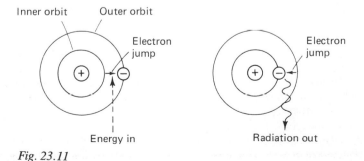

Inner orbit   Outer orbit

Electron jump

Energy in

Electron jump

Radiation out

Fig. 23.11

vapour atoms are ionized by bombardment with electrons accelerated by p.d.s to known energies.

(iii) **Modern model.** Although it is still useful for some purposes, the Bohr model has now been replaced by a mathematical model which is not easy to picture. The best we can do, without using advanced mathematics, is to say that the atom consists of a nucleus surrounded by a hazy cloud of electrons. On a diagram, we can use dense shading to represent regions of the atom where the mathematics predicts that electrons are likely to be found (Fig. 23.12(a)).

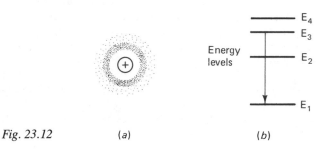

Fig. 23.12   (a)   (b)

The modern theory does away with the idea of electrons moving in definite orbits and replaces them by *energy levels*. When an electron jumps from one level, say E_3 in Fig. 23.12(b), to a lower one E_1, a photon of electromagnetic radiation is emitted with energy equal to the difference in energy of the two levels.

23.8 Radioactive Decay

A radioactive atom breaks up (disintegrates) into an atom of another element when it emits an alpha- or a beta-particle. It is said to *decay*. A new nucleus is formed, with a different number of protons and neutrons, which is more stable but may itself decay further. Eventually a stable end-nuclide is formed. The decay process happens of its own accord and cannot be controlled; it is unaffected by temperature changes, and occurs whether the material is pure or combined chemically with other elements.

(i) **Alpha-decay.** An alpha particle ($^4_2$He) is a helium nucleus having two protons and two neutrons, and when an atom decays by alpha-emission its nucleon number decreases by 4 and its proton number by 2. For example, when radium of nucleon number 226 and proton number 88 emits an alpha-particle, it decays to radon of nucleon number 222 and proton number 86. The change is written:

$$^{226}_{88}\text{Ra} \rightarrow \, ^{222}_{86}\text{Rn} + \, ^4_2\text{He}$$

The superscripts and subscripts must balance on both sides of the equation

(226 = 222 + 4 and 88 = 86 + 2) since nucleons (superscripts) and total charge (subscripts) are conserved during the process.

(ii) **Beta-decay.** Here a neutron changes to a proton and an electron. The proton remains in the nucleus and the electron is emitted as a beta-particle. The new nucleus has the same nucleon number, but its proton number increases by one since it has one more proton. Radioactive carbon, called carbon-14, decays by beta-emission to nitrogen:

$$^{14}_{6}C \rightarrow {}^{14}_{7}N + {}^{0}_{-1}e$$

A beta-particle—that is, an electron—is written as $_{-1}^{0}e$, because it has negligible mass compared with a proton or neutron, and carries a charge of -1 unit. Again the superscripts and subscripts balance $(14 + 0 = 14$ and $6 = 7 - 1)$, since nucleons and charge are conserved.

(iii) **Gamma-emission.** After emitting an alpha- or beta-particle some nuclei are left in an 'excited' state. Rearrangement of the protons and neutrons occurs in the nucleus and a burst of gamma-rays is released. This happens in the decay of the radium-226 nucleus.

23.9 Half-life

(i) **Definition.** Every radioactive nuclide has its own definite decay rate, expressed in terms of its *half-life T/2*.

*The half-life of a radioactive nuclide is the time
for half the nuclei present in a given sample to decay.*

Half-lives vary from millionths of a second to millions of years. The half-life of radium is 1600 years: that means that if 20 million undecayed nuclei are present in a certain sample, 1600 years later 10 million will have decayed. This number will be halved after another 1600 years, leaving 5 million still undecayed and so on. It would take an impossibly long time to measure the 'full-life' of radium; the half-life is a much more practical quantity which can be found experimentally.

Despite the great age of the earth, nuclides with short half-lives exist because many are formed from nuclides with very long half-lives; others are radioisotopes made in nuclear reactors.

(ii) **Decay curve.** The average number of disintegrations (decaying atoms) per second of a sample is its *activity*. If the activity is measured at different times (for example, by finding the count-rate using a G–M tube and ratemeter) and plotted against time, a *decay curve* can be drawn. The one in Fig. 23.13 shows that the activity decreases by the *same fraction* in successive equal time intervals, that is, it is an *exponential curve*: the activity falls from 80 to 40 disintegrations per second in 10 minutes, from 40 to 20 in the next 10 minutes, from 20 to 10 in the third 10 minutes, and so on. The half-life is thus 10 minutes.

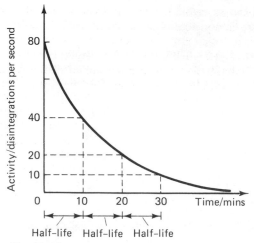

Fig. 23.13

(iii) **Half-life of radon-220.** This radon isotope (sometimes called thoron) is an alpha-emitting gas whose half-life can be found from a decay curve using the apparatus in Fig. 23.14(*a*). The plastic bottle is squeezed three or four times to transfer some radon to the flask. The clips are then closed, the bottle removed and the stopper of the flask replaced by a G–M tube so that it seals the top (Fig. 23.14(*b*)). When the ratemeter has reached its maximum reading and started to fall, the count-rate is noted every 15 seconds for 2 minutes and then every minute for the next few minutes. (**The G–M tube must be left in the flask for at least an hour until the radioactivity has decayed.**) The background count-rate is then found separately and subtracted from each count-rate measurement since the G–M tube detects it as well as radiation from the thoron. The graph of count-rate against time (the decay curve) is then plotted and the half-life (52 s) estimated from it.

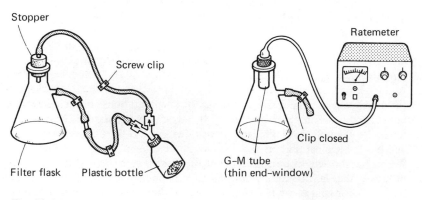

Fig. 23.14   (a)   (b)

During this experiment it becomes evident that the count-rate varies irregularly; the loudspeaker of the ratemeter 'clicks' erratically, not at a steady rate. The reason is that radioactive decay is a *random process*, in that it is a matter of pure chance whether or not a particular nucleus will decay during a given period of time. All we can say is that about half the nuclei in a sample will decay during the half-life: we cannot say which nuclei these will be, nor can we influence the process in any way.

(iv) **Worked example.** In an experiment to find the half-life of radioactive iodine the count-rate falls from 200 to 25 counts per second (c.p.s.) in 75 minutes. What is the half-life?

After one half-life count-rate = 100 c.p.s.
After two half-lives count-rate = 50 c.p.s.
After three half-lives count-rate = 25 c.p.s.
But count-rate after 75 minutes = 25 c.p.s.
∴ Three half-lives = 75 minutes
∴ One half-life = 25 minutes

23.10 Nuclear Energy

(i) $E=mc^2$. Einstein predicted that if the energy of a body changes by an amount E, its mass changes by an amount m given by the equation

$$E=mc^2$$

where c is the speed of light (3×10^8 m/s). The implication is that any reaction in which there is a decrease of mass, called a *mass defect*, is a source of energy. The energy and mass changes in physical and chemical changes are very small; those in some nuclear reactions, such as radioactive decay, are millions of times greater.

For example, when one radium atom decays according to the equation

$$^{226}_{88}\text{Ra} \rightarrow {}^{222}_{86}\text{Rn} + {}^4_2\text{He}$$

radium   radon   alpha-particle

the mass of the decay products—one radon atom and one alpha-particle—is *less* than the mass of the radium atom by 8.8×10^{-30} kg. (Information about the mass of single atoms can be obtained with great accuracy using an instrument called a mass spectrometer.) The energy equivalent E is given by

$$E=mc^2 = 8.8 \times 10^{-30} \times (3.0 \times 10^8)^2 \text{ J}$$
$$= 7.9 \times 10^{-13} \text{ J}$$

The alpha-particle carries off most of this energy as k.e. Although E is very small for one disintegration, considerable amounts of energy are released by sources of large activity. The k.e. is changed to heat when the alpha-particles collide with other atoms and make them move faster. The high temperature of rocks deep in the earth is due to radioactive decay and is a source of geothermal energy (see Unit 6.6(iii)).

(ii) **Fission.** The heavy metal uranium is found naturally as a mixture of isotopes, mainly uranium-238 (over 99 per cent) and uranium-235, the latter being the more important for energy production. Some atoms of this isotope decay spontaneously, emitting high-speed neutrons. If one of these hits the nucleus of a neighbouring uranium-235 atom (being uncharged the neutron is not repelled by the nucleus), this may break (*fission*) into two nearly equal radioactive nuclei, often of barium and krypton, with the production of two or three more neutrons:

$$\underset{\text{neutron}}{\overset{235}{_{92}}\text{U} + \overset{1}{_{0}}\text{n}} \rightarrow \underset{\text{fission fragments}}{\overset{144}{_{56}}\text{Ba} + \overset{90}{_{36}}\text{Kr}} + \underset{\text{neutrons}}{2\overset{1}{_{0}}\text{n}}$$

The mass defect is large and appears mostly as k.e. of the fission fragments. These fly apart at great speed, colliding with surrounding atoms and raising their average k.e., that is, their temperature. Heat is therefore produced.

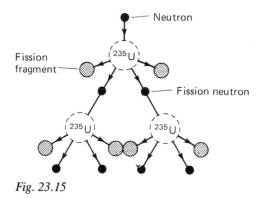

Fig. 23.15

If the fission neutrons split other uranium-235 nuclei, a *chain reaction* is set up (Fig. 23.15). In practice some fission neutrons are lost by escaping from the surface of the uranium before this happens. The ratio of those escaping to those causing fission decreases as the mass of uranium-235 increases. This must exceed a certain *critical mass* for a chain reaction to start.

(iii) **Nuclear reactor.** In a nuclear power station a nuclear reactor produces the steam for the turbines instead of a coal- or oil-burning furnace. Fig. 23.16 is a simplified diagram of an advanced gas-cooled reactor (AGR).

The chain reaction proceeds at a steady rate which is controlled by inserting or withdrawing neutron-absorbing rods of boron among the uranium fuel rods. These are made from uranium dioxide, extra uranium-235 being used to enrich the natural uranium. The graphite core is called the *moderator* and slows down

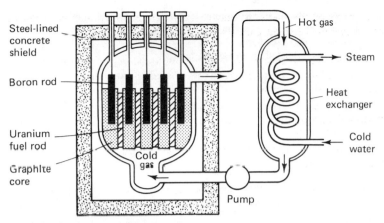

Fig. 23.16

the fission neutrons: fission of uranium-235 occurs more readily with slow than with fast neutrons. Carbon dioxide gas is pumped through the core and carries off heat to the heat exchanger where steam is produced. The steel-lined concrete shield gives protection from gamma-rays and neutrons.

The fuel rods have to be removed and reprocessed from time to time to separate radioactive waste products and small amounts of plutonium-239 from unused uranium. Plutonium-239 is produced in the reactor when uranium-238 absorbs fast fission neutrons; like uranium-235, it undergoes fission and is used in fast-breeder reactors and to make nuclear weapons.

In an *atomic bomb* an accelerating uncontrolled chain reaction occurs when, for example, two pieces of uranium-235 come together and exceed the critical mass.

(iv) **Fusion.** The union of light nuclei into heavier ones can also lead to a loss of mass and, as a result, the release of energy. At present, research is being done on the controlled fusion of isotopes of hydrogen (deuterium and tritium) to give helium. Temperatures of about 100 million °C are required to start it off and nuclear fusion is therefore called a *thermonuclear* reaction because thermal energy has to be supplied before energy is released. Fusion is believed to be the source of the sun's energy.

23.11 Revision Questions and Problems

Radioactivity
1. State which type of radiation from radioactive materials
   (*a*) has a positive charge,
   (*b*) is the most penetrating,
   (*c*) is easily deflected by a magnetic field,
   (*d*) consists of waves,

(e) causes the most intense ionization,

(f) has the shortest range in air,

(g) has a negative charge,

(h) is not deflected by an electric field.

2. Describe the effect of radiation on (a) a charged electroscope, (b) a photographic film, (c) a fluorescent screen.

3. (a) Name two sources of background radiation.
   (b) State three safety precautions that should be taken when using a radioactive source.
   (c) Give three uses of radioactive sources.

4. Describe the function of (a) a G–M tube, (b) a ratemeter, (c) a scaler.

5. How would you distinguish between a source which emits only alpha-particles and another which emits only beta-particles?

6. How do alpha-particle tracks in a cloud chamber differ from those of beta-particles?

Atomic Structure
7. (a) What evidence is there for the nuclear model of the atom?
   (b) State the charge, relative mass and location of each of the three basic particles in the atom.
   (c) How does an element in the Periodic Table differ in structure from the element before it?

8. (a) Explain the terms *mass number* and *atomic number*. Give their other names.
   (b) What is (i) a nucleon, (ii) a nuclide?
   (c) A nuclide of carbon has the symbol $^{14}_{6}C$. How many (i) nucleons, (ii) protons, (iii) neutrons, (iv) electrons does it have?

9. What are *isotopes*? Give two examples. Why are they difficult to separate chemically?

10. Use Bohr's model of the atom to explain (a) what electron shells are, (b) how atoms emit light.

Radioactive Decay
11. State what changes (if any) occur in the proton number of a radioactive atom when it emits (a) an alpha-particle, (b) a beta-particle, (c) a gamma-ray.

12. The equation for the radioactive decay of four nuclides, represented by the letters A, B, C, D, is

$$^{232}_{90}A \rightarrow \,^{228}_{88}B \rightarrow \,^{228}_{89}C \rightarrow \,^{228}_{90}D$$

$$\text{(i)} \qquad \text{(ii)} \qquad \text{(iii)}$$

   (a) Name the particles emitted in each decay.
   (b) Which letters represent isotopes?

13. (a) In nuclear equations what symbols are used to represent (i) an alpha-particle, (ii) a beta-particle?
    (b) Uranium-238 ($^{238}_{92}U$) decays by alpha-emission to thorium (Th), which then decays by beta-emission to protactinium (Pa). Write the equations for these decay processes.

Half-life

14. (a) What is meant by the *half-life* of a radioactive nuclide? Why is it a more practical measure of the decay rate of a nuclide than the *full-life*?
    (b) Why are nuclides with short half-lives still found on the earth?

15. A radioactive nuclide has a half-life of 15 minutes. What fraction of it is left after 1 hour?

16. In an experiment to find the half-life of a certain nuclide the following count-rates (corrected for background) were obtained at hourly intervals:

Time (hours)	0	1	2	3	4	5
Corrected count-rate (c.p.s.)	78	49	31	20	12	8

Plot a decay curve and find the half-life from it.

17. If the half-life of a radioactive gas is 2 minutes, to what fraction of its initial value will the activity have fallen after 8 minutes?

18. Radium-226 has a half-life of 1600 years.
    (a) What fraction *remains* after 4800 years?
    (b) What fraction has *decayed* after 6400 years?
    (c) How many half-lives does it have in 9600 years?

Nuclear Energy

19. (a) State Einstein's mass–energy equation.
    (b) What is the energy equivalent of 1 g (0.001 kg) of matter? (Speed of light $=3 \times 10^8$ m/s.)

20. Explain the terms (a) fission, (b) chain reaction, (c) critical mass, (d) fusion.

21. In an advanced gas-cooled nuclear reactor, what is the purpose of (a) the graphite moderator, (b) the boron control rods, (c) the carbon dioxide gas, (d) reprocessing the uranium fuel rods?

Electronics

24.1 Electrons

The discovery of the electron was a landmark in physics and has led to great technological advances. Experiments with streams of 'escaped' electrons have taught us much about their nature.

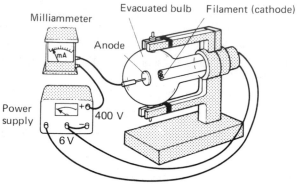

Fig. 24.1

(i) **Thermionic emission.** The evacuated bulb in Fig. 24.1 contains a small coil of wire, the *filament*, and a metal plate which is called the *anode* because it is connected to the positive of the 400 V d.c. power supply. The negative of the supply is joined to the filament which is also called the *cathode*. The filament is heated by current from a 6 V supply (a.c. or d.c.).

With the circuit as shown, the meter deflects, indicating current flow in the circuit containing the gap between anode and cathode. The current stops if the 400 V supply is reversed to make the anode negative, or if the filament is not heated.

This demonstration supports the view that negative charges, in the form of electrons, escape from the filament when it is hot because they have enough energy to get free from the metal surface. The process is known as *thermionic emission*. The electrons are attracted to the anode if it is positive and are able to reach it because there is a vacuum in the bulb.

(ii) **Cathode rays.** Streams of electrons moving at high speed are called *cathode rays*. Some of their properties can be studied using the *Maltese cross tube* (Fig. 24.2(*a*)). Electrons emitted by the hot cathode are accelerated

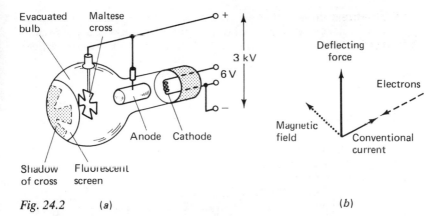

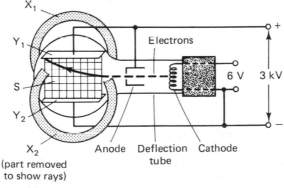

Fig. 24.2   (a)   (b)

towards the anode but most pass through the hole in it and travel on along the
tube. Some are stopped by the cross, but those that miss it cause the screen to
fluoresce with a green light, and a shadow of the cross is cast on it. The cathode
rays evidently travel in straight lines.

If the N pole of a magnet is brought up to the neck of the tube, the rays (and
the non-fluorescent shadow) move upwards. The rays are deflected by a
magnetic field and, using Fleming's left-hand rule (see Unit 21.9(ii)), we see
that they behave like conventional current (positive charge flow) travelling
from anode to cathode, that is, like negative charge moving from cathode to
anode (Fig. 24.2(b)).

The cathode emits light as well as electrons, so that the Maltese cross also
casts an optical shadow on the screen, but this is unaffected by the magnet.

The *deflection tube* in Fig. 24.3 may be used to show the deflection of
cathode rays by electric and magnetic fields. Electrons from a hot cathode
strike a fluorescent screen S set at an angle. A p.d. applied across two
horizontal metal plates Y_1Y_2 creates a *vertical* electric field which deflects the
rays upwards if Y_1 is positive (as shown) and downwards if it is negative.

Fig. 24.3

When current flows in the two coils X_1X_2 (in series) outside the tube, a *horizontal* magnetic field is produced across the tube. It can be used instead of a magnet to deflect the rays, or to cancel the deflection due to an electric field.

(iii) **Measuring e/m and e.** The ratio of the charge e of an electron to its mass m is called its *specific charge e/m* and can be found from experiments in which cathode rays are deflected by electric and magnetic fields. This was first done by J. J. Thomson in 1897 using a deflection-type tube. His work is regarded as proving the existence of the electron as a negatively charged particle of very small mass (about 1/2000 of that of a hydrogen atom) rather than, as some scientists thought, a form of electromagnetic radiation like light.

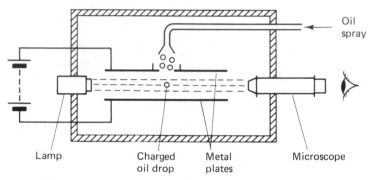

Fig. 24.4

The actual value of e was first measured accurately by Millikan in 1911. The apparatus he used is shown in simplified form in Fig. 24.4. Tiny oil drops, which became charged when they were sprayed, were observed as they fell through the air between two horizontal metal plates connected to a high p.d. In the electric field so created, their time of fall depended on the charge they carried. Millikan measured the charge on a large number of drops, and found that it was always a multiple of 1.6×10^{-19} C. Since the drops gain or lose a certain number of electrons when they become charged, he concluded that the charge on *one* electron—that is, the *electronic charge e*—was 1.6×10^{-19} C.

Knowing e/m and e, m can be calculated. Its value is 9.1×10^{-31} kg.

24.2 Cathode Ray Oscilloscope (C.R.O.)

The C.R.O. is one of the most important instruments ever to be developed. It consists of a cathode ray tube together with electronic circuits operated by controls on a panel at the front of the case that houses the whole instrument (Fig. 24.5). A cathode ray tube has three main parts (Fig. 24.6).

(i) **Electron gun.** This produces a narrow beam of high-speed electrons

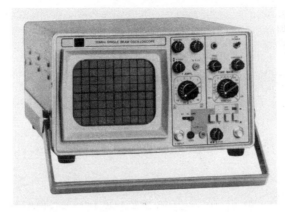

Fig. 24.5

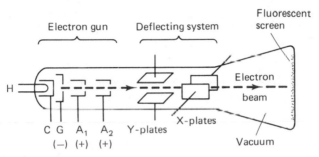

Fig. 24.6

(cathode rays). It consists of a filament or *heater* H which heats a small metal cylinder called the *cathode* C (coated with an electron-emitting material), a ring-shaped electrode known as the *grid* G, and two *anodes* A_1 and A_2 in the shape of cylinders with open ends.

The grid is connected to the power supply so that it is negative with respect to the cathode. It controls the number of electrons passing through its central hole from cathode to anodes and acts as the *brilliance* control: the more negative the grid, the smaller the number of electrons emerging from it. The anodes are at different high positive p.d.s with respect to the cathode. They accelerate the electrons along the highly evacuated glass tube and altering the p.d. between them (by adjusting the *focus* control) makes the beam narrower or wider.

(ii) **Fluorescent screen.** The inside of the wide end of the tube is coated with a fluorescent substance, such as zinc sulphide, which produces a bright spot of light where the electron beam hits it.

(iii) **Deflecting system.** Beyond the anodes are two pairs of deflecting plates to which p.d.s can be applied. The Y-plates are horizontal and create a vertical electric field which deflects the beam vertically. The X-plates are vertical and deflect the beam horizontally.

The p.d. to create the electric field between the Y-plates is applied to the *Y-input* terminals (often marked 'high' and 'low') on the front of the C.R.O. The input is usually amplified, by an amount depending on the setting of the *Y-amp gain* control, before it is applied to the Y-plates. It is then large enough to give a suitable vertical deflection of the beam.

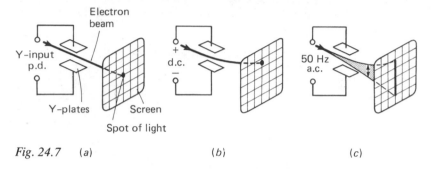

Fig. 24.7   (*a*)   (*b*)   (*c*)

In Fig. 24.7(*a*) the p.d. between the plates is zero, and so is the deflection. In Fig. 24.7(*b*) the d.c. input p.d. makes the upper plate positive and deflects the beam upwards. In Fig. 24.7(*c*) the 50 Hz a.c. input makes the beam move up and down so rapidly that it produces a continuous vertical line, whose length increases when the Y-amp gain control is turned up.

The p.d. applied to the X-plates is also amplified, by the *X-amplifier*, and can be either from an external source connected to the *X-input* terminal or, more commonly, from the *time base* circuit in the C.R.O.

The time base deflects the beam horizontally in the X-direction and makes the spot sweep across the screen from left to right at a steady speed determined by the setting of the time base controls (usually 'coarse' and 'fine'). It must then make the spot 'fly back' very rapidly to its starting point, ready for the next sweep. The p.d. from the time base should therefore have a sawtooth

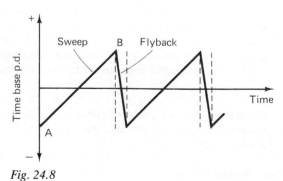

Fig. 24.8

waveform like that in Fig. 24.8. Since AB is a straight line, the distance moved by the spot is directly proportional to time and the horizontal deflection becomes a measure of time, that is, a time axis or base.

In Fig. 24.9 the time base is on. In (a) the Y-input p.d. is zero, while in (b) the Y-input is d.c. which makes the upper Y-plate positive; in both cases the spot traces out a continuous horizontal line if the time base frequency is high enough. With an a.c. input p.d. to the Y-plates, the time base draws it out in a wavy line, that is, the waveform of the a.c. is displayed. When the time base frequency equals that of the input, one complete wave is produced (Fig. 24.9(c)); if it is half that of the Y-input, two waves are formed (Fig. 24.9(d)).

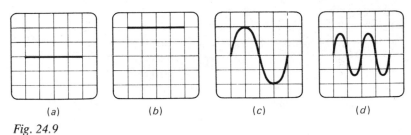

(a)   (b)   (c)   (d)

Fig. 24.9

24.3 Using the C.R.O.

(i) **Practical points.** The brilliance (brightness or intensity) control, which is usually the on/off switch as well, should be turned as low as possible when there is just a spot on the screen, to avoid damage to the fluorescent material by *screen burn*. If possible it is best to defocus the spot or draw it into a line by running the time base.

When preparing the C.R.O. for use, set the brilliance, focus, X- and Y-shift controls (which allow the spot to be moved 'manually' over the screen in these directions) to their mid-positions. The time base and Y-amp gain controls can then be adjusted to suit the input.

When the a.c./d.c. selector switch is in the 'd.c.' (or 'direct') position, both d.c. and a.c. can pass to the Y-input; in the 'a.c.' (or 'via *C*') position, a capacitor blocks d.c. in the input but allows a.c. to pass.

(ii) **P.d. (voltage) measurement.** A C.R.O. can be used as a d.c./a.c. voltmeter if the p.d. to be measured is connected across the Y-input terminals; the deflection of the spot is proportional to the p.d. When the Y-amp gain control is on, say, 1 V/div, a deflection of 1 vertical division on the screen is given by a 1 V d.c. Y-input. A line 1 division long would be produced by an a.c. input of 1 V peak-to-peak, that is, where peak voltage = 0.5 V and r.m.s. voltage = 0.7 × peak voltage = 0.7 × 0.5 = 0.35 V.

While there are more accurate ways of measuring p.d.s, the C.R.O. can measure alternating p.d.s at frequencies of several megahertz.

(iii) **Waveform display.** In this widely used role, the C.R.O. acts as a 'graph-plotter' to show the waveform (the variation with time) of the p.d. applied to its Y-input when the time base is on. The displays in Fig. 24.9(c) and (d) are for alternating p.d.s with sine waveforms.

Sound waveforms can be obtained if a microphone is connected to the Y-input terminals of a C.R.O. (see Unit 17.7(iv)).

(iv) **Time and frequency measurements.** These can be made if the C.R.O. has a calibrated time base. For example, when it is set on 10 ms/div the spot takes 10 milliseconds to move 1 division horizontally across the screen. If this is the time base setting for the waveform in Fig. 24.9(d) then, since 1 complete wave occupies 2 horizontal divisions,

$$\text{time for 1 complete wave} = 2 \text{ divs} \times 10 \text{ ms/div}$$
$$= 20 \text{ ms}$$
$$= 20/1000 = 1/50 \text{ s}$$
$$\therefore \text{ number of complete waves per second} = 50$$
$$\therefore \text{ frequency of the a.c.} = 50 \text{ Hz}$$

24.4 Television

(i) **Black and white.** A television receiver is basically a C.R.O. with two time bases. Magnetic deflection is used, however; it is obtained by having two pairs of current-carrying coils outside the tube at right angles to each other (Fig. 24.10(a)). The horizontal or *line time base* acts as in the C.R.O. The vertical or *frame time base* operates at the same time and draws the spot at a much slower rate down to the bottom of the screen and then returns it almost at once to the top. The spot thus 'draws' a series of parallel lines of light (625) which cover the screen (Fig. 24.10(b)).

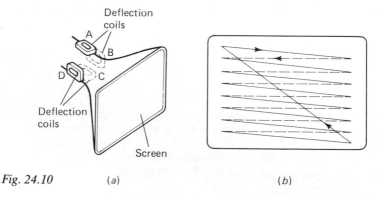

Fig. 24.10   (a)   (b)

A picture is produced by the incoming signal altering the number of electrons which travel from the electron gun to the screen: the greater the number, the brighter the spot. The brightness of the spot varies from white through grey to black as it sweeps across the screen. A complete picture appears every 1/25 s, but because of the persistence of vision (see Unit 15.3) we see the picture as continuous. If each picture is just slightly different from its predecessor, the resultant effect is that of a 'movie' and not a sequence of 'stills'.

(ii) **Colour.** One type of colour television receiver has three electron guns and the screen is coated with about a million tiny light-emitting 'dots' arranged in triangles. One 'dot' in each triangle emits red light when hit by electrons, another green light and the third blue light (red, green and blue being the primary colours—see Unit 14.10(ii)).

As the three electron beams scan the screen, an accurately placed 'shadow mask' consisting of a perforated metal plate with about one-third of a million holes ensures that each beam strikes only dots of one 'colour'—for instance, electrons from the 'red' gun strike only 'red' dots (Fig. 24.11).

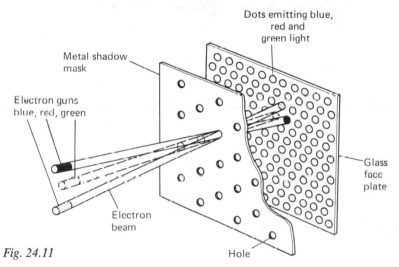

Fig. 24.11

When a triangle of dots is struck it may be that the 'red' and 'green' electron beams are intense but not the 'blue'. The triangle will emit red and green light strongly and appear yellowish. The triangles of dots are struck in turn, and since the dots are so small and the scanning so fast, we see a continuous colour picture.

24.5 Semiconductor Diode

(i) **Semiconductors.** Semiconductor materials, of which silicon and germanium are the two best known, are insulators if they are very pure, especially at low temperatures. Their conductivity can be greatly increased, however, by adding tiny but controlled amounts of certain other substances or *impurities* by a process known as *doping*, and they can then be used to make devices such as diodes, transistors and integrated circuits. Two types of semiconductor material are obtained in this way.

In *n-type* silicon (Fig. 24.12), the silicon (Si) is doped with phosphorus (P) atoms which increase the number of negative electrons that are free to move through the material.

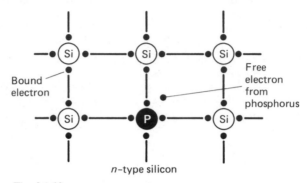

Fig. 24.12

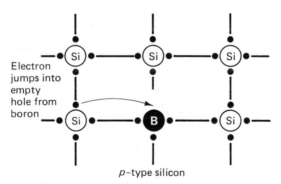

Fig. 24.13

In *p-type* silicon, boron (B) atoms are used for doping. They create gaps, called positive 'holes', in the material and conduction occurs by electrons jumping from one hole to another (Fig. 24.13). The effect is just as if positive holes were moving in the opposite direction, and for that reason we usually consider that conduction in a *p*-type semiconductor is due to positive holes.

(ii) **The *p–n* junction diode.** A *diode* is a two-terminal device which lets current pass through it in one direction only. One can be made by doping a crystal of pure silicon (or germanium) so as to form a region of *p*-type material

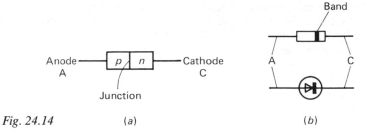

Fig. 24.14   (a)   (b)

in contact with a region of *n*-type material, the boundary between them being called the *junction*. The connection to the *p*-side is the *anode* (A) and that to the *n*-side the *cathode* (C) (Fig. 24.14(*a*)). A diode and its symbol are shown in Fig. 24.14(*b*)).

If a p.d. is connected as in Fig. 24.15(*a*) so that the *p*-type region is positive and the *n*-type negative, the positive holes drift from *p*- to *n*-material and negative electrons go from *n*- to *p*-material across the junction. (You can think of the positive and negative terminals of the p.d. as repelling positive holes and negative electrons respectively, so helping them to move towards each other across the junction.) The diode conducts. It has a *low* resistance and is said to be *forward biased*.

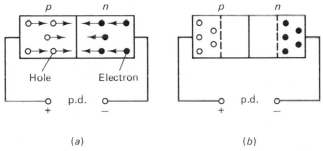

(a)   (b)

Fig. 24.15 (a) Forward bias, (b) reverse bias

If the p.d. is applied the other way round (Fig. 24.15(*b*)), the electrons and holes are attracted to opposite ends of the diode away from the junction so that there is no flow of charge across it. The diode hardly conducts. It has a *high* resistance and is said to be *reverse biased*.

To sum up, a diode has an 'easy' and a 'difficult' direction for current to pass. Its one-way action can be shown with the circuit of Fig. 24.16 in which the lamp only lights when the diode is forward biased.

(iii) **Characteristic curve.** Fig. 24.17(*a*) shows a circuit to find how the current *I* through a junction diode varies with the p.d. *V* across it. Altering the rheostat changes *V*; the corresponding values of *I* are noted. Reversing the battery connections reverse biases the diode.

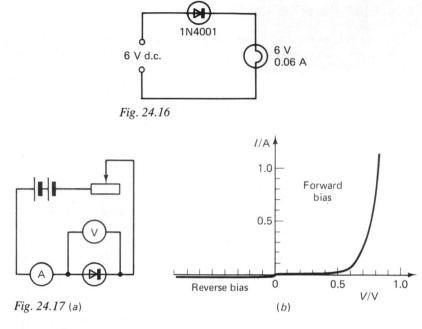

Fig. 24.16

Fig. 24.17 (a)   (b)

A graph of I against V, called the *characteristic curve*, is given in Fig. 24.17(b) for a typical silicon diode. Conduction starts when the forward bias value of V is about 0.6 V (for germanium the value is about 0.1 V), and thereafter a very small change in V causes a sudden, large increase in I. In reverse bias I is almost zero. The forward resistance of this diode is about 1 Ω.

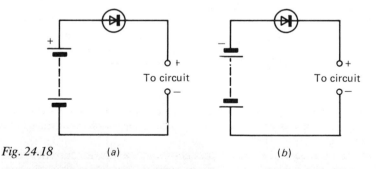

Fig. 24.18   (a)   (b)

(iv) **Uses.** Junction diodes are used (a) as *rectifiers* to change a.c. to d.c. (see Unit 24.6), and (b) to *prevent damage to a circuit (or device) by a reversed power supply*. In Fig. 24.18(a), for example, the battery is correctly connected to the circuit and forward biases the diode, and current passes. In Fig. 24.18(b) the battery is incorrectly connected but it reverse biases the diode, no current passes and so no damage is done to the circuit.

24.6 Rectification and Smoothing

The conversion of a.c. to steady d.c. is often necessary for electronic equipment, such as a radio or television set, which is supplied by the a.c. mains but requires d.c.

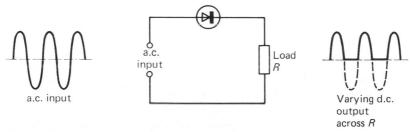

Fig. 24.19

(i) **Half-wave rectification.** In the simple circuit of Fig. 24.19 the diode removes the negative half-cycles of the a.c. input to give a varying but one-way (direct) p.d. across the 'load' R (in practice R would be a piece of electronic equipment requiring a d.c. supply).

If the Y-input terminals of a C.R.O are connected first across the a.c. input, then across R, the output waveform is seen to be the positive half-cycles of the a.c. This accounts for the term 'half-wave' rectification.

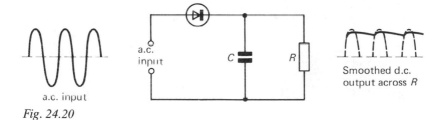

Fig. 24.20

(ii) **Smoothing.** The 'humps' in the varying d.c. from a rectifier circuit can be smoothed to give a much steadier d.c. by connecting a large capacitor C across R, as in Fig. 24.20.

On the positive half-cycles of the a.c. input the diode conducts; current passes through R and also into C to charge it up. On the negative half-cycles the diode is reverse biased and non-conducting, and C partly discharges through R. The charge-storing action of C thus maintains current in R and a steadier p.d. across it, as the output waveform shows.

(iii) **Full-wave rectification.** Here both half-cycles of the a.c. to be rectified are used. In the bridge rectifier circuit of Fig. 24.21, the current follows the

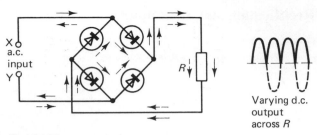

Fig. 24.21

solid arrows when X is positive and Y negative, and the broken arrows on the negative half-cycles when the polarities of X and Y are reversed. During both half-cycles, current passes through R and in the *same* direction, giving a p.d. that varies as shown. It can be smoothed as in (ii), by connecting a large capacitor across R.

24.7 Transistors

Transistors are the tiny semiconductor devices which have revolutionized electronics. They have three connections. They are made as separate devices, like those in Fig. 24.22(a) in their cases, and also as parts of *integrated circuits* (ICs) where many thousands of transistors may be packed on a slice or 'chip' of silicon perhaps only 1.5 cm long (Fig. 24.22(b)).

They are used as amplifiers and as high-speed switches.

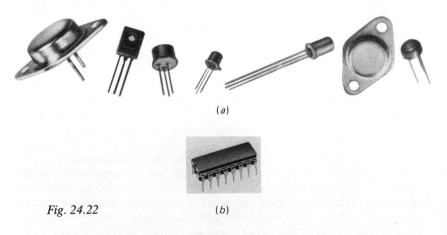

(a)

Fig. 24.22   (b)

(i) **Action.** The simplified structure of the n–p–n junction transistor, the commonest type, is shown in Fig. 24.23 together with its symbol. It consists of

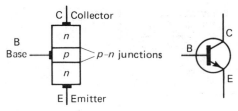

Fig. 24.23

two *p–n* junctions (in effect two diodes back to back) arranged as a sandwich with a thin *p*-type 'filling', the *base*, between two thicker slices of *n*-type material, called the *collector* and the *emitter*. The arrow on the symbol gives the direction in which conventional (positive) current would flow; electron flow is in the opposite direction.

There are two current paths through a transistor. One is the *base–emitter path* and the other is the *collector–emitter* (via base) *path*. The transistor is valuable because it can link circuits connected to each path so that the current in one controls that in the other.

If a p.d., say +6 V, is applied across an *n–p–n* transistor so that the collector becomes positive with respect to the emitter, the base being unconnected, the base–collector junction is reverse biased (since the + of the supply goes to the *n*-type collector). Current cannot pass through the transistor (Fig. 24.24).

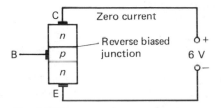

Fig. 24.24

If the base–emitter junction is now *forward biased* by applying a p.d. V_{BE} (of about +0.6 V for a silicon transistor, +0.1 V for germanium), electrons flow from the *n*-type emitter across the junction—as they would in a diode—into the *p*-type base (Fig. 24.25). Their loss is made good by electrons entering the emitter from the external circuit to form the emitter current I_E.

In the base only a small proportion of the electrons from the emitter combine with holes, because the base is very thin and is lightly doped. The loss of holes that does occur is made good by some flowing to the base from the base power supply. This creates a small base current I_B. Most electrons pass through the base under the strong attraction of the positive collector. They cross the base–collector junction and become the collector current I_C in the external circuit.

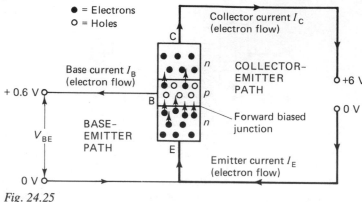

Fig. 24.25

If we regard I_B as the *input* current and I_C as the *output* current, then a transistor acts

1. as a *switch* in which I_B turns on and controls I_C, that is, $I_C = 0$ if $I_B = 0$ and I_C increases when I_B does (but note that $I_B = 0$ until $V_{BE} \approx 0.6$ V, the 'turn-on' p.d.),

2. as a *current amplifier*, since I_C is greater than I_B and a small change in I_B causes a larger change in I_C.

(ii) **Further points.** Here are some more points about using transistors.

1. For an *n–p–n* transistor the collector and base must be positive with respect to the emitter.

2. The input (base–emitter) and output (collector–emitter) circuits in Fig. 24.25 have a common connection at the emitter. The transistor is said to be in *common-emitter* connection.

3. Typically I_C is 10 to 1000 times I_B, depending on the type of transistor. The *current gain* is an important property of a transistor and is defined by

$$\text{current gain} = \frac{I_C}{I_B}$$

For example, if $I_C = 5$ mA and $I_B = 50$ μA $= 0.05$ mA, the current gain $= 5/0.05 = 100$.

4. Since the current leaving a transistor equals that entering it, we have

$$I_E = I_B + I_C$$

5. Silicon is generally preferred to germanium for making transistors, the reason being that it can work at higher temperatures (175 °C compared with 75 °C). A popular silicon type is the BC109.

6. Transistors are damaged if they get too hot—from carrying too large a collector current, for example. Having a *heat sink* (Fig. 24.26) on the transistor helps to prevent overheating, the excess heat being lost from the black plastic cooling fins.

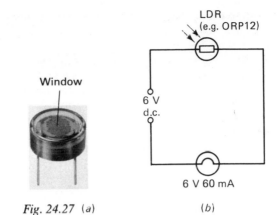

Fig. 24.26   *Fig. 24.27* (a)   (b)

24.8 Other Semiconductor Devices

(i) **Light-dependent resistor (LDR).** The action of an LDR depends on the fact that the resistance of samples of certain semiconductors, such as cadmium sulphide, decreases as the intensity of the light falling on them increases; for example, that of the resistor ORP12 is several megohms in the dark but only a few kilohms in daylight.

An LDR, its symbol and a circuit which shows its action are given in Fig. 24.27(a) and (b). When light falls on the 'window' of the LDR, its resistance decreases and the increased current is large enough to bring the bulb on. LDRs are used in photographic meters.

(ii) **Thermistor.** A thermistor (see Unit 19.7(ii)) contains semiconducting metallic oxides whose resistance decreases markedly when the temperature rises, either because the thermistor is heated directly or because a current is passed through it. Fig. 24.28(a) and (b) shows a thermistor, its symbol and a

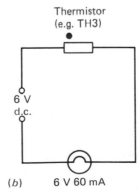

Fig. 24.28   (a)   (b)   6 V 60 mA

circuit to demonstrate its action. Heating the thermistor with a match flame lights the bulb.

(iii) **Thyristor or silicon-controlled rectifier (SCR).** This is a silicon diode with a third connection called the *gate*. When forward biased it does not conduct until a small gate current enters it. Conduction continues even if the gate current is removed; it stops only if the battery to the diode itself is disconnected or if the diode current falls below a certain value.

A thyristor and its symbol, together with a circuit which shows its action when S_1 and S_2 are closed, are given in Fig. 24.29(*a*) and (*b*).

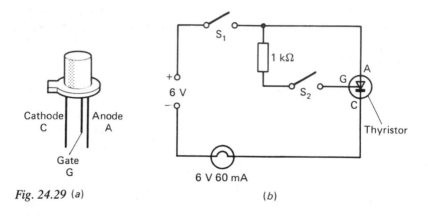

Fig. 24.29 (a)   (b)

(iv) **Light-emitting diode (LED).** An LED, shown in Fig. 24.30(*a*) and (*b*) with its symbol, is a junction diode made from the semiconductor gallium arsenide phosphide. When forward biased it conducts and emits red, yellow or green light. No light is emitted on reverse bias which, if it exceeds 5 V, may damage the LED.

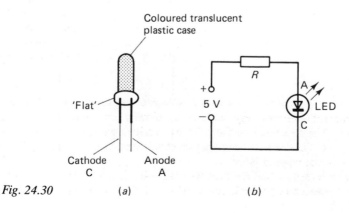

Fig. 24.30   (a)   (b)

When in use, an LED must have a suitable resistor R connected in series with it to limit the current, which typically may be 10 mA (0.01 A). The value of R depends on the supply p.d. For example, in Fig. 24.30(b) it is 5.0 V and if we take the p.d. across a forward biased LED as 2 V, then R is given by

$$R = \frac{(\text{supply p.d.} - 2)\,V}{0.01\,A}$$

$$= \frac{(5-2)\,V}{0.01\,A}$$

$$= 300\,\Omega$$

LEDs are used as indicator lamps in radio receivers and other electronic equipment. Many calculators, clocks, cash registers and measuring instruments have seven-segment red or green displays (Fig. 24.31(a)). Each segment is an LED and, depending on which segments are energized, the display lights up the numbers 0 to 9 as in Fig. 24.31(b)).

LEDs are small, reliable and have a long life; their operating speed is high and their current requirement is very modest.

LED
segment

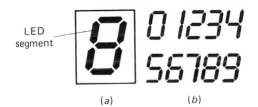

Fig. 24.31   (a)   (b)

24.9 Transistor as a Switch

(i) **Advantages.** Transistors have many advantages over other electrically operated switches such as relays and reed switches. They are small, cheap, reliable and have no moving parts; their life is almost indefinite (in well-designed circuits) and they can switch on and off millions of times a second.

Digital electronics is concerned with the use of transistors as switches in devices such as computers, pocket calculators, digital watches and weighing machines.

(ii) **'On' and 'off' states.** A transistor is considered to be 'off' when the collector current is zero or very small. It is 'on' when the collector current is much larger. The resistance of the collector–emitter path is large when the transistor is 'off' (as it is for an ordinary mechanical switch) and small (ideally it should be zero) when it is 'on'.

To switch a transistor 'on' requires the base voltage, and therefore the base current, to exceed a certain minimum value (+0.6 V for silicon).

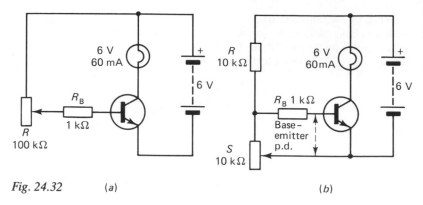

Fig. 24.32   (a)   (b)

(iii) **Basic switching circuits.** Two are shown in Fig. 24.32(*a*) and (*b*). In both, only one battery is used to obtain the positive voltages for the collector and base of the transistor and the 'on' state is shown by the lamp in the collector circuit becoming fully lit.

In (*a*), forward biasing of the base–emitter junction to 'switch on' is achieved by reducing the *rheostat R* until the base current is large enough to make the collector light the lamp. (The base resistor R_B is essential in case R becomes zero and results in +6 V from the battery being applied directly to the base. This would produce very large base and collector currents and destroy the transistor by overheating.)

In (*b*), 'switch-on' is obtained by adjusting the variable resistor S in the *potential divider R–S* (see Unit 19.10(ii)) until the p.d. across S (which is the base–emitter p.d. and depends on the value of S compared with that of R) exceeds +0.6 V or so.

24.10 Alarm Circuits

In many alarm circuits LDRs, thermistors and microphones are used in potential divider arrangements to detect small changes of light intensity, temperature and sound level respectively. These changes then cause a transistor to switch on and activate an alarm, such as a lamp or bell.

(i) **Light-operated circuit.** In the circuit of Fig. 24.33 the LDR is part of a potential divider. The lamp comes on when the LDR is shielded due to more of the battery p.d. being dropped across the increased resistance of the LDR (that is, more than 0.6 V) and less across R. Hence in the dark the base–emitter p.d. increases, as does the base current and so also the collector current.

If the LDR and R are interchanged the lamp goes off in the dark; the circuit could then act as a light-operated intruder alarm.

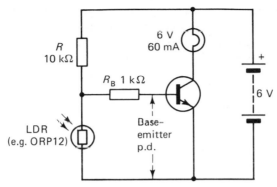

Fig. 24.33

(ii) **Temperature-operated circuit.** In the high-temperature alarm circuit of Fig. 24.34 a thermistor and resistor R form a potential divider across the 6 V supply. When the temperature of the thermistor rises, its resistance decreases and a larger fraction of the 6 V supply is dropped across R, that is, the base–emitter p.d. increases. When it exceeds 0.6 V or so the transistor switches 'on' and collector current (too small to ring the bell directly) goes through the relay coil. The relay contacts close, enabling the bell to obtain the larger current it needs directly from the 6 V supply.

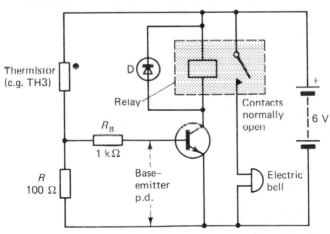

Fig. 24.34

The diode D protects the transistor from damage by the large e.m.f. induced in the relay coil (due to its inductance—see Unit 22.10) when the collector current falls to zero at switch-off. The diode is forward biased to the induced e.m.f. (which tries to maintain the current through the relay coil) and, because of its low forward resistance (1 Ω or so), offers an easy path to it. To the 6 V supply the diode is reverse biased and its high resistance does not short-circuit the relay coil when the transistor is on.

If the thermistor and R are interchanged the circuit could be used as a frost-warning device.

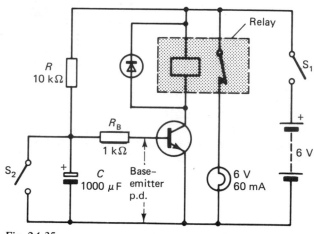

Fig. 24.35

(iii) **Time-operated circuit.** In the circuit of Fig. 24.35 when S_1 and S_2 are closed, the lamp is on and the transistor is off because the base–emitter p.d. is zero (due to S_2 short-circuiting C and stopping it from charging up). If S_2 is opened, C starts to charge through R and, *after a certain time*, the base–emitter p.d. exceeds 0.6 V causing the transistor to switch on. This operates the relay; its contacts open and switch off the lamp. The *time delay* between opening S_2 and the lamp going off increases if either C or R or both are increased.

The circuit is reset by opening S_1 and closing S_2 to let C discharge. It could be used as a timer to control a lamp in a photographic dark room.

(iv) **Sound-operated circuit with latching.** The variable resistor R in Fig. 24.36 is adjusted so that the transistor switches 'on' only when someone speaks into the microphone. The emitter current then provides the gate current which triggers the thyristor and allows current to flow through the lamp. The lamp stays on till the 6 V supply is disconnected, that is, the thyristor acts as a *latching switch*.

The capacitor C stops d.c. from the battery passing via R through the microphone and upsetting the operation of the transistor. But it allows the a.c. produced in the microphone by the sound to pass to the base.

If a relay and bell are used instead of the lamp (as in Fig. 24.34) the circuit could form the basis of a sound-operated intruder alarm.

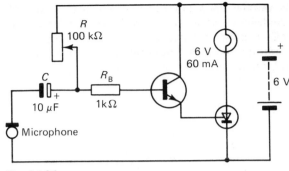

Fig. 24.36

24.11 Multivibrator Circuits

Multivibrators are switching circuits containing two transistors and when one is 'on' the other is 'off'. There are three types.

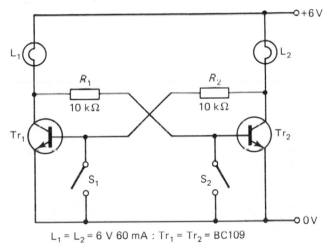

$L_1 = L_2 = 6$ V 60 mA : $Tr_1 = Tr_2 = $ BC109

Fig. 24.37

(i) **Bistable.** The circuit is given in Fig. 24.37. If L_1 comes on when it is first connected then Tr_1 is 'on' (the collector current is large). The circuit stays in this state, that is, it *latches* on to it and *remembers* it.

However, closing S_1 momentarily connects the base of Tr_1 to 0 V, that is, it is no longer forward biased and so switches 'off'. L_1 therefore goes off and L_2 lights up because Tr_2 comes 'on', since its base is now connected via R_1 and L_1 to +6 V, that is, it is forward biased. The circuit will stay in this second stable state (hence the term *bistable*) until S_2 is closed momentarily, when L_1 lights again.

Adding a few more components to a bistable gives a circuit which changes from one stable state to the other every time a switching pulse is applied to an input called the 'trigger'. The pulse can be obtained either by connecting and disconnecting 'trigger' to +6 V or from an astable multivibrator (see (ii) below). Each lamp then comes on only at every second trigger pulse, that is at *half* the frequency of the trigger pulses. The bistable is a *divide-by-two* circuit and many joined together make up a *binary counter*. Bistables are used as dividers in digital watches.

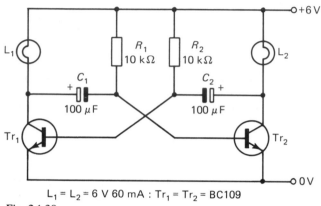

$L_1 = L_2 = 6$ V 60 mA : $Tr_1 = Tr_2 = $ BC109

Fig. 24.38

(ii) **Astable.** A circuit is shown in Fig. 24.38. In this case Tr_1 and Tr_2 switch 'on' and 'off' automatically causing L_1 and L_2 to flash in turn. The action is due to C_1 charging and discharging through R_1 while C_2 does the same through R_2. The circuit is used for the flashing lights that give warning of road works.

The flashing rate depends on the values of $C_1 \times R_1$ and $C_2 \times R_2$. For example, if C_1 and C_2 are replaced by 0.1 μF capacitors and L_2 by a headphone or a small loudspeaker, the transistors switch 'on' and 'off' so quickly that L_1 seems to be on all the time and an audible note (that is, a string of very rapid 'clicks') is heard in the headphone.

An astable has no stable states but switches from one state to the other of its own accord at a rate determined by the circuit components. It is used as an *oscillator* to produce the notes in an electronic organ, and also as a *timer* or *clock* to control and operate an electronic system.

(iii) **Monostable** (Fig. 24.39). This circuit has one stable state in which it normally rests with Tr_1 'on' and Tr_2 'off'. It can be switched to its unstable state for a certain time, depending on the values of C_1 and R_1, if the base of Tr_1 is connected momentarily to 0 V by closing S_1. During this time L_2 is alight.

A monostable can be used as a *timer* to bring on a light for a known time.

All three types of multivibrator are made as ICs.

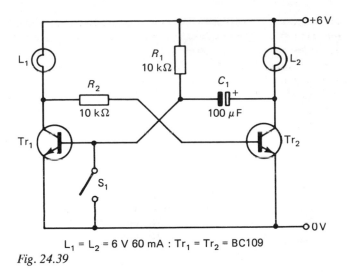

$$L_1 = L_2 = 6 \text{ V } 60 \text{ mA} : Tr_1 = Tr_2 = BC109$$

Fig. 24.39

24.12 Logic Gates

Logic gates are switching circuits used in computers and other digital electronic systems. A gate is 'opened', that is, made to give a 'high' output voltage or signal of around 5 V—by a certain voltage or combination of voltages at its input or inputs (it usually has more than one).

There are six basic types of gate, all made from transistors in IC form. The behaviour of each is described by a *truth table* showing what the output is for all possible inputs. 'High' outputs and inputs (typically about 5 V) and 'low' ones (near 0 V) are represented by 1 and 0 respectively and are referred to as *logic levels* 1 and 0.

(i) **NOT gate or inverter.** This is the simplest gate, with one input and one output. It produces a 'high' output if the input is 'low', that is, NOT high and vice versa: whatever the input, the gate inverts it. The symbol and truth table are given in Fig. 24.40.

Input	Output
0	1
1	0

Fig. 24.40

(ii) **OR, NOR, AND, NAND gates.** All these have two or more inputs and one output (F). The truth tables and symbols for two-input gates are shown in Fig. 24.41. Try to remember the following:

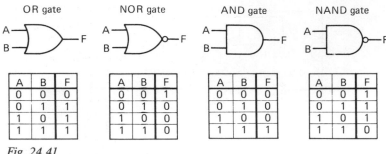

Fig. 24.41

> **OR**: output is 1 if input A **OR** input B **OR** both are 1
> **NOR**: output is 1 if neither input A **NOR** input B is 1
> **AND**: output is 1 if input A **AND** input B are 1
> **NAND**: output is 1 if input A **AND** input B are **NOT** both 1.

Note that the outputs of the NOR and NAND gates are the inverted forms of those of the OR and AND gates respectively. Their symbols have a small circle at the output end to signify this inversion.

(iii) **Exclusive OR gate.** This gate gives a 'high' output when *either* input is 'high' but not when *both* are 'high'. Unlike the ordinary OR gate (sometimes called the *inclusive* OR gate), it excludes the case of both inputs being 'high' for a 'high' output. It is sometimes called the *difference* gate because the output is 'high' when the inputs are different.

The symbol and truth table are shown in Fig. 24.42.

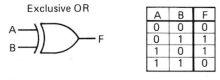

Fig. 24.42

(iv) **Testing logic gates.** The truth tables for the various gates can be conveniently checked by having the logic IC mounted on a small board with sockets for the power supply, inputs A and B and output F (Fig. 24.43). A 'high' input (logic level 1) is obtained by connecting the input socket to the positive of the power supply, say $+5\,V$, and a 'low' one (logic level 0) by connecting it to $0\,V$.

The output can be detected using an indicator module containing an LED which lights up for a '1' and stays off for a '0'.

(v) **Using gates to build logic circuits.** During a counting operation in say a computer, it may be necessary to know when a certain total has been reached

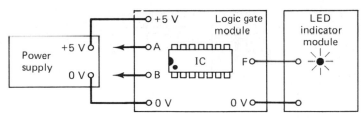

Fig. 24.43

before moving on to the next part of the program. This involves comparing two numbers.

To take a very simple example, suppose the logic circuit required has to produce a logic 1 output F when its inputs A and B are equal, either both 0s or both 1s. The block diagram and truth table for this circuit are given in Fig. 24.44(*a*) and (*b*) and the actual circuit using AND, OR and NOT gates in Fig. 24.44(*c*).

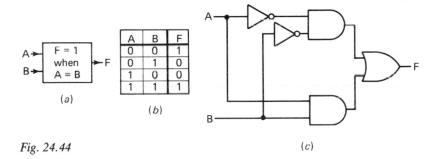

Fig. 24.44   (*c*)

24.13 Transistor as an Amplifier

This is the other main use for transistors and is what *analogue electronics* (such as radio and television) is chiefly concerned with.

In a transistor amplifier a small a.c. signal, such as that due to sound falling on a microphone, is applied as the *input* to its base–emitter circuit. This causes small changes of the steady base current which result in much larger changes of collector current. These produce as the *output* an amplified version of the original sound in an earphone in the collector circuit. For the amplification to be free from distortion, the output waveform must be an exact copy of the input waveform and this is achieved only if the base current changes about a suitable steady value.

In the simple circuit of Fig. 24.45(*a*) the steady base current is decided by the resistance of R_B which should be about 100 times greater than the resistance of

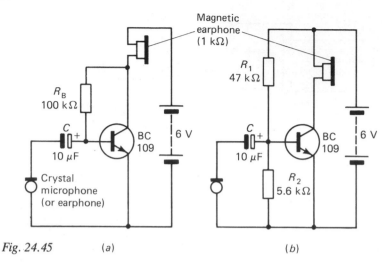

Fig. 24.45   (a)   (b)

the earphone. Capacitor *C* stops d.c. from the battery passing through the microphone (and upsetting the biasing) but allows the a.c. signal from the microphone to pass to the base.

Fig. 24.45(*b*) shows an alternative arrangement for forward biasing the base–emitter junction to the required value using a potential divider R_1–R_2.

In practice, amplifiers have several transistors, with the output of one fed to the input of the next. This increases the amplification.

24.14 Operational Amplifier

(i) **About op amps.** Operational amplifiers (op amps) were originally designed to solve mathematical equations electronically by performing operations such as addition. Today, in IC form, they have many uses, two of the most important being (*a*) as high-gain d.c. and a.c. voltage amplifiers and (*b*) as switches. A typical op amp contains about twenty transistors.

An op amp has one output and two inputs, called the *inverting* input (marked −) and the *non-inverting* input (marked +), as shown on its symbol in Fig. 24.46. It operates from a dual power supply giving equal positive and negative d.c. voltages in the range ±5 V to ±15 V. The centre point on the power supply is common to the input and output circuits and is taken as 0 V.

If a small *positive* voltage V_1 is applied to the inverting input (−), with the non-inverting input (+) connected to 0 V so that $V_2 = 0$, the output is an amplified *negative* voltage V_o. On the other hand if V_1 is negative, V_o is positive. In both cases V_o is of opposite sign to V_1, that is, it is inverted and in antiphase with V_1.

If a small *positive* voltage V_2 is applied to the non-inverting input, with the inverting input connected to 0 V so that $V_1 = 0$, the output in this case is an amplified *positive* voltage V_o. Similarly if V_2 is negative, V_o is negative. In both

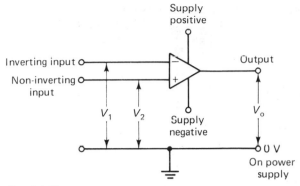

Fig. 24.46

cases V_o has the same sign as V_2, that is, it is not inverted and is in phase with V_2.

(ii) **Op amp voltage amplifier.** In this role op amps almost always use *negative feedback*, that is, part of the output is fed back to the external input so that it is in antiphase with it. The feedback subtracts from the input, thereby reducing both the input and the output, as shown in Fig. 24.47.

(*a*) No negative feedback

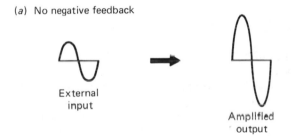

External
input

Amplified
output

(*b*) With negative feedback

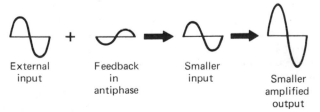

External   Feedback   Smaller
input   in   input
                  antiphase

Smaller
amplified
output

Fig. 24.47

The *voltage gain A* of the amplifier, defined by

$$A = \frac{\text{output voltage}}{\text{input voltage}} = \frac{V_o}{V_i}$$

is thus reduced but this is more than compensated for by the gain becoming *accurately predictable* and *more constant over a wider range of input frequencies*.

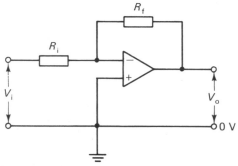

Fig. 24.48   N.B. Power supply connections not shown

In the basic circuit of Fig. 24.48 for an inverting op amp voltage amplifier, the non-inverting terminal is held at 0 V and the input voltage V_i (a.c. or d.c.) is applied via resistor R_i to the inverting terminal. The output voltage V_o is therefore in antiphase with the input. The feedback resistor R_f, by feeding back a certain fraction (depending on the value of R_f) of the output to the *inverting* terminal, ensures that the feedback is negative.

It can be proved that the gain is given by

$$A = \frac{V_o}{V_i} = \frac{R_f}{R_i} \qquad\qquad \textbf{1}$$

For example, if $R_f = 100\,\text{k}\Omega$ and $R_i = 10\,\text{k}\Omega$, $A = -10$. The negative sign shows that V_o is negative if V_i is positive, and vice versa.

From equation 1 we see that A depends only on the values of the two resistors R_f and R_i (which can be known accurately) and not on the particular op amp used. Also note that the maximum value of the output voltage cannot exceed the range between the positive and negative of the power supply (18 V peak-to-peak on a ± 9 V supply).

To check the gain equation experimentally, V_i (at about 1 kHz) can be obtained from a signal generator and measured, along with V_o, using a C.R.O. as an a.c. voltmeter (see Unit 24.3(ii)), with the time base on so that the waveforms of V_i and V_o are seen to be undistorted as in Fig. 24.49(a).

To show that the gain decreases as the frequency of V_i increases, the signal generator should be set at different frequencies up to 100 kHz and a graph plotted of gain against frequency using a frequency scale that increases by powers of ten (to accommodate the wide range of values—see Fig. 24.49(b)). The frequency range over which the gain is nearly constant is called the

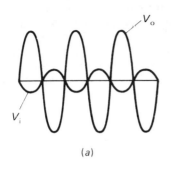

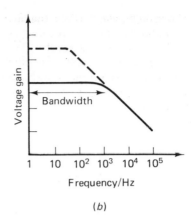

(a)

Fig. 24.49

(b)

bandwidth of the amplifier; the bandwidth decreases if the gain is increased (by making R_f/R_i greater), as shown by the dotted graph.

(iii) Op amp voltage comparator. When both inputs of an op amp are used at the same time, the amplified output voltage V_o is the *difference* between the two input voltages V_1 and V_2. But because of the very high gain (which may be up to 10^5 for d.c. and low-frequency a.c. without negative feedback), in theory V_o could exceed the power supply voltage when the difference between V_1 and V_2 is greater than about 0.1 mV. In practice, however, this cannot happen. Hence where the difference between V_1 and V_2 is more than this, V_o remains constant at the supply voltage (for instance, at +9 V or −9 V on a ±9 V supply) and the op amp is said to be *saturated*. In this condition it can be used as a switch.

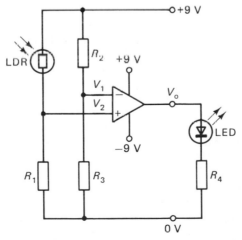

Fig. 24.50

For example, in the light-operated alarm circuit of Fig. 24.50, the inputs V_1 and V_2 are supplied by potential dividers and the op amp compares them. In the dark, the resistance of the LDR is much greater than R_1, making V_2 less than the 'reference' voltage (set by the values of R_2 and R_3), the difference being large enough to saturate the op amp. Since V_1 (at the inverting input) is positive, V_o will be negative and about -9 V. If light falls on the LDR its resistance decreases and V_2 increases. When V_2 (the non-inverting input) exceeds V_1, the op amp switches to its other saturated state with V_o about $+9$ V. This positive voltage lights the LED (that is, the alarm).

24.15 Radio

Radio waves (see Unit 16.10) are emitted by aerials when a.c. flows in them, but the length of the aerial must be comparable with the wavelength of the wave produced for the radiation to be appreciable. A 50 Hz a.c. corresponds to a wavelength of 6×10^6 m (since $v = f\lambda$ where $v = 3 \times 10^8$ m and $f = 50$ Hz).

Alternating currents with frequencies below about 20 kHz are called *audio frequency* (a.f.) currents; those with frequencies greater than this are *radio frequency* (r.f.) currents. Therefore, so that aerials are not too large, they are supplied with r.f. currents. Speech and music generate a.f. currents, however, and so some way of combining a.f. with r.f. is required if they are to be sent over a distance.

(i) **Transmitter.** In this, an *oscillator* produces an r.f. current which would cause an aerial connected to it to send out an electromagnetic wave, called a *carrier wave*, of constant amplitude and having the same frequency as the r.f. current. If a normal receiver picked up such a signal nothing would be heard. The r.f. signal has to be modified or *modulated* so that it 'carries' the a.f. This is done in various ways.

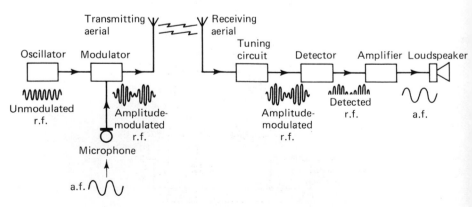

Fig. 24.51 (*a*) Transmitter   (*b*) Receiver

In *amplitude modulation* (a.m.) the amplitude of the r.f. is varied so that it depends on the a.f. current from the microphone, the process occurring in a *modulator*. Fig. 24.51(*a*) is a block diagram for a transmitter of this type, which is used for medium- and long-wave broadcasting in Britain.

(ii) **Receiver.** A block diagram of a simple a.m. receiver is shown in Fig. 24.51(*b*). The *tuning circuit* selects the wanted signal from the aerial. The *detector* (or demodulator) separates the a.f. (speech or music) from the r.f. carrier. The *amplifier* then boosts the a.f. which produces sound in the loudspeaker.

In *detection* or *demodulation* the a.f. which was 'added' to the r.f. in the transmitter is recovered in the receiver.

Suppose the amplitude-modulated r.f. signal *V* of Fig. 24.52(*a*) is applied to the detector circuit of Fig. 24.52(*d*). The diode produces rectified pulses of r.f. current *I* (Fig. 24.52(*b*)). These charge up *C* during the positive half-cycles, as well as flowing through the earphone. During the negative half-cycles, when the diode is non-conducting, *C* *partly* discharges through the earphone.

The p.d. V_c across *C* (and the earphone) varies as in Fig. 24.52(*c*) if *C* and *R* have suitable values. Apart from the slight r.f. ripple, V_c has the same frequency and shape as the modulating a.f. and produces the original sound in the earphone.

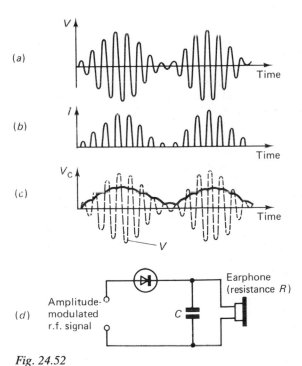

Fig. 24.52

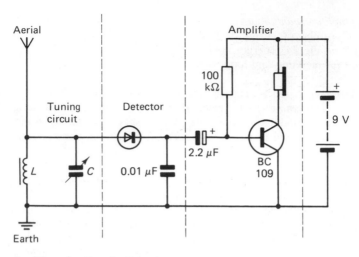

L = 50-turn coil on ferrite rod
C = 0.0005 μF variable capacitor
Fig. 24.53

A simple radio receiver circuit is shown in Fig. 24.53.

24.16 Revision Questions and Problems

Electrons

1. A thermionic tube is shown in Fig. 24.54.
    (a) Explain the term *thermionic*.
    (b) Copy and complete the diagram so that a current will flow through the tube.
    (c) What does the current consist of?
    (d) Why do these current carriers move to the anode?
    (e) Why is the tube evacuated?

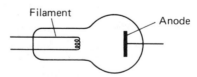

Fig. 24.54

2. (a) What are cathode rays?
    (b) State four properties of cathode rays.
    (c) In Fig. 24.55(a), to which terminals on a power supply must plates A and B be connected to deflect the cathode rays downwards?
    (d) In Fig. 24.55(b), in which direction will the cathode rays be deflected?

3. Outline briefly (a) how Thomson measured the specific charge e/m for the electron, and (b) how Millikan measured the electronic charge e.

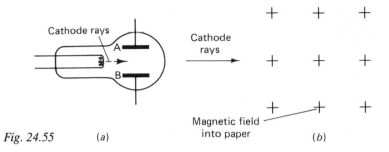

Fig. 24.55   (a)   Magnetic field
                                          into paper   (b)

4. Calculate the *e/m* for an electron if $e = 1.6 \times 10^{-19}$ C and $m = 9.1 \times 10^{-31}$ kg.

Cathode Ray Oscilloscope: Television

5. (*a*) Name the three main parts of the cathode ray tube in an oscilloscope and say what each part does.
   (*b*) In a C.R.O., how does (i) the brilliance control, (ii) the focus control, vary the brightness and sharpness respectively of the spot on the screen?
   (*c*) What does the time base do in a C.R.O.?
   (*d*) State three uses of a C.R.O.

6. An end-on view of the screen S and deflecting plates A, B, C, D of a C.R.O. are shown in Fig. 24.56(*a*), (*b*) and (*c*).
   (*a*) Which are the Y-plates?
   (*b*) In Fig. 24.56(*b*), which plate or plates must be positive and which negative? State two ways of increasing the deflection.
   (*c*) In Fig. 24.56(*c*), which plate or plates must be positive and which negative?
   (*d*) If an alternating p.d. of 1 Hz was applied to plates B and D in Fig. 24.56(*a*), what would you see on S?
   (*e*) If an alternating p.d. of 50 Hz was applied to plates A and C in Fig. 24.56(*a*), what would you see on S?

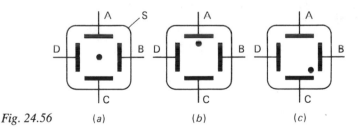

Fig. 24.56   (a)   (b)   (c)

7. When the Y-amp gain control on a C.R.O. is set on 2 V/div, an a.c. input produces a vertical line 10 divisions long. What is (*a*) the peak voltage, (*b*) the r.m.s. voltage, of the input?

8. What is the frequency of an alternating p.d. which is applied to the Y-plates of a C.R.O. and produces five complete waves covering 10 horizontal divisions of the screen when the time base setting is 10 ms/div?

9. (a) In a television receiver, what is the function of (i) the line time base, (ii) the frame time base?

(b) In Fig. 24.10(a), which are the line (that is, the x-direction) time base coils? (Use Fleming's left-hand rule.)

Semiconductor Diode: Rectification and Smoothing

10. (a) Name two semiconductor materials.

(b) Explain the following terms: doping, n-type semiconductor, p-type semiconductor.

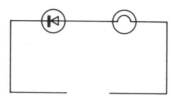

Fig. 24.57

11. (a) What is a diode?

(b) Explain the terms *forward bias* and *reverse bias*.

(c) Copy and complete the circuit in Fig. 24.57 with a battery connected so that the diode is forward biased.

12. (a) Draw a typical diode characteristic curve.

(b) Draw the circuit you would use to find the characteristic curve of a diode.

13. Which lamps light in the circuits of Fig. 24.58(a), (b) and (c)?

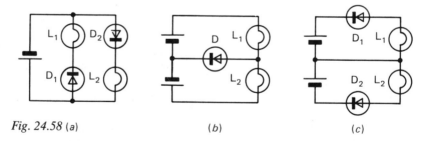

Fig. 24.58 (a)   (b)   (c)

Transistors: Alarm Circuits

14. (a) Draw the symbol for an n–p–n junction transistor and label its three connections.

(b) Why are most transistors made of silicon?

(c) How many p–n junctions are there in a junction transistor and which is/are forward biased?

(d) Name the two current paths in a transistor in common-emitter connection. Which is the input circuit and which the output circuit?

(e) What is the value of the 'turn-on' p.d. in a silicon junction transistor?

(f) State two uses of transistors.

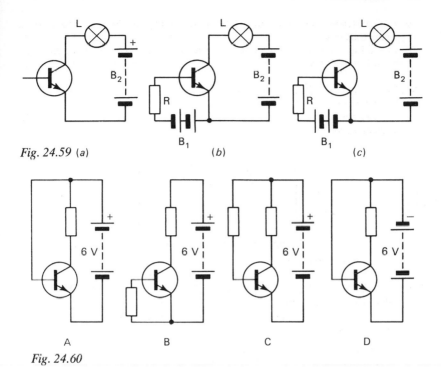

Fig. 24.59 (a)   (b)   (c)

Fig. 24.60

15. In which circuit(s) of Fig. 24.59 will lamp L light if B_1 =3 V, B_2 =6 V, R =1 kΩ and L =6 V 60 mA?

16. In which circuit(s) of Fig. 24.60 is the transistor (a) correctly connected, (b) likely to overheat, if the resistors have suitable values?

17. (a) Explain the term *current gain* as applied to a transistor.
    (b) What is the current gain of a transistor for which the collector current is 10 mA when the base current is 20 μA?

18. (a) A lamp in series with an LDR is just alight. What happens if the intensity of the light on the LDR increases?
    (b) A lamp in series with a thermistor is just alight. Does it get brighter if the thermistor is cooled?

19. (a) Draw the symbol for an LED.
    (b) State two precautions that should be taken to prevent damage when using one.

20. (a) Give six advantages of using transistors as switches.
    (b) When is a transistor considered to be (i) off, (ii) on, if it is used as a switch?
    (c) Draw the two basic transistor switching circuits.

21. The circuit in Fig. 24.61 when completed is to be used as an early-morning alarm which rings a bell when it gets light.
    (a) Copy and complete the circuit by adding in the correct gaps an LDR, a variable resistor, a relay, a diode and an electric bell.

(b) What is the purpose of (i) R_B, (ii) the diode?

(c) What is the advantage of using a variable resistor rather than a fixed one?

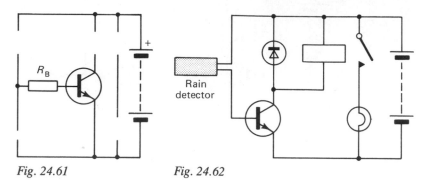

Fig. 24.61   *Fig. 24.62*

22. A simple rain warning circuit is shown in Fig. 24.62 in which the rain detector is two closely spaced copper rods.

(a) How does the circuit work when it rains?

(b) If the relay operates with a current of 30 mA and the current gain of the transistor is 60, what base current is needed for the relay to work?

Multivibrators: Logic Gates

23. (a) What is a multivibrator?

(b) Describe what each of the three types does.

(c) State one use for each.

24. Copy and complete the truth tables for each of the two-input logic gates.

Inputs		Outputs				
A	B	OR	NOR	AND	NAND	Exclusive OR
0	0					
0	1					
1	0					
1	1					

25. What do the symbols represent in Figs. 24.63(a), (b), (c), (d), (e) and (f)?

26. Write down the truth table for the logic circuit in Fig. 24.64.

Amplifiers: Transistor and Op Amp

27. (a) Draw the circuit for a single-stage common-emitter amplifier which includes a microphone, an earphone, a resistor and a capacitor.

(b) What is the function of each of the components mentioned in (a)?

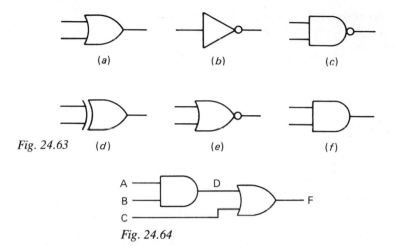

Fig. 24.63

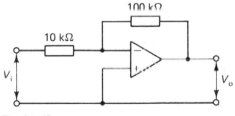

Fig. 24.64

28. (a) State two important uses of op amps.
   (b) Explain the terms *inverting* and *non-inverting* inputs with reference to an op amp.
   (c) Draw the symbol for an op amp.

29. (a) Explain the term *negative feedback*.
   (b) Give two reasons why op amp voltage amplifiers use negative feedback.

30. (a) The circuit of Fig. 24.65 is for an inverting op amp voltage amplifier. What is its voltage gain and the output voltage if the input is an alternating voltage of peak value (i) ± 1 V, (ii) ± 2 V, and the supply voltage is ± 15 V?

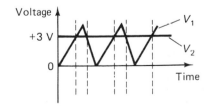

Fig. 24.65

Fig. 24.66

(*b*) How does the voltage gain of an op amp vary with the frequency of the input?

31. (*a*) How is an op amp used to compare two voltages?

(*b*) Voltages V_1 and V_2 with waveforms like those in Fig. 24.66 are applied simultaneously to the inverting and non-inverting inputs respectively of an op amp on a ± 6 V supply. Copy Fig. 24.66 and draw the waveform of the output voltage V_o below it.

Radio

32. Explain the following terms: audio frequency, radio frequency, modulation, detection.

33. Draw a block diagram for a radio transmitter and receiver.

Mathematics for Physics

Use this section as the need arises

Equations—type 1

An equation has sometimes to be changed round before it can be solved. In the equation $x = a/b$, the subject is x. To change it we *multiply or divide both sides* of the equation by the same quantity.

(i) To change the subject to a. We have

$$x = \frac{a}{b}$$

If we multiply both sides by b the equation will still be true.

$$\therefore \quad x \times b = \frac{a}{b} \times b$$

The bs on the right-hand side cancel,

$$\therefore \quad b \times x = \frac{a}{\not b} \times \not b = a$$

$$\therefore \quad a = b \times x$$

(ii) To change the subject to b. We have

$$x = \frac{a}{b}$$

Multiplying both sides by b as before, we get

$$a = b \times x$$

Divide both sides by x,

$$\therefore \quad \frac{a}{x} = \frac{b \times x}{x} = \frac{b \times \not x}{\not x} = b$$

$$\therefore \quad b = \frac{a}{x}$$

Now try the following questions using these ideas.

Questions

1. Find the value of x if

   (a) $2x=6$ (b) $3x=15$ (c) $3x=8$ (d) $\dfrac{x}{2}=10$

   (e) $\dfrac{x}{3}=4$ (f) $\dfrac{2x}{3}=4$ (g) $\dfrac{4}{x}=2$ (h) $\dfrac{9}{x}=3$ (i) $\dfrac{x}{6}=\dfrac{4}{3}$

2. Change the subject to

   (a) f in $v=f\lambda$ (b) λ in $v=f\lambda$ (c) I in $V=IR$

   (d) R in $V=IR$ (e) m in $d=\dfrac{m}{V}$ (f) V in $d=\dfrac{m}{V}$

   (g) s in $v=\dfrac{s}{t}$ (h) t in $v=\dfrac{s}{t}$ (i) a in $F=ma$

   (j) I in $Q=It$ (k) Q in $C=\dfrac{Q}{V}$ (l) A in $p=\dfrac{F}{A}$

   (m) p_1 in $p_1V_1=p_2V_2$ (n) a in $x=abc$ (o) t in $W=ItV$

   (p) $\Delta\theta$ in $E_H=mc\,\Delta\theta$

3. Change the subject to

   (a) I^2 in $P=I^2R$ (b) I in $P=I^2R$ (c) a in $s=\frac{1}{2}at^2$

   (d) t^2 in $s=\frac{1}{2}at$ (e) t in $s=\frac{1}{2}at^2$ (f) v in $\frac{1}{2}mv^2=mgh$

   (g) y in $\lambda=\dfrac{ay}{D}$ (h) ρ in $R=\dfrac{\rho l}{A}$ (i) V_1 in $\dfrac{V_1}{T_1}=\dfrac{V_2}{T_2}$

   (j) T_1 in $\dfrac{V_1}{T_1}=\dfrac{V_2}{T_2}$ (k) V_2 in $\dfrac{p_1V_1}{T_1}=\dfrac{p_2V_2}{T_2}$ (l) T_2 in $\dfrac{p_1V_1}{T_1}=\dfrac{p_2V_2}{T_2}$

4. By replacing (substituting) find the value of v in $v=f\lambda$ if

   (a) $f=5$ and $\lambda=2$ (b) $f=3.4$ and $\lambda=10$
   (c) $f=\frac{1}{4}$ and $\lambda=\frac{8}{3}$ (d) $f=\frac{3}{5}$ and $\lambda=\frac{1}{6}$
   (e) $f=100$ and $\lambda=0.1$ (f) $f=3\times10^5$ and $\lambda=10^3$

5. By changing the subject and replacing find

   (a) f in $v=f\lambda$ if $v=3.0\times10^8$ and $\lambda=1.5\times10^3$
   (b) h in $p=10hd$ if $p=10^5$ and $d=10^3$
   (c) a in $n=a/b$ if $n=4/3$ and $b=6$
   (d) b in $n=a/b$ if $n=1.5$ and $a=3.0\times10^8$
   (e) F in $p=F/A$ if $p=100$ and $A=0.2$
   (f) s in $v=s/t$ if $v=1500$ and $t=0.2$
   (g) t in $V=At$ if $V=10^{-3}$ and $A=10^4$
   (h) V_2 in $p_1V_1=p_2V_2$ if $p_1=10^5$, $V_1=30$ and $p_2=2\times10^5$
   (i) t in $s=\frac{1}{2}gt^2$ if $s=125$ and $g=10$
   (j) b in $x=abc$ if $x=0.0016$, $a=1$ and $c=80$
   (k) $\Delta\theta$ in $E_H=mc\,\Delta\theta$ if $E_H=8000$, $m=2$ and $c=400$
   (l) V_2 in $p_1V_1/T_1=p_2V_2/T_2$ if $p_1=1$, $p_2=2$, $V_1=2$, $T_1=300$ and $T_2=500$

Equations—type 2

To change the subject in the equation $x = a + by$ we *add or subtract the same quantity from each side.* We may also have to divide or multiply as in a type 1 equation. Suppose we wish to change the subject to y in

$$x = a + by$$

Subtract a from both sides,

$$\therefore \quad x - a = a + by - a = by$$

Divide both sides by b,

$$\therefore \quad \frac{x-a}{b} = \frac{by}{b} = y$$

$$\therefore \quad y = \frac{x-a}{b}$$

Questions

6. What is the value of x if

(a) $x + 1 = 5$ (b) $2x + 3 = 7$ (c) $x - 2 = 3$

(d) $2(x-3) = 10$ (e) $\dfrac{x}{2} - \dfrac{1}{3} = 0$ (f) $\dfrac{x}{3} + \dfrac{1}{4} = 0$

(g) $2x + \dfrac{5}{3} = 6$ (h) $7 - \dfrac{x}{4} = 11$ (i) $\dfrac{3}{x} + 2 = 5$

7. By changing the subject and replacing find the value of a in $v = u + at$ if

(a) $v = 20$, $u = 10$ and $t = 2$
(b) $v = 50$, $u = 20$ and $t = 0.5$
(c) $v = 5/0.2$, $u = 2/0.2$ and $t = 0.2$

8. Change the subject in $v^2 = u^2 + 2as$ to a.

Proportion (or variation)

One of the most important mathematical operations in physics is finding the relation between two sets of measurements.

(i) **Direct proportion.** Suppose that in an experiment two sets of readings are obtained for the quantities x and y as in Table 1 (units omitted).

Table 1

x	1	2	3	4
y	2	4	6	8

We see that when x is doubled, y doubles; when x is trebled, y trebles; when x is halved, y halves and so on. There is a one-to-one relationship between each value of x and the corresponding value of y.

We say that y *is directly proportional* to x, or y *varies directly* as x. In symbols,

$$y \propto x$$

Also, the *ratio* of one to the other, say of y to x, is always the same, that is, it has a constant value which in this case is 2. Hence we can write

$$\frac{y}{x} = \text{a constant} = 2$$

The constant, called the *constant of proportionality* or *variation*, is given a symbol, such as k, and the relation between y and x is then summed up by the equation

$$\frac{y}{x} = k \text{ or } y = kx$$

Notes

1. In practice, because of inevitable experimental errors, the readings seldom show the relation so clearly as here.

2. If instead of using numerical values for x and y we use letters, such as x_1, x_2, $x_3 \ldots$ and $y_1, y_2, y_3 \ldots$ then we can also say

$$\frac{y_1}{x_1} = \frac{y_2}{x_2} = \frac{y_3}{x_3} = \ldots = k$$

or
$$y_1 = kx_1, y_2 = kx_2, y_3 = kx_3 \ldots$$

(ii) **Inverse proportion.** Two sets of readings for the quantities p and V are given in Table 2.

Table 2

p	3	4	6	12
V	4	3	2	1

There is again a one-to-one relationship between each value of p and the corresponding value of V, but here when p is doubled, V is halved; when p is trebled, V has one-third its previous value and so on.

We say that V is *inversely proportional* to p, or V *varies inversely* as p, that is,

$$V \propto \frac{1}{p}$$

Also, the product $p \times V$ is always the same $(=12)$ and we write

$$V = \frac{k}{p} \text{ or } pV = k$$

where k is the constant of proportionality or variation and equals 12 in this case.

Using letters for values of p and V, we can also say

$$p_1 V_1 = p_2 V_2 = p_3 V_3 = \ldots = k$$

Graphs

Another useful way of finding the relation between two quantities is by a graph.

(i) **Straight-line graphs.** When the readings in Table 1 are used to plot a graph of y against x, a *continuous* line joining the points is *a straight line passing through the origin* 0 (Fig. 1). Such a graph shows that there is direct proportionality between the quantities plotted, that is, that $y \propto x$. But note that the line must go through 0.

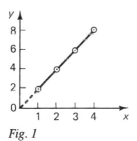

Fig. 1

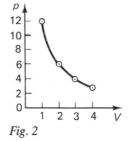

Fig. 2

A graph of p against V using the readings in Table 2 is a curve (Fig. 2). But if we plot p against $1/V$ (or V against $1/p$) we get a straight line through the origin, showing that $p \propto 1/V$ (or $V \propto 1/p$) (Fig. 3).

(ii) **Slope or gradient.** The slope or gradient of a straight-line graph equals the constant of proportionality. In Fig. 1, the slope is $y/x - 2$; in Fig. 3 it is $p/(1/V) = pV = 12$.

In practice, points plotted from actual measurements may not lie exactly on a straight line, because of experimental errors. The 'best straight line' is then

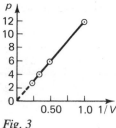

p	V	$1/V$
3	4	0.25
4	3	0.33
6	2	0.50
12	1	1.0

Fig. 3

drawn 'through' them so that they are equally distributed about it. This automatically averages the results. Any points that are well off the line stand out and may be investigated further.

(iii) **Practical points.**
(*a*) Label the axes, giving the quantities being plotted and their units (current in amperes, for example).
(*b*) If possible the origin of both scales should be on the paper. Choose the scales so that the points are spread out along the graph.
(*c*) Mark the points ⊙ or ×.

Questions

9. In an experiment different masses were hung from the end of a spring held in a stand, and the extensions produced were as shown below.

Mass (g)	100	150	200	300	350	500	600
Extension (cm)	1.9	3.1	4.0	6.1	6.9	10.0	12.2

(*a*) Plot a graph of *extension* along the vertical (*y*) axis against *mass* along the horizontal (*x*) axis.
(*b*) What is the relation between *extension* and *mass*? Give a reason for your answer.

10. Pairs of readings of the quantities *m* and *v* are given below.

m	0.12	1.5	2.5	3.5
v	20	40	56	72

(*a*) Plot a graph of *m* along the vertical axis and *v* along the horizontal axis.
(*b*) Is *m* directly proportional to *v*? Explain your answer.
(*c*) Use the graph to find *v* when *m*=1.

11. The distances s (in metres) travelled by a car at various times t (in seconds) are shown below.

s	0	2	8	18	32	50
t	0	1	2	3	4	5

Draw graphs of (a) s against t, (b) s against t^2. What can you conclude?

Powers of Ten Notation

There are three rules for performing calculations involving the multiplication and division of numbers that are in powers of ten form.

Rule 1. When the number is changed from numerator (top) to denominator (bottom) or vice versa, the sign of the power of ten is changed. For example:

$$10^3 = \frac{1}{10^{-3}} : \ 10^{-6} = \frac{1}{10^6}$$

$$\frac{6}{2 \times 10^{-6}} = \frac{6 \times 10^6}{2} = 3 \times 10^6$$

Rule 2. When two numbers are multiplied, the powers of ten are added. For example:

$$10^2 \times 10^6 = 10^{2+6} = 10^8$$
$$10^5 \times 10^{-3} = 10^{5-3} = 10^2$$
$$10^4 \times 10^{-9} = 10^{4-9} = 10^{-5}$$
$$3 \times 10^{12} \times 2 \times 10^{\ 5} = 3 \times 2 \times 10^{12\ 5} = 6 \times 10^7$$
$$4 \times 10^6 \times 2 \times 10^{-6} = 4 \times 2 \times 10^{6-6} = 8 \times 10^0 = 8 \times 1 = 8$$

Rule 3. When one number is divided by another, their powers of ten are subtracted. For example:

$$\frac{10^8}{10^3} = 10^{8-3} = 10^5$$

$$\frac{8 \times 10^{-5}}{2 \times 10^{-3}} = \frac{8 \times 10^{-5+3}}{2} = 4 \times 10^{-2}$$

$$\frac{10^{-2}}{10^{-6}} = 10^{-2+6} = 10^4$$

Questions

12. Find the value of

(a) $10^4 \times 10^5$ (b) $10^{12} \times 10^{-9}$ (c) $10^7/10^3$ (d) $10^2/10^5$

(e) $\dfrac{6 \times 10^3}{3 \times 10^2}$ (f) $\dfrac{5.0 \times 10^5}{2.0 \times 10^{-3}}$ (g) $2 \times 10^4 \times 4 \times 10^{-3}$ (h) $\dfrac{8}{4 \times 10^6}$

(i) $3.5 \times 10^{-4} \times 2 \times 10^4$ (j) $5 \times 10^6/10^6$

13. Find the value of

(a) $3 \times 10^3 + 2 \times 10^3$ (b) $6 \times 10^5 + 3 \times 10^4$

(c) $5 \times 10^3 - 4 \times 10^2$ (d) $7 \times 10^6 - 9 \times 10^5$

Appendix 1

Basic Quantities and Units

The five basic quantities and their units are listed in Table A1.

Table A1

Basic quantity		Unit	
Name	Symbol	Name	Symbol
length	l	metre	m
mass	m	kilogram	kg
time	t	second	s
temperature:			
Celsius	θ	degree Celsius	°C
Kelvin	T	kelvin	K
electric current	I	ampere	A

θ is a Greek letter, pronounced 'theta'.

Derived Quantities and Units

The units of derived quantities are obtained from the basic units by multiplication or division. Table A2 lists some that have combined names.

Table A2

Derived quantity		Unit	
Name	Symbol	Name	Symbol
area	A	square metre	m^2
volume	V	cubic metre	m^3
density	d	kilogram per cubic metre	kg/m^3 or $kg\,m^{-3}$
velocity	v	metre per second	m/s or $m\,s^{-1}$
acceleration	a	metre per second squared	m/s^2 or $m\,s^{-2}$
momentum	p	kilogram metre per second	$kg\,m/s$ or $kg\,m\,s^{-1}$

The units of some derived quantities would be rather complex if written in terms of the basic units, and these are named after famous scientists. Some are listed in Table A3.

Table A3

Derived quantity		Unit	
Name	Symbol	Name	Symbol
force	F	newton	N
pressure	p	pascal	Pa
energy	E	joule	J
work	W	joule	J
power	P	watt	W
frequency	f	hertz	Hz
electric charge	Q	coulomb	C
resistance	R	ohm	Ω
electromotive force (e.m.f.)	E	volt	V
potential difference (p.d.)	V	volt	V

Ω is a Greek letter, pronounced 'omega'. Note that the unit symbols all have capital letters.

A few quantities, such as relative density, do not have units. They consist of a number only and are said to be *dimensionless* quantities.

Appendix 2

Proof of Equations for Uniform Acceleration

First equation. If a body is moving with uniform acceleration a and its velocity increases from u to v in time t, then

$$a = \frac{\text{change of velocity}}{\text{time taken}} = \frac{v-u}{t}$$

$$\therefore \quad at = v - u$$
$$\text{or} \quad v = u + at \qquad \qquad \textbf{1}$$

Remember that the initial velocity u and the final velocity v refer to the start and the finish of the timing, not necessarily to the start and finish of the motion.

Second equation. The velocity of a body moving with uniform acceleration increases steadily. Its average velocity therefore equals half the sum of its initial and final velocities, that is,

$$\text{average velocity} = \frac{u+v}{2}$$

If s is the distance moved in time t, then since average velocity = distance/time $= s/t$,

$$\frac{s}{t} = \frac{u+v}{2} \qquad \qquad \textbf{2}$$

Third equation. From equation 1, $v = u + at$

From equation 2, $\quad \text{average velocity} = \dfrac{u+u+at}{2} = \dfrac{2u+at}{2}$

$$= u + \tfrac{1}{2}at$$

$$\therefore \quad \frac{s}{t} = u + \tfrac{1}{2}at$$

$$s = ut + \tfrac{1}{2}at^2 \qquad \qquad \textbf{3}$$

Fourth equation. This is obtained by eliminating t from equations 1 and 3. We have

$$v = u + at$$
$$\therefore \quad v^2 = u^2 + 2uat + a^2t^2$$
$$= u^2 + 2a(ut + \tfrac{1}{2}at^2)$$
$$\text{But} \quad s = ut + \tfrac{1}{2}at^2$$
$$\therefore \quad v^2 = u^2 + 2as \qquad \qquad \textbf{4}$$

Further Reading

Books

Gordon, J. E.: *The New Science of Strong Materials*. Penguin (London, 1968).

Kentzer, M.: *Strength*. Collins (London, 1977).

Gordon, J. E.: *Structures or Why Things Don't Fall Down*. Penguin (London, 1978).

Boyle, D.: *Visual Science—Energy*. Macdonald Educational (London, 1980).

Satchwell, J.: *Future Sources*. Franklin Watts (London, 1981).

Kentzer, M.: *Waves*. Collins (London, 1977).

Seymour, P.: *Adventures with Astronomy*. John Murray (London, 1983).

Duncan, T.: *Success in Electronics*. John Murray (London, 1983).

Mintern, H.: *The Kingfisher Book of Electronics*. Grisewood and Dempsey (London, 1984).

Kerrod, R.: *The World of Tomorrow*. Longman (London, 1980).

ILEA Physics Project Team: *APPIL* (Advanced Physics Project for Independent Learning) *Students' Guides: Structure of Matter; Forces and Motion; Electrical Properties; Wave Properties*. John Murray (London, 1979).

Periodicals

New Scientist
Scientific American

Answers to Revision Questions and Problems

(where appropriate)

Unit 1.5

1. Matter and energy.
2. (a) A compound contains two or more elements. (b) A molecule contains two or more atoms which may be the same or different.
3. A quantity which can be measured and helps to 'explain' the behaviour of matter and/or energy. For examples see Units 4.2 and 4.3.
4. The relationship between concepts. For examples see Units 5.4 and 19.6.
5. To help us to think about and 'explain' things we cannot see. For examples see Unit 8.2.
6. Washing machine, electric refrigerator, food mixer (there are many other examples).
7. Starter motor, windscreen-wiper motor, radiator cooling-fan motor are examples.
8. (a) To do calculations very quickly; to control industrial processes or robots in a factory. (b) To control missiles in warfare; to store secret personal information, and make it available to other people.

Unit 2.13

2. 4×10^3; 2×10^5; 1×10^6; 2.5×10^3; 1.86×10^5; 1×10^{-1}; 5×10^{-2}; 2.9×10^{-1}; 7.6×10^{-3}; 1.3×10^{-6}.
3. (a) has been measured to the nearest 0.1 cm and (b) to the nearest 0.01 cm.

Unit 2.14

1. (a) 10; (b) 40; (c) 5; (d) 67; (e) 1000.
2. (a) 3.00; (b) 5.50; (c) 8.70; (d) 0.43; (e) 0.100.
3. (a) Wrap a piece of string round the ball once, then measure its length. (b) Measure the thickness of say 100 sheets, then divide by 100.
4. 10.4 mm $(100 \times 0.10\,\text{mm} + 2 \times 0.20\,\text{mm} = 10\,\text{mm} + 0.4\,\text{mm})$.
5. (a) 53.3 mm; (b) 95.8 mm.
6. (a) 2.31 mm; (b) 14.97 mm.
7. 40 cm³; 5.
8. 80.
9. $4.1\,\text{cm} \times 2.8\,\text{cm} \times 2.1\,\text{cm} = 25.108\,\text{cm}^3$, but to give that result would be to claim an accuracy much greater than that of each measurement. 24 cm³ would be a reasonable answer.
10. (a) (i) 0.5 g, (ii) 1 g, (iii) 5 g; (b) (i) 10 g/cm³, (ii) 3 kg/m³; (c) (i) 2 cm³, (ii) 5 cm³.

11. (*a*) $8.0 \, \text{g/cm}^3$; (*b*) $8.0 \times 10^3 \, \text{kg/m}^3$.
12. $15\,000 \, \text{kg}$.
13. $130 \, \text{kg}$.
14. (*a*) $72 \, \text{cm}^3$; (*b*) $2.5 \, \text{g/cm}^3$.
15. $0.88 \, \text{g/cm}^3$. (Volume of mixture $=200+300=500 \, \text{cm}^3$; mass of mixture $=200 \times 1 + 300 \times 0.80 = 440 \, \text{g}$; density of mixture $=440 \, \text{g}/500 \, \text{cm}^3 = 0.88 \, \text{g/cm}^3$.)
16. $3.5 \times 10^{-2} \, \text{kg}$.
17. $1.0 \times 10^{-3} \, \text{m}$ (1 mm): treat the mercury thread as a cylinder.

Unit 3.12

10. (*b*) 1: unstable; 2: neutral; 3: stable.

Unit 3.13

1. (*a*) $1 \, \text{N}$; (*b*) $50 \, \text{N}$; (*c*) $0.5 \, \text{N}$.
2. (*a*) $120 \, \text{N}$; (*b*) $20 \, \text{N}$.
3. (*a*) $13 \, \text{cm}$; (*b*) $45 \, \text{g}$.
4.

Mass on spring (g)	0	100	200	300	400	500	600	700	800
Stretching force (N)	0	1	2	3	4	5	6	7	8
Length of spring (mm)	60	72	84	96	108	120	132	150	180
Extension (mm)	0	12	24	36	48	60	72	90	120

5. (*a*) $X=5 \, \text{N}$; (*b*) $X=5 \, \text{N}$; (*c*) $X=Y=2.5 \, \text{N}$.
6. (*a*) Balanced: clockwise moment $=2 \times 2 = 4$, anticlockwise moment $=1 \times 4 = 4$ (taking 1 disc and 5 cm as units of force and distance). (*b*) Turns anticlockwise: clockwise moment $=3 \times 3 = 9$, anticlockwise moment $=1 \times 2 + 2 \times 4 = 10$.
7. (*a*) $20 \, \text{N m}$; (*b*) $10 \, \text{N m}$.
8. (*a*) Moment $=F \times 2 = 4 \times 3 = 12 \, \text{N m}$; (*b*) $F=6 \, \text{N}$, $\therefore R=6+4=10 \, \text{N}$.
9. Clockwise moment $=10 \, \text{N} \times 0.1 \, \text{m} = 1 \, \text{N m}$, anticlockwise moment $=3 \, \text{N} \times 0.3 \, \text{m} = 0.9 \, \text{N m}$ $\therefore$ bar tips clockwise to the right.
10. (*a*) Moment of 500 N force $=500 \times 1 \, \text{N m}$ (clockwise)
    moment of 200 N force $=200 \times 2 \, \text{N m}$ (clockwise)
    moment of $Q=Q \times 3 \, \text{N m}$ (anticlockwise)
    moment of $P=P \times 0=0$

    (*b*) Total clockwise moment $=$ anticlockwise moment
    $$500+400=3\,Q$$
    $$\therefore \qquad Q=300 \, \text{N}$$
    (*c*) $P+Q=500+200=700 \, \text{N}$; (*d*) $400 \, \text{N}$.

11. 15 N m.
12. (a) 0; (b) between 0 and 5 N m; (c) 5 N m.
13. (a) 7 N; (b) 1 N; (c) 5 N at $37°$ to 4 N.
14. (a) 50 N at $37°$ to 40 N; (b) 60.8 N at $25°$ to 40 N.
15. 198 N at $142°$ to 100 N.
16. (a) Vertical component $= 100$ N (200 sin 30 by calculation), horizontal component $= 173$ N (200 cos 30 by calculation); (b) $500 + 100 = 600$ N; (c) $500 - 100 = 400$ N.

Unit 4.14

1. (a) 20 m/s, (b) $6\frac{1}{4}$ m/s.
2. (a) 15 m/s; (b) 900 m.
3. 2 m/s^2.
4. (a) 6 m/s; (b) 14 m/s.
5. 4 s.
6. 50 s.
7. A: acceleration; B: constant velocity; C: deceleration; D: at rest.
8. (a) Uniform acceleration; (b) constant speed.
9. (a) 100 m; (b) 20 m/s; (c) decelerates.
10. (a) $1\frac{1}{4}$ m/s^2; (b) (i) 10 m, (ii) 50 m; (c) 22 s.
11. 2.5 m/s^2.
12. (a) 10 m/s; (b) 25 m; (c) 10 s.
13. 96 m.
14. (a) 4 s; (b) 24 m.
15. (a) 1 s; (b) (i) 10 cm/tentick^2, (ii) 10 cm/$\frac{1}{5}$ s every tentick $= 50$ cm/s per tentick, (iii) 250 cm/s^2.
16. (a) Uniform acceleration of 3 cm/tentick^2; (b) 75 cm/s^2.
17. (a) (i) 10 m/s, (ii) 20 m/s, (iii) 30 m/s, (iv) 50 m/s; (b) (i) 5 m, (ii) 20 m, (iii) 45 m, (iv) 125 m.
18. (a) 4 s; (b) 40 m/s
19. (a) (i) 20 m/s, (ii) 10 m/s, (iii) 0, (iv) 20 m/s, (v) 30 m/s; (b) 45 m.
20. (a) 10 s; (b) 2000 m.
21. B, because the bullet continues to travel with the same horizontal velocity as car B.

Unit 5.15

2. Opposition to change of motion. Mass is a measure of inertia.
3. All explained by inertia.
4. (a) Forward pull in tow rope = backward force due to resistance of air and water; (b) weight of parachutist downwards = upwards force due to air resistance; (c) forward push of air on propellers = backward force due to resistance of air and water.
7. (b) One pair consists of weight of book (i.e. downward gravitational pull of earth on book) and upward gravitational pull of book on earth. Other pair is downward force of book on table and upward force of table on book (i.e. the reaction). All are equal. The two forces acting on the book are its weight and the reaction.
8. (a) Weight; (b) air resistance; (c) falls at constant speed (i.e. with its terminal velocity).

Unit 5.16

1. **D.**
2. 20 N.
3. 5000 N; 10 000 N.
4. 15 m/s^2; 60 m/s^2.
5. (a) 2 m/s^2; (b) 1000 N; (c) due to overcoming friction and air resistance.
6. (a) 4 m/s^2; (b) 2 N.
7. (a) 5000 N; (b) 20 000 N, 40 m/s^2.
8. (a) 40 kg m/s; (b) 80 kg m/s; (c) 20 kg m/s per s; (d) 20 N.
9. (a) 10 N s; (b) 20 N s; (c) velocity increases by 2 m/s.
10. (a) 10 kg m/s; (b) 10 N s; (c) 400 N.
11. (a) 3 kg m/s; (b) 3 N s; (c) 30 N.
12. (a) 300 N; (b) 30 000 N.
13. (a) X: 2 kg m/s, Y: 0 kg m/s; (b) X: 0 kg m/s, Y: 2 kg m/s; (c) 2 m/s.
14. (a) 280 kg m/s; (b) 4 m/s.
15. 6 m/s.
16. 0.5 m/s. (Initial momentum of girl+boat=0. Therefore final momentum =0. Momentum is a vector, therefore the momentum of the girl in one direction is equal and opposite to that of the boat in the other direction.)
17. (a) Force =change of momentum per second =200 ×50 =10 000 N; (b) 10 m/s^2. (Acceleration =net force/mass =(10 000 − 5000)/500 = 10 m/s^2.)
18. Apple is torn from stalk when centripetal force needed to keep it in 'orbit' exceeds the force required to break the stalk.
19. (a) Sideways friction between tyres and road acts towards centre of circle and pushes car inwards; (b) (i) larger, (ii) smaller, (iii) larger.
20. (a) Gravitational attraction of earth for shuttle; (b) smaller centripetal force required which is provided by smaller gravitational attraction; (c) (i) decrease, (ii) decrease.

Unit 6.11

3. (a) Lamp; (b) microphone; (c) battery; (d) pile-driver, catapult; (e) electric motor.
9. See Fig. 1.

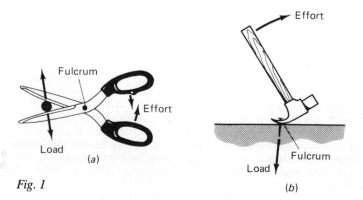

Fig. 1

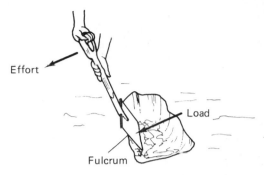

Effort

Load

Fulcrum

Fig. 1 continued   (c)

Unit 6.12

1. (a) 50 J; (b) 180 J.
2. 200 000 J = 200 kJ.
3. (a) 2 J; (b) 500 J; (c) 2000 J; (d) 100 000 J = 100 kJ.
4. 20 m/s.
5. (a) 400 J; (b) $F \times s = \frac{1}{2}mv^2$, i.e. $F \times 2 = 400$, ∴ $F = 200$ N.
6. (a) 150 J; (b) 300 J.
7. 2 m.
8. (a) 800 J; (b) 800 J; (c) 20 m.
9. (a) 1.8 J; (b) 1.8 J; (c) 6 m/s; (d) 1.25 J; (e) 5 m/s.
10. (a) 1 J; (b) 100 N.
11. 250 W.
12. 2 kW.
13. 8 s.
14. 3500 MW.
15. (a) 250 N; (b) 4; (c) 0.4 m; (d) 4.
16. (a) 5000 J; (b) 7500 J; (c) 67%.
17. (a) (i) 10/7, (ii) 2, (iii) 71%; (b) (i) 2, (ii) 3, (iii) 67%; (c) (i) 10/3, (ii) 6, (iii) 56%.
18. (a) 3; (b) 50 N; (c) (i) 10 m, (ii) 500 J, (iii) 200 J.
19. (a) 4000 J; (b) 500 W.
20. (a) 5; (b) 10; (c) 50%.
21. 2½ times.

Unit 7.14

2. (b) The area of contact between two walnuts is much less than that between one walnut and the hand. The pressure is therefore very large and the walnut with the weaker shell breaks.
9. (c) 74 cm.

Unit 7.15

1. (a) (i) 25 Pa, (ii) 0.5 Pa, (iii) 100 Pa; (b) 30 N.
2. (a) 0.20 m^3; (b) 400 kg; (c) 4000 N; (d) 20 000 Pa; (e) (i) none, (ii) less.
3. 1 150 000 Pa (1.15×10^6 Pa).
4. (a) 100 Pa; (b) 200 N.
5. 20 m.
6. 10 m.
7. 860 mmHg.
8. 0.2 m.
9. (a) 10 N; (b) 8 N; (c) 6 N; (d) 5 N.
10. (a) 4800 N; (b) $(4800 - 1600) = 3200$ N.
11. (a) $12/(12 - 7) = 12/5 = 2.4$; (b) $(12 - 8)/(12 - 7) = 4/5 = 0.8$.
12. (a) 10 N; (b) 10 N; (c) 10 N; (d) 1 kg; (e) $1/1000 = 0.001$ m^3; (f) floats higher.
13. $(25 000 - 20 000) = 5000$ N.
14. Vol. of water displaced $= 8$ cm $\times 2$ cm$^2 = 16$ cm^3
  mass of water displaced $= 16$ cm$^3 \times 1$ g/cm$^3 = 16$ g
 weight of water displaced $= 16 \times g = 16 \times 10 = 160$ N
 $\therefore$ by principle of flotation,
   weight of weighted tube $= 160$ N
    vol. of liquid displaced $= l$ cm $\times 2$ cm$^2 = 2l$ cm^3
 (where $l =$ length under surface in liquid)
   mass of liquid displaced $= 2l$ cm$^3 \times 0.8$ g/cm^3
                            $= 1.6 l$ g
 weight of liquid displaced $= 1.6 l \times g$ N $= 16 l$ N
                            $=$ weight of weighted tube
     therefore $16 l = 160$
                         $l = 10$ cm.

Unit 8.10

1. (a) Matter consists of molecules. The molecules are in rapid motion; (b) kinetic energy and potential energy.
2. (b) Molecules in gases are much farther apart than in liquids or solids.
3. (c) Diffusion.
4. (a) Molecules in a gas can travel farther before colliding with other molecules but (b) even so they are slowed down to some extent.
6. Adhesion is greater for water than cohesion; opposite is true for mercury.
9. Crystal models of different shapes and sizes can be built using model 'particles' (e.g. polystyrene balls).

Unit 8.11

1. (2.0×10^3) cm$^3/(50 \times 40)$ cm$^2 = 1$ cm.
2. (6.0×10^{-11}) m$^3/(3.0 \times 10^{-3})$ m$^2 = 2.0 \times 10^{-8}$ m.
3. (6×10^{-10}) m$^3 = \pi (0.1$ m$)^2 \times h$ $\therefore h = 2 \times 10^{-8}$ m.

Unit 9.11

5. **E** (since heat passes quickly to the mercury).
10. (*a*) Metal A.

Unit 9.12

1. (*a*) (i) 50 °F, (ii) 60 °F, (iii) 70 °F, (iv) 80 °F; (*b*) 'Subtract 30 from the temperature in °F and halve the result'; (i) 5 °C, (ii) 13 °C, (iii) 19 °C, (iv) 30 °C.
2. (*a*) (i) 0 K, (ii) 273 K, (iii) 290 K, (iv) 373 K; (*b*) (i) 600 °C, (ii) 273 °C, (iii) −50 °C, (iv) −200 °C.
3. (*a*) 0.000 02 m; (*b*) 0.000 02 cm; (*c*) 0.01 cm.
4. (*a*) Aluminium; (*b*) 1.009 m; (*c*) has same linear expansivity as concrete; (*d*) platinum.
5. (*a*) 0.1 m; (*b*) 0.04 cm; (*c*) 0.3 m.
6. 0.0016/80 = 0.000 02/K.
7. 400 m^3.
8. 91 K (−182 °C).
9. 178 cm^3.
10. Using $p_1V_1 = p_2V_2$, 40 m × 3.0 cm^3 = 10 m × v_2, ∴ $v_2 = 12$ cm^3.

Unit 10.13

7. (*a*) 60 °C; (*b*) (i) CD, (ii) AB, (iii) BC.

Unit 10.14

1. 15 000 J.
2. A: 2000 J/(kg K); B: 200 J/(kg K); C: 1000 J/(kg K).
3. 88 000 (8.8 × 10^4) J.
4. (*a*) 20 000 (2 × 10^4) J; (*b*) 120 000 (1.2 × 10^5) J.
5. (*a*) 2400 J; (*b*) 4800 J/(kg K).
6. 1050 W.
7. 45 kg.
8. (*a*) 990 000 (9.9 × 10^5) J, (*b*) 1 650 000 (1.65 × 10^6) J.
9. (*a*) 270 000 (2.7 × 10^5) J; (*b*) 1680 J.
10. 660 s = 11 min.
11. (*a*) 0 °C; (*b*) 0.030 kg (30 g).
12. (*a*) 23 000 000 = 2.3 × 10^7 J; (*b*) 27 000 = 2.7 × 10^4 J.
13. 0.3 kg.
14. 2 400 000 (2.4 × 10^6) J/kg.

Unit 11.10

4. **E**.
7. **D**.

8. The matt black can, because it has the best emitting surface.
10. (a) Rate at which earth re-emits radiation equals rate at which it receives solar radiation; (b) on a cloudy night earth does not cool down as much by losing radiation into space.
11. **B**.
12. **C**.

Unit 13.13

1. 30°.
2. (a) 30°; (c) 60°.
3. 10°.
4. 4 m.
5. 14 m.
6. 12.45.
7. Real image 13 cm from mirror, 0.70 cm high.
8. (a) Real image 21 cm in front of mirror, 1.3 cm high; (b) virtual image, 30 cm behind mirror, 9.0 cm high.
9. 15/5.0 = 3.0.

Unit 14.12

1. 1.3 (1.25).
2. (a) 17°; (b) 37°.
3. 64°.
4. 250 000 km/s.
5. (a) 0.8 m; (b) 6 cm.
6. 2.5.
7. 30°.
8. 13 cm from lens, 2.5 cm high, real.
9. 10 cm from lens, 4.0 cm high, virtual.
10. 5.0 cm.

Unit 15.9

1. (a) Iris; (b) retina; (c) ciliary muscles.
2. **E**.
3. (a) (i) No, (ii) yes, (iii) no; (b) concave.
4. (a) (i) No, (ii) yes; (b) convex.
5. Closer object.
6. Aperture made larger.
8. (a) 4 cm; (b) (i) larger, blurred, less bright, (ii) moved closer to the slide.
9. (a) 4 cm; (b) 8 cm behind lens, virtual, $m = 2$.
10. **C**.

Unit 16.12

2. (a) 1 cm; (b) 1 Hz; (c) 1 cm/s.
3. (a) 50 mm/s; (b) 10 mm.

5. (a) Speed of wave depends on depth of water; (b) AB, since waves travel more slowly towards it, therefore water shallower in this direction.

6. (a) 4 cm; (b) $\sin i = \dfrac{30}{20} \sin r = \dfrac{3}{2} \sin 30 = \dfrac{3}{2} \times \dfrac{1}{2} = \dfrac{3}{4}$ $\therefore i = 49°$.

7. (a) Diffraction occurs; (b) diffraction less marked since gap width and wavelength must be comparable.

8. (a) Reinforce each other, (b) cancel each other: interference.

9. Waves diffracted (i.e. circular waves on right side of gap) and of shorter wavelength (since water shallower).

10. (a) Trough; (b) (i) 3 mm, (ii) 15 mm/s, (iii) 5 Hz; (c) reinforce at B (two troughs), cancel at C (trough + crest).

11. (a) Due to its very small wavelength; (b) they do not produce coherent sets of light waves.

12. (a) $S_1O = S_2O$; (b) $S_1O_1 - S_2O_1 = \lambda/2$; (c) $S_1O_2 - S_2O_2 = \lambda$.

13. (a) Fringes closer together; (b) fringes farther apart but dimmer; (c) fringes farther apart; (d) central fringe white, all others coloured.

19. (a) 3 m; (b) 2×10^{-4} s.

Unit 17.12

4. (b) (i) 1 m, (ii) 2 m.

5. 3.3 km.

6. (a) When he sees the flash of light from the pistol, because light travels about 1 million times faster than sound; (b) error $= 110/330 = 1/3$ s: this should be added to his timing.

7. (a) 0.5 m; (b) $1500 = 2d/0.6$ where d is depth of sea-bed, $\therefore d = 450$ m.

8. $5 \times 330 = 1650$ m (about 1 mile).

9. (a) $2 \times 160 = 320$ m/s; (b) the clapping interval is $\frac{3}{4}$ s during which time sound travels 2×120 m $= 240$ m, $\therefore$ speed of sound $= 240$ m $\div \frac{3}{4}$ s $= \frac{4}{3} \times 240 = 320$ m/s; (c) 320 m.

Unit 18.11

7. (a) C; (b) electrons flow from sphere to earth and leave sphere with a positive charge.

8. A charge of opposite sign to that on the balloon is induced on the wall and attracts the balloon.

12. (a) (i) 540 mA, (ii) 85 mA, (iii) 2 mA; (b) (i) 1.5 A, (ii) 0.61 A, (iii) 0.035 A; (c) (i) 1000 µA, (ii) 470 µA, (iii) 15 µA.

13. $Q = I \times t$ or $I = Q/t$.

14. (a) 5 C; (b) 50 C; (c) 1500 C.

15. (a) 5 A; (b) 0.50 A; (c) 2.0 A.

18. (a)

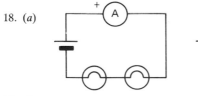

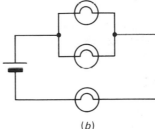

Fig. 2   (a)   (b)

19. (a) Ammeters A_2 and A_3 read 0.2 A; (b) 0.5 A.
20. All read 0.25 A.

Unit 19.14

1. (a) 12 J; (b) 60 J.
2. (a) 4.5 V; (b) 1.5 V; (c) 1.5 V; (d) 3 V.
3. $W = ItV$ ∴ $V = W/It = 48$ J/(2 A × 1 s) = 48/2 = 24 J/C = 24 V.
4. (a) 4.5 V; (b) 3.5 V; (c) 1.0 V.
5. $V = 18$ V; $V_2 = 2$ V; $V_1 = 8$ V.
6. (a) Voltmeter V_1 reads 6 V; $W = V_1It = 6$ V × 0.5 A × 60 s = 180 J; (b) in Fig. 19.21 the 'left' sides of voltmeters V, V_1 and V_2 and the 'right' side of ammeter A are +.
7. (a) 3 Ω; (b) 20 V; (c) 2 A; (d) 4 V. (*Note:* if I is in mA and R in k Ω, V is in V.)
8. (a) L reads 2 A; (b) M reads 6 V, N reads 2 V.
9. (a) 10 Ω; (b) 2 Ω; (c) 1.5 Ω; (d) 6 Ω; (e) 12 Ω; (f) 3 Ω.
10. (a) 15 Ω; (b) 1.5 Ω.
11. (a) 4 Ω; (b) 0.5 A; (c) 0.25 A; (d) 0.5 V; (e) 1.5 V.
12. $I = 3$ A, $I_1 = 2$ A, $I_2 = 1$ A.
13. (a) P, R and T ammeters reading 2 A: Q and S voltmeters, Q reading 4 V, S reading 6 V; (b) B, C and D ammeters, B reading 1 A, C and D reading 0.5 A: E, F and G voltmeters, E and F reading 1 V and G 3 V.
14. (a) 1 A; (b) 1.5 A.
15. (a) 3 V; (b) 2 V; (c) 8 V.
16. (a) 1 V; (b) 3 V; (c) 2 V.
17. (a) 3.0 V; (b) 2.6 V; (c) 0.4 V; (d) 2 Ω; (e) 13 Ω.
18. 1.9 V; 2.0/0.01 = 200 A.

Unit 20.11

1. (a) 100 J; (b) 500 J; (c) 6000 J.
2. (a) 24 W; (b) 3 J/s.
3. (a) 3 Ω; (b) 4 A.
4. 3.12 kW.
5. (a) (i) 10 W, (ii) 40 W; (b) (i) 2 W, (ii) 8 W.
6. $ItV = mc\Delta\theta$, i.e. 3.5 × 300 × 12 = 0.6 × 4200 × $\Delta\theta$, ∴ $\Delta\theta$ = 3.5 × 300 × 12/(0.6 × 4200) = 4200 × 3/(0.6 × 4200) = 3/0.6 = 5 °C.
7. $Pt = mc\Delta\theta$, i.e. 2100 × t = 1.2 × 4200 × 90, ∴ t = 2.4 × 90 = 216 s.
11. (a) 3 A; (b) 3 A; (c) 13 A; (d) 13 A.
12. (a) (7 × 100 + 2 × 150) × 5 = 1 × 5 kW h = 5 units, costing 25 p; (b) 2 units, costing 10 p.
13. 48 p.
14. (a) Total power P = 6 kW = 6000 W, supply p.d. V = 240 V, ∴ $I = P/V$ = 6000/240 = 25 A: 30 A fuse would be suitable; (b) assuming all parts are on at full heat, energy used = 3 kW × 2 hrs + 3 kW × 0.5 hr = 6 + 1.5 = 7.5 units: cost = 7.5 × 5 p = 37.5 p.

Unit 21.12

2. C.
3. (a) Steel; (b) A.

4. S.
8. (a) A; (b) A.
11. A is N; B is N; C is S; D is S; E is N; F is S.
12. (b) (i) P is N, (ii) L is N, (iii) M is S.
13. (a) N; (b) E.
18. When the door is closed the magnetic field due to the magnet in the door jamb is cancelled out by that due to the magnet in the door, so the reed switch is open and the alarm bell does not ring. When the door is open the reed switch closes (due to its reeds being magnetized by the door jamb magnet only) and rings the bell.
21. (b) A couple; (c) maximum; (d) zero.

Unit 22.11

1. (b) From B to A; (d) alternating.
4. (a) E.m.f. waveform has double the amplitude but same frequency as first graph; (b) amplitude and frequency both twice as great as in first graph.
9. (a) 24 V; (b) 240 V.
10. (a) 120; (b) (i) 1 A, (ii) 1/40 A.
13. (a) $1/50 = 0.02$ s.
14. (a) 12 V; (b) $12/0.7 \approx 17$ V.

Unit 23.11

8. (c) (i) 14, (ii) 6, (iii) 8, (iv) 6.
12. (a) (i) alpha, (ii) beta, (iii) beta; (b) A and D.
13. (a) (i) $^4_2$He, (ii) $_{-1}^0$e; (b) $^{238}_{92}$U $\rightarrow$ $^{234}_{90}$Th $+ ^4_2$He; $^{234}_{90}$Th $\rightarrow$ $^{234}_{91}$Pa $+ _{-1}^0$e.
15. $\frac{1}{2} \times \frac{1}{2} \times \frac{1}{2} \times \frac{1}{2} = 1/16$.
16. 1.5 hours.
17. 1/16.
18. (a) 1/8; (b) 15/16; (c) 6.
19. (b) 9×10^{13} J.

Unit 24.16

2. (c) A negative, B positive; (d) down.
4. 1.8×10^{11} C/kg.
6. (a) A and C; (b) A +, C − : make A more positive, increase Y-amp gain control; (c) B and C +, A and D −; (d) spot moving slowly forwards and backwards horizontally across S; (e) a continuous vertical line.
7. (a) 10 V; (b) 7 V.
8. 50 Hz.
9. (b) A and C.
13. (a) L_1, since D_2 is reverse biased; (b) L_1 and L_2, since D is forward biased by both cells; (c) L_2 since D_1 is reverse biased.
14. (e) About 0.6 V.
15. (c).

16. (*a*) C; (*b*) A.
17. (*b*) $10\,\text{mA}/20\,\mu\text{A} = 10 \times 1000\,\mu\text{A}/20\,\mu\text{A} = 500$.
18. (*a*) Lamp brightens; (*b*) no, gets less bright.
21. (*c*) Allows light level at which transistor 'turns on' to be varied.
22. (*a*) Water is a conductor and raindrops complete the circuit between the two copper rods, thereby allowing base current to flow; (*b*) $60 = 30/\text{base current}$, $\therefore$ base current $= 30/60 = 0.5\,\text{mA}$.

26.

A	B	D	C	F
0	0	0	0	0
0	1	0	0	0
1	0	0	0	0
1	1	1	0	1
0	0	0	1	1
0	1	0	1	1
1	0	0	1	1
1	1	1	1	1

30. (*a*) $100/10 = 10$; (i) $\pm10\,\text{V}$, (ii) $\pm15\,\text{V}$ (in theory $\pm20\,\text{V}$ but op amp saturates before this happens).
31. (*b*)

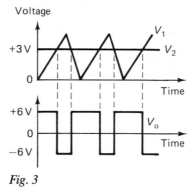

Fig. 3

Mathematics for Physics

1. (*a*) 3; (*b*) 5; (*c*) 8/3; (*d*) 20; (*e*) 12; (*f*) 6; (*g*) 2; (*h*) 3; (*i*) 8.

2. (*a*) $f = \dfrac{v}{\lambda}$; (*b*) $\lambda = \dfrac{v}{f}$; (*c*) $I = \dfrac{V}{R}$; (*d*) $R = \dfrac{V}{I}$; (*e*) $m = d \times V$;

 (*f*) $V = \dfrac{m}{d}$; (*g*) $s = vt$; (*h*) $t = \dfrac{s}{v}$; (*i*) $a = \dfrac{F}{m}$; (*j*) $I = \dfrac{Q}{t}$;

 (*k*) $Q = VC$; (*l*) $A = \dfrac{F}{p}$; (*m*) $p_1 = p_2 \times \dfrac{V_2}{V_1}$; (*n*) $a = \dfrac{x}{bc}$;

 (*o*) $t = \dfrac{W}{IV}$; (*p*) $\Delta\theta = \dfrac{E_H}{mc}$.

3. (a) $I^2 = \dfrac{P}{R}$;   (b) $I = \sqrt{\dfrac{P}{R}}$;   (c) $a = \dfrac{2s}{t^2}$;   (d) $t^2 = \dfrac{2s}{a}$;

(e) $t = \sqrt{\dfrac{2s}{a}}$;   (f) $v = \sqrt{2gh}$;   (g) $y = \dfrac{D\lambda}{a}$;   (h) $\rho = \dfrac{AR}{l}$;

(i) $V_1 = V_2 \times \dfrac{T_1}{T_2}$;   (j) $T_1 = \dfrac{V_1}{V_2} \times T_2$;   (k) $V_2 = \dfrac{p_1}{p_2} \times \dfrac{T_2}{T_1} \times V_1$;

(l) $T_2 = \dfrac{p_2}{p_1} \times \dfrac{V_2}{V_1} \times T_1$.

4. (a) 10; (b) 34; (c) $\frac{2}{8}$; (d) 1/10; (e) 10; (f) 3×10^8
5. (a) 2.0×10^5; (b) 10; (c) 8; (d) 2.0×10^8; (e) 20; (f) 300; (g) 10^{-7}; (h) 15; (i) 5; (j) $0.00002 = 2 \times 10^{-5}$; (k) 10; (l) 5/3.
6. (a) 4; (b) 2; (c) 5; (d) 8; (e) $\frac{2}{3}$; (f) $= -\frac{3}{4}$; (g) 13/6; (h) $= -16$; (i) 1.
7. $a = \dfrac{v - u}{c}$: (a) 5; (b) 60; (c) 75.

8. $a = \dfrac{v^2 - u^2}{2s}$

9. (b) Extension $\propto$ mass since the graph is a straight line through the origin.
10. (b) No: although the graph is a straight line it does not pass through the origin; (c) 32.
11. (a) is a curve; (b) is a straight line through the origin, therefore $s \propto t^2$ or $s/t^2 = a$ constant $= 2$.
12. (a) 10^9; (b) 10^3; (c) 10^4; (d) 10^{-3}; (e) 20; (f) 2.5×10^8; (g) 80; (h) 2×10^{-6}; (i) 7; (j) 5.
13. (a) 5×10^3; (b) 6.3×10^5; (c) 4.6×10^3; (d) 6.1×10^6.

Index